Conformation
of Biopolymers

Volume 1

Conformation
of Biopolymers

PAPERS READ AT AN INTERNATIONAL SYMPOSIUM
HELD AT THE UNIVERSITY OF MADRAS
18–21 JANUARY 1967

Volume 1

Edited by

G. N. Ramachandran
Centre of Advanced Study in Biophysics
University of Madras, India

1967

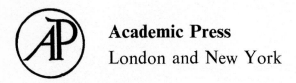

Academic Press
London and New York

ACADEMIC PRESS INC. (LONDON) LTD
Berkeley Square House
Berkeley Square
London, W.1

U.S. Edition published by
ACADEMIC PRESS INC.
111 Fifth Avenue
New York, New York 10003

Library of Congress Catalog Card Number: 67–24320

Printed in Great Britain by
The Whitefriars Press Limited, London and Tonbridge

List of Contributors

ACHARYA, A. S., *Indian Institute of Science, Bangalore, India* (p. 291)

ADAMS, M. J., *University of Oxford, Oxford, England* (p. 9)

ANDREEVA, N. S., *Academy of Sciences of U.S.S.R., Moscow, U.S.S.R.* (p. 469)

APPLEQUIST, J., *Iowa State University, Ames, Iowa, U.S.A.* (p. 403)

AVEY, H. P., *Birkbeck College, London, England* (p. 17)

BAGCHI, B., *Saha Institute of Nuclear Physics, Calcutta, India* (p. 663)

BALASUBRAMANIAM, D., *Indian Institute of Technology, Kanpur, India* (p. 147)

BALL, J. T., *Bradford Technical College, Yorkshire, England* (p. 623)

BANKS, W., *The University, Edinburgh, Scotland* (p. 739)

BASU, S., *Saha Institute of Nuclear Physics, Calcutta, India* (p. 663)

BLOUT, E. R., *Harvard Medical School, Boston, Massachusetts, U.S.A.* (p. 123)

BOLES, M. O., *Birkbeck College, London, England* (p. 17)

BRADBURY, E. M., *College of Technology, Portsmouth, England* (p. 583)

CARLISLE, C. H., *Birkbeck College, London, England* (p. 17)

CHACKO, K. K., *University of Madras, Madras, India* (p. 607)

CHAO, C. C. W., *Northwestern University, Chicago, Illinois, U.S.A.* (p. 499)

CHATTERJEE, R., *Bose Institute, Calcutta, India* (p. 235)

COLEMAN, R., *Carlsberg Laboratory, Copenhagen, Denmark* (p. 123)

CRANE-ROBINSON, C., *College of Technology, Portsmouth, England* (p. 583)

CRIGHTON, J. S., *Bradford Institute of Technology, Yorkshire, England* (p. 623)

DAS GUPTA, N. N., *Saha Institute of Nuclear Physics, Calcutta, India* (p. 663)

DODSON, E., *University of Oxford, Oxford, England* (p. 9)

DODSON, G., *University of Oxford, Oxford, England* (p. 9)

ENGEL, J., *Max-Planck-Institut für Eiweiss-und Lederforschung, Munich, Germany* (p. 483)

ESIPOVA, N. G., *Academy of Sciences of U.S.S.R., Moscow, U.S.S.R.* (p. 469)

EVANS, S. A., *Birkbeck College, London, England* (p. 17)

FLORY, P. J. *Stanford University, Stanford, California, U.S.A.* (p. 339)

FUKUSHIMA, K., *Osaka University, Osaka, Japan* (p. 557)

GIBSON, K. D., *Cornell University, Ithaca, New York, U.S.A.* (p. 43)

GORBUNOFF, M. J., *Brandeis University, Waltham, Massachusetts, U.S.A.* (p. 173)

GREEN, D. B., *Institute of Technology, Bradford, Yorkshire, England* (p. 617)

GREENWOOD, C. T., *The University, Edinburgh, Scotland* (p. 739)

HAPPEY, F., *Institute of Technology, Bradford, Yorkshire, England* (pp. 617, 623)
HARRINGTON, W. F., *The Johns Hopkins University, Baltimore, Maryland, U.S.A.* (p. 513)
HAUGLAND, R. P., *Stanford University, Stanford, California, U.S.A.* (p. 321)
HODGKIN, D. C., *University of Oxford, Oxford, England* (p. 9)
JEHLE, H., *George Washington University, Washington, D.C., U.S.A.* (p. 703)
KAUFMAN, E., *St. Mary's College, Winona, Minnesota, U.S.A.* (p. 499)
KRIMM, S., *University of Michigan, Ann Arbor, Michigan, U.S.A.* (p. 439)
KÜHN, K., *Max-Planck-Institut für Eiweiss-und Lederforschung, Munich, Germany* (p. 533)
KUMOSINSKI, T. F., *Eastern Regional Research Laboratory, Philadelphia, Pennsylvania, U.S.A.* (p. 173)
KUROIWA, K., *Laboratory of Tokyo Customs, Tokyo, Japan* (p. 439)
LAKSHMINARAYAN, A. V., *University of Madras, Madras, India* (pp. 61, 641)
LEACH, S. J., *Commonwealth Scientific Industrial and Research Organization, Parkville, Victoria, Australia* (p. 43)
MANJULA, B. N., *Indian Institute of Science, Bangalore, India* (p. 291)
MARCHESSAULT, R. H., *State University of New York, Syracuse, New York, U.S.A.* (p. 709)
MARGOLIASH, E., *Abbott Laboratories, North Chicago, Illinois, U.S.A.* (p. 253)
MASUDA, Y., *Japan Women's University, Tokyo, Japan* (p. 557)
MEISTER, A., *Tufts University School of Medicine, Boston, Massachusetts, U.S.A.* (p. 279)
MILLIONOVA, M. I., *Institute of Biophysics, Academy of Sciences of U.S.S.R., Moscow, U.S.S.R.* (p. 469)
MISRA, D. N., *Saha Institute of Nuclear Physics, Calcutta, India* (p. 663)
MIYAZAWA, T., *Osaka University, Osaka, Japan* (p. 557)
MORRIS, S. J., *Birkbeck College, London, England* (p. 17)
NÉMETHY, G., *The Rockefeller University, New York, New York, U.S.A.* (pp. 43, 365)
NIELSEN, E. B., *University of Oregon, Eugene, Oregon, U.S.A.* (p. 109)
NISONOFF, A., *University of Illinois School of Medicine, Chicago, Illinois, U.S.A.* (p. 253)
OOI, T., *Nagoya University, Nagoya, Japan* (p. 43)
OKAMURA, K., *State University of New York, Syracuse, New York, U.S.A.* (p. 709)
PALMER, R. A., *Birkbeck College, London, England* (p. 17)
PAULING, L., *Center for the Study of Democratic Institutions, Santa Barbara, California, U.S.A.* (p. 1)
PAWSE, A. R., *Bhabha Atomic Research Centre, Bombay, India* (p. 309)
PTITSYN, O. B., *Institute of High Molecular Compounds, Academy of Sciences of U.S.S.R., Leningrad, U.S.S.R.* (p. 381)

RAMACHANDRAN, G. N., *University of Madras, Madras, India* (pp. 61, 82, 429, 641, 721)

RAMAKRISHNAN, C., *University of Madras, Madras, India* (pp. 429, 721)

RAO, V. S. R., *University of Madras, Madras, India* (p. 721)

RATTLE, H. W., *College of Technology, Portsmouth, England* (p. 583)

RAY, A., *Bose Institute, Calcutta, India* (p. 235)

REBANE, T., *University of Michigan, Ann Arbor, Michigan, U.S.A.* (p. 439)

REICHLIN, M., *State University of New York, Buffalo, New York, U.S.A.* (p. 253)

ROGULENKOVA, V. N., *Institute of Biophysics, Academy of Sciences of U.S.S.R., Moscow., U.S.S.R.* (p. 469)

RUDALL, K. M., *The University, Leeds, England* (p. 751)

SAMPATHKUMAR, K. S. V., *Bhabha Atomic Research Centre, Bombay, India* (p. 309)

SANKARAN, K., *Bhabha Atomic Research Centre, Bombay, India* (p. 309)

SARKAR, P. K., *Bose Institute, Calcutta, India* (p. 197)

SASISEKHARAN, V., *University of Madras, Madras, India* (pp. 61, 641)

SCHELLMAN, J. A., *University of Oregon, Eugene, Oregon, U.S.A.* (p. 109)

SCHERAGA, H. A., *Cornell University, Ithaca, New York, U.S.A.* (p. 43)

SCOTT, R. A., *University of Hawaii, Honolulu, Hawaii, U.S.A.* (p. 43)

SHALL, S., *University of Sussex, Sussex, England* (p. 17)

SHIBNEV, V. A., *Academy of Sciences of U.S.S.R., Moscow, U.S.S.R.* (p. 469)

SHMUELI, V., *Tel Aviv University, Tel Aviv, Israel* (p. 449)

SIRSAT, S. M., *Indian Cancer Research Centre, Bombay, India* (p. 545)

SPERLING, R., *Weizmann Institute of Science, Rehovoth, Israel* (p. 215)

SRINIVASAN, R., *University of Madras, Madras, India* (p. 607)

STEINBERG, I. Z., *Weizmann Institute of Science, Rehovoth, Israel* (p. 215)

STEINRAUF, L. K., *Indiana University Medical School, Indianapolis, Indiana, U.S.A.* (p. 27)

STEPHENS, R. M., *College of Technology, Portsmouth, England* (p. 583)

STEVENS, L., *Eastern Region Research Laboratory, Philadelphia, Pennsylvania, U.S.A.* (p. 173).

STRYER, L., *Stanford University School of Medicine, Palo Alto, California, U.S.A.* (p. 321)

SUGANO, S., *Osaka University, Osaka, Japan* (p. 557)

SUNDARARAJAN, P. R., *University of Madras, Madras, India* (p. 721)

SUSI, H., *Eastern Regional Research Laboratory, Philadelphia, Pennsylvania, U.S.A.* (p. 173)

SUWALSKY, M., *Weizmann Institute of Science, Rehovoth, Israel* (p. 449)

TATARINOVA, L. I., *Institute of Crystallography, Academy of Sciences of U.S.S.R., Moscow, U.S.S.R.* (p. 569)

TIMASHEFF, S. N., *Brandeis University, Waltham, Massachusetts, U.S.A.* (p. 173)

Tkocz, C., *Max-Planck-Institut für Eiweiss-und Lederforschung, Munich, Germany* (p. 533)

Townend, R., *Brandeis University, Waltham, Massachusetts, U.S.A.* (p. 173)

Traub, W., *Weizmann Institute of Science, Rehovoth, Israel* (p. 449)

Tsuboi, M., *University of Tokyo, Tokyo, Japan* (p. 689)

Vanderkooi, G., *Cornell University, Ithaca, New York, U.S.A.* (p. 43)

Vainshtein, B. K., *Institute of Crystallography, Academy of Sciences of U.S.S.R., Moscow, U.S.S.R.* (p. 569)

Veis, A., *Northwestern University, Chicago, Illinois, U.S.A.* (p. 499)

Venkatappa, M. P., *Bangalore University, Bangalore, India* (p. 27)

Venkatachalam, C. M., *University of Madras, Madras, India* (pp. 83, 429)

Venkateswara Rao, N., *University of Madras, Madras, India* (p. 513)

Vithayathil, P. J., *Indian Institute of Science, Bangalore, India* (p. 291)

Wada, A., *Tokyo University, Tokyo, Japan* (p. 655)

Watson, B. M., *Institute of Technology, Bradford, Yorkshire, England* (p. 617)

Wetlaufer, D. B., *University of Minnesota, Minneapolis, Minnesota, U.S.A.* (p. 147)

Woolhouse, B. A., *Birkbeck College, London, England* (p. 17)

Yonath, A., *Weizmann Institute of Science, Rehovoth, Israel* (p. 449)

Yang, J. T., *University of California, San Francisco Medical Center, San Francisco, California, U.S.A.* (pp. 157, 197)

Zimmermann, B., *Max-Planck-Institut für Eiweiss-und Lederforschung, Munich, Germany* (p. 533)

Preface

An International Symposium on Conformation of Biopolymers was organized at the University of Madras by the Centre of Advanced Study in Biophysics of the University, from 18 to 21 January 1967. The Symposium, which had the sponsorship of the International Union of Pure and Applied Biophysics, was presided over by Professor Linus Pauling and was in the hands of an Organizing Committee consisting of Dr C. B. Anfinsen, Bethesda, U.S.A., Dr W. F. Harrington, Baltimore, U.S.A., Dr F. M. Richards, New Haven, U.S.A., Dr H. A. Scheraga, Ithaca, U.S.A., Dr G. N. Ramachandran, Madras (Convener), Dr C. Ramakrishnan, Madras (Secretary), Dr S. Thyagaraja Rao, Madras (Secretary) and Dr V. S. R. Rao, Madras (Treasurer).

The possibility of holding a Workshop on Protein Conformation, attended by some of the leading workers in the field, was the stimulus for the organization of the Symposium on the wider subject on Conformation of Biopolymers at Madras. It is gratifying to note that forty-eight papers were offered for the Symposium by scientists from different countries. Most of them (thirty-nine) deal with the conformation of proteins and polypeptides, five with nucleic acids and nucleotides and four with polysaccharides. The papers cover a wide variety of techniques used for the study of conformational aspects of these macromolecules, such as X-ray, chemical, optical and theoretical methods.

These volumes will be found to be of interest by all biochemists who are working on the study of proteins, nucleic acids and polysaccharides. In particular, they will appeal to those who are interested in the conformational aspects of these materials and the relation between conformation and biological activity. Those dealing with physical and chemical techniques for the study of conformation would find the papers particularly useful, as they deal with the latest developments in these fields.

The organizers would like to thank the Commission on Molecular Biophysics of the IUPAB, particularly Dr R. C. Williams, the Chairman, and Dr J. A. V. Butler, the Secretary, for their sponsorship of the Symposium, which enabled many of the scientists to attend the Symposium. Financial support for the Symposium came from various sources in India—in particular the University Grants Commission, the Council of Scientific and Industrial Research and the Atomic Energy Commission and we would like to thank all these for their generous assistance. The Organizers would also like to record the continuous support and encouragement given to them by Dr D. S. Kothari, Chairman, University Grants Commission and Dr A. L. Mudaliar, Vice-Chancellor, University of Madras. They are grateful to all the members of the Centre of Advanced Study in Physics for their assistance in the actual conduct of the conference—in particular Dr R. Srinivasan for the organization of the Symposium and Dr V. Sasisekharan for that of the Workshop.

The Editor wishes to thank Academic Press for providing preprints from galleys for the Symposium and for their assistance in various ways for the speedy publication of the volumes. He would like to thank in particular Dr C. Ramakrishnan and his other colleagues for assistance in editing and in correcting the proofs.

March 1967
Madras   G. N. RAMACHANDRAN

Contents of Volume 1

Proteins and Polypeptides

A. X-Ray diffraction and stereochemical studies

B. Optical rotation studies

Contents of Volume 2

Proteins and Polypeptides

PRESIDENTIAL ADDRESS

Molecular Structure of Proteins

Linus Pauling

Research Professor of the Physical and Biological Sciences, Center for the Study of Democratic Institutions, Santa Barbara, California, U.S.A.

addressed The Symposium as follows

I begin by expressing to Professor Ramachandran and his associates in the University of Madras my deep appreciation of the honor of having been chosen as President of this Symposium on Conformation of Biopolymers, and as Raman Visiting Professor of Physics in the University of Madras.

The problem of the structure of proteins is one that has interested me for 33 years. So far as I can remember, I had not developed any significant interest in this field until 1934, when I began work on hemoglobin, as I shall describe later on.

It was the discovery of the phenomenon of X-ray diffraction by Max von Laue, in 1912, and its successful application to the determination of the structure of crystals by W. H. Bragg and W. L. Bragg, in 1913, that was ultimately responsible for the great progress in the field of protein structure made during the last two decades. The first X-ray diffraction photographs of proteins were made in 1913 by S. Nishikawa and S. Ono, in Japan. In 1914, Nishikawa continued this task, but the diffraction patterns were so diffuse as to discourage further work. Better diffraction photographs were then made by Herzog and Jancke in 1920. They studied muscle, nerve, sinew, hair and silk, and a year later Brill made the suggestion that in silk the polypeptide chains are essentially in the extended form, in which each amino acid residue has a length along the fiber axis of about 3·5 Å. Then, in 1931, Astbury and Street pointed out that hair, wool and related fibers exist in both a contracted form, called α-keratin, and an extended form, called β-keratin. They suggested that in β-keratin the polypeptide chains are in the extended conformation, and that a chemical change involving the formation of rings of atoms held together by covalent bonds takes place on contraction to α-keratin. Astbury and Woods in 1933 described β-keratin as involving sheets of extended polypeptide chains, the chains being held together in the

1

sheets by interaction of carbonyl and imino groups of the amide groups. In 1936 Alfred E. Mirsky and I discussed the general problem of the structure of proteins and the phenomenon of denaturation, and suggested that the inter-action between the chains in silk is the formation of hydrogen bonds between the carbonyl oxygen atom and the hydrogen atom attached to the amide nitrogen atom. The same suggestion about hydrogen bonding in silk was made at nearly the same time by Maurice L. Huggins. Several possible con-figurations for the coiled polypeptide chain in α-keratin were suggested by Astbury, Huggins, Bragg, Kendrew and Perutz, and finally, in 1949, the discovery of the α-helix was reported by Professor Robert B. Corey, Dr Herman R. Branson and me.

I have already mentioned that I became interested in the structure of proteins by way of hemoglobin. Between 1922 and 1934 I was engaged in the determination of the structure of many crystals by the X-ray diffraction method and of some gas molecules by the electron-diffraction method, as well as in theoretical work dealing with the nature of the chemical bond and the structure of molecules and crystals. The matter of the magnetic properties of substances also engaged my interest, and one day in 1934, when I happened to run across a discussion of the question of the nature of the attachment of oxygen molecules to hemoglobin in the red cells of the blood, the idea occurred to me that some significant information could be obtained by measuring the magnetic susceptibility of hemoglobin. The oxygen molecule is almost unique among gas molecules in having a permanent magnetic moment, corresponding to two electrons with parallel spin. I argued that if the oxygen molecules were attached to the hemoglobin molecule by physical interactions they would retain their magnetic moment, whereas if they formed chemical bonds with the hemoglobin molecule, presumably with the iron atoms, the unpaired electrons would be involved in the formation of pairs and the permanent magnetic moment would be lost. Charles Coryell and I carried out this experiment. We found that oxyhemoglobin is completely diamagnetic, with no magnetic moment; and in this way we proved that the oxygen molecules have entered into chemical combination with the hemo-globin molecule. A striking observation made in the course of these studies was that the hemoglobin molecule with oxygen removed from it has a large magnetic moment, which is the result of a deep-seated change in the electronic structure of the iron atoms that takes place on the removal of the oxygen molecules.

Before embarking, with Coryell, on these magnetic studies, I had carried out a theoretical discussion of the oxygen equilibrium curve of hemoglobin, in relation to the change in interaction energy of the four heme groups with one another that accompanies their oxygenation. Having decided that it would be well worth while to carry out some experimental investigations of hemoglobin, I was faced with the fact that my background of experience did not include the handling of such delicate and complex chemical substances as hemoglobin, and that I would be wise to seek the help of an expert. Fortunately, I was successful in getting Dr Alfred E. Mirsky, of the Rockefeller Institute for Medical Research, to come to Pasadena for a year, and to give me (and Dr Coryell) instruction in the ways of preparing and handling hemoglobin solutions. In the course of this work Mirsky and I developed the idea that proteins in general are held in their native configurations through the formation of hydrogen bonds between one part of a polypeptide chain and another part.

The magnetic studies on hemoglobin were continued for several years. They led to the discovery of several previously unknown compounds of hemoglobin and to much information about equilibrium constants, rate of reactions and electronic structure of hemoglobin and hemoglobin derivatives. Moreover, this work on hemoglobin, which I described in a seminar at the Rockefeller Institute in 1936, caused Dr Karl Landsteiner, the discoverer of the blood groups, to ask me to discuss with him the question of the structure of antibodies and the nature of serological reactions, and this discussion led ultimately to a large amount of work on the subject in our Pasadena laboratories.

Moreover, Dr Robert B. Corey, who had been working at the Rockefeller Institute with Ralph W. G. Wyckoff, decided that he would spend a year of absence from the Rockefeller Institute working in our laboratories in Pasadena. When he arrived in Pasadena in the summer of 1937 he found me engrossed in the effort to formulate a structure for α-keratin. I had decided that the resonance of the double bond in the amide group would require this group of six atoms (including the two α-carbon atoms) to be planar, and that the acceptable ways of folding the polypeptide chain would be those in which the planarity of the amide groups was preserved, but that different orientations around the two single bonds to the α-carbon atoms were possible, and that in addition the hydrogen atom attached to nitrogen in the amide group should be directed toward the oxygen atom of a neighboring amide group, with a normal hydrogen-bond length, about 2·8 or 3·0 Å. I had constructed some ball-and-stick models, in the effort to get a repeating structure that would account for the strong 5·1 Å meridional reflection observed in the X-ray diffraction pattern of the α-keratin proteins. After several weeks of this effort, with no success in accounting for the 5·1 Å reflection, I gave up the search. I preserved some of the models for a year or two, and then dismantled them. It is my memory that my greatest effort was expended on ways of folding the polypeptide chain in which the chain lay in essentially one plane, as had been suggested by Astbury, and that I did not make a very serious effort to discuss three-dimensional models, especially helical ones, as was done by Huggins and by Bragg, Kendrew and Perutz, as well as by Corey, Branson and me, a decade or two later.

Corey had made some X-ray diffraction photographs of proteins while he was with Wyckoff at the Rockefeller Institute, and when he came to discuss with me his program of work for the year the question of the structure of proteins was brought up. I mentioned that I felt some doubt as to whether we were justified in assuming, as I had been doing, that the structure of the amide group in the polypeptide chains of proteins had the planarity, bond lengths and bond angles that I had predicted, and also whether the assumption that I had been making about the formation of hydrogen bonds was justified. The decision was made by Corey and me that he would attack the experimental problem of determining the structure of some amino acids and simple peptides. This decision led to his determination of the structure of diketopiperazine in 1938, of glycine (with Gustav Albrecht) in 1939, and of alanine (with Henry Levy) in 1941, and ultimately, through the efforts also of E. W. Hughes, Jerry Donohue, Werner Shomaker, David Shoemaker, Walter Moore, Kenneth Trueblood, R. A. Pasternak, Gene Carpenter, Harry Yakel, Jr., and others, to accurate structure determinations of many amino acids and simple peptides. Corey's year in Pasadena turned out to be 30 years, so far.

By 1948 it has become quite clear that the conclusions about the planarity of the amide group, values of bond lengths and bond angles, and formation and properties of hydrogen bonds that I had reached in 1937 were, in fact, valid. One day, in the spring of 1948, when I was in bed with a cold in Oxford, England, where I was serving as Eastman Visiting Professor, I decided to attack again the problem of the structure of the α-keratin proteins. Starting with the idea that the operation of a rotation and a translation, when repeated, gives rise to a helical structure of equivalent groups, I soon found, with the aid only of a sheet of paper which I could twist into cylindrical form, that helical configurations of polypeptide chains could be devised in which the structural parameters have the accepted values and hydrogen bonds are formed between amide groups and their neighbors in adjacent turns of the helix. During the next few years this idea led to a tremendous amount of work, in the prediction of many alternative helical structures, some with several strands of helices. Much of this work remained unpublished. In particular, our results about the effect of different amino acid residues in influencing the bending of the polypeptide chain from one α-helix segment to another has not been published in detail.

I shall not discuss, in this lecture, the recent history of the field of protein structure, except in relation to collagen. In 1951 Professor Corey and I proposed a structure for collagen, involving three polypeptide chains twisted about one another. In devising this structure we had found it necessary to assume that in each polypeptide chain there is an alternation of two amide groups with the *cis*-configuration and one with the *trans*-configuration. It is well known that our structure turned out not to be right. In a lecture on the stochastic method and the structure of proteins that I gave in Stockholm in 1953, at the Thirteenth International Congress of Pure and Applied Chemistry, I pointed out that in applying the stochastic method the first step is to make a hypothesis, a guess. The second step is to test the hypothesis, by some comparison with experiment. In general the test cannot be sufficiently thorough to provide rigorous proof that the hypothesis is correct: it may happen that it can easily be shown that the hypothesis is incorrect, through the discovery of a significant disagreement with experiment, but agreement on a limited number of points cannot be accepted as verification of the hypothesis. In order for the stochastic method to be significant, the principles used in formulating the hypothesis must be restrictive enough to make the hypothesis itself essentially unique; in other words, an investigator who makes use of this method should, I contended, be allowed only one guess. If he were allowed many guesses he would sooner or later make one that was not in disagreement with the limited number of test points, but there would then be little justification for accepting that guess as correct. At that time (1953), however, I contended that Professor Corey and I together should be allowed two guesses on collagen, and I stated that we were determined that our second one would be right.

As you all know, it turned out that Professor Corey and I did not get to make our second guess. In 1955 Professor Ramachandran and his co-worker G. Kartha described the striking triple-helical structure of collagen that is now generally accepted as being essentially correct. Although I may have some feeling of regret that Professor Corey and I did not succeed in making our second guess (which I trust would have turned out to be the right one), I may point out that the problem was a very difficult one, and that Professor Ramachandran and his co-workers deserve great credit for their successful attack on it, and for their continuing vigorous effort in the solution of the many difficult problems in the field of protein structure and other aspects of structural chemistry to which they have devoted themselves for many years.

PROTEINS AND POLYPEPTIDES

A. X-Ray Diffraction and Stereochemical Studies

A Report on Recent Calculations on Rhombohedral Insulin Crystals Containing Lead

M. J. Adams, G. Dodson, E. Dodson and
Dorothy Crowfoot Hodgkin

Chemical Crystallography Laboratory, University of Oxford, England

Lead-containing rhombohedral insulin crystals can be prepared by removing the zinc from 2Zn insulin crystals by soaking overnight in 0·1% EDTA and then soaking in lead acetate containing buffer. The crystals give X-ray photographs showing marked anomalous dispersion effects; they contain two lead atoms per unit cell which can be placed by difference Patterson calculations along the three-fold axis. Measurements have been made of the intensities of all reflections to spacings of 4·5 Å and phase angles assigned to about 2/3 of these. Very approximate electron density maps derived from these terms show features suggesting some parts of the molecule have α-helix character.

1. Introduction

In the presence of zinc and sodium chloride, insulin crystallises from aqueous solutions in two rhombohedral forms which contain a minimum of two zinc ions and four zinc ions respectively per six insulin molecules; the two rhombohedral unit cells contain six insulin molecules of weight varying according to species. Most of our experiments have been carried out on specially purified pig insulin (molecular weight 5778), given to us by Dr J. Schlichtkrull (Novo-Terapeutisk Laboratorium, Copenhagen) and recrystallized according to methods described by him. Occasionally we have also worked with beef insulin given us by Boots Pure Drug Co. Ltd. Table 1 records preliminary X-ray data on 2Zn and 4Zn insulin crystals (Harding *et al.*, 1966; Dodson *et al.*, 1966, report work on these).

When D. A. Scott first discovered that zinc was present in rhombohedral insulin crystals, he experimented on the replacement of zinc by other metals

TABLE 1. Data on rhombohedral insulin crystals

	$a_H(\text{Å})$	$c_H(\text{Å})$	$a_R(\text{Å})$	α_R	Solvent content
2Zn Insulin	82·5	34·0	49·0	114·8°	30%
4Zn Insulin	80·7	37·6	48·2	113·4°	34%

and showed that similar crystals would grow in the presence of iron, cobalt, nickel and cadmium as well as zinc. Schlichtkrull (1956) also investigated the behaviour of these metals and also of copper in promoting the growth of insulin crystals. An early attempt to grow crystals containing lead was made by Dr F. Bertinotti at Oxford; very small crystals grew in one preparation but it was found impossible to repeat the crystallization. Recently, B. G. Malmström, P. O. Nyman, B. Strandberg and B. Tilander (private communication) showed that it was possible to remove zinc from crystals of human erythrocyte carbonic anhydrase by chelating agents and then to replace the zinc by other metals. Following their suggestions, we have tried similar experiments on zinc insulin crystals. It proves to be easy to remove zinc from 2Zn crystals and also to introduce certain alternative metals, which include lead, into the crystals. No success has so far been achieved in replacing zinc in 4Zn crystals by similar measures, as the crystals break up when the zinc is removed.

2. Lead Insulin Crystals

To prepare lead insulin, well-formed 2Zn insulin rhombohedra are left for several days in a citrate buffer solution containing 0·1 % EDTA solution. The buffer is then changed first to acetate buffer alone and then to acetate buffer containing 0·01 M lead acetate. Crystals photographed after a few hours show changes in intensity; they are generally left for 24 h at least in the lead containing solutions, after which further changes have not been observed. Spectrophotometric analysis with dithizone proves the presence in the crystals of 2–3 Pb atoms per six molecules of insulin. The lead-containing crystals appear a little cloudy to the eye but give good X-ray reflections out to a limit of 1·8 Å. These reflections show markedly the effects of anomalous dispersion due to the presence of lead in the crystals. An example is the evident trigonal symmetry of the reflections of type (3030) on Fig. 1.

Measurements were first made of the intensities of reflections from 2Zn insulin on the linear diffractometer out to a limit of 2·0 Å and 2Pb insulin crystals for $hkl(+)$ reflections only to a limit of 2·2 Å. To make use, for phasing purposes, of the anomalous dispersion effects, more careful measurements were next made of the complete sphere of reflections for Pb insulin initially out to a spacing of 4·5 Å only. These were achieved by mounting a crystal to rotate about its c-axis, measuring the reflections first on the $+l$ side, then reversing the tube with the crystal, remounting and measuring on the $-l$ side. The flat rhombohedra were oriented into a suitable position across thin-walled glass tubes by careful manipulation of both crystal and mother liquor with fine glass threads. Normal corrections were applied to the intensity data and absorption corrections derived through measurements on the variation of the axial reflections. The data were scaled by Wilson's method assuming no solvent of crystallization.

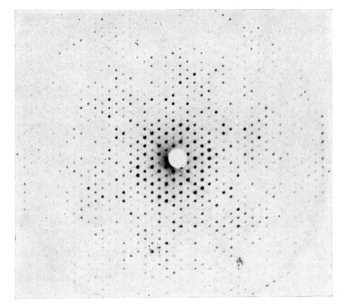

FIG. 1. Precession photograph showing $hik0$ reflections for 2Pb insulin.

3. Use of Anomalous Dispersion Data

From the scaled intensities recorded for the individual reflections for each $hkil$ index type, and the derived figures for $F^2_{2\text{Zn I}}$, $F^{2(+)}_{2\text{Pb I}}$ and $F^{2(-)}_{2\text{Pb I}}$, a value could be calculated in many cases for an estimate of the real part of the lead structure factor, F_{Pb} (cf. Matthews, 1966; Singh & Ramaseshan, 1966). This estimate, which excludes possible zinc contributions, was derived from the expression:

$$F^2_{\text{Pb}} = \left|F_{2\text{Zn I}}\right|^2 + \left|F_m\right|^2 \pm 2F_{2\text{Zn I}}\left\{\left|F_m\right|^2 - \left(\frac{\Delta}{F_{2\text{Zn I}}}\frac{f'_{\text{Pb}}}{4f''_{\text{Pb}}}\right)^2\right\}^{\frac{1}{2}}$$

where

$$\left|F_m\right|^2 = \tfrac{1}{2}(F^{2(+)}_{2\text{Pb I}} + F^{2(-)}_{2\text{Pb I}}) \text{ and } \Delta = F^{2(+)}_{2\text{Pb I}} - F^{2(-)}_{2\text{Pb I}}$$

Patterson distributions were then calculated with the lower of the two possible estimates, F^2_{LPb}, as coefficients (Fig. 2) and also with $F^2_{2\text{Pb I}} - F^2_{2\text{Zn I}}$ and $(F_{2\text{Pb I}} - F_{2\text{Zn I}})^2$ as coefficients. Limits were set for the terms used at both 6 Å and 4·5 Å. All the distributions calculated were very similar. All showed two peaks as most prominent along the threefold axis with z close to $\pm0\cdot115$, implying the presence of two lead atom positions along the threefold axis separated by 7·8 Å. Evidence was later obtained from difference-Fourier

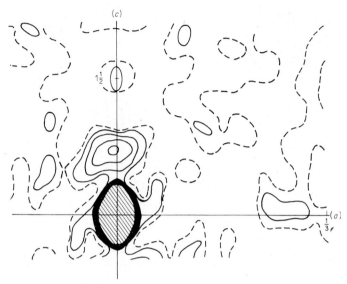

FIG. 2. Section of three-dimensional Patterson function for Pb insulin calculated with coefficients F_{LPb}, showing Pb–Pb vector peak, 4·5 Å, section at $y = 0$.

maps calculated with coefficients $F_{2PbI} - F_{2ZnI}$ and the phase angles derived for lead insulin that the zinc atoms were probably placed differently from the lead atoms and at $z = \pm 0·21$. Though there are indications of this parameter from the Patterson series they are far from precise.

Two separate series of approximate electron density calculations have been made from the data so far described, one for lead insulin and the other for 2Zn insulin.

For 2Pb insulin, $\sin \alpha_{2PbI}$ was calculated from the expression (Ramachandran & Raman, 1956):

$$\sin \alpha_{2PbI} = \frac{F_{2PbI}^{2(+)} - F_{2PbI}^{2(-)}}{4F'_{2PbI}F''_{Pb}}$$

and the relative magnitude of F_{2ZnI} and F_{2PbI} was then used to determine the quadrant of the phase angle. After the first evaluation, a correction was introduced to allow for the probable contribution of zinc to the difference between F_{2ZnI} and F_{2PbI}. Very few zinc contributions were, however, sufficiently large to affect the quadrant chosen. In all, 182/241 phase angles were defined in the 6 Å sphere and 350/450 phase angles in the 4·5 Å sphere. Among those omitted were all reflections where either F_{2ZnI} and $F_{2PbI}^{(+)}$ or $F_{2PbI}^{(-)}$ were zero, also all terms with $l = 2$, since F''_{Pbcalc} is only four electrons for reflections with $l = 2$.

For 2Zn insulin phase angles, $\alpha_{2\text{ZnI}}$ were derived by regarding $F^{(+)}_{2\text{PbI}}$ and $F^{(-)}_{2\text{PbI}}$ as two independent isomorphous derivatives. In the 6-Å sphere 209/241 phases were defined and in the 4·5-Å sphere 400/470. Again, where $F_{2\text{ZnI}}$, $F^{(+)}_{2\text{PbI}}$ or $F^{(-)}_{2\text{PbI}}$ were zero, the phase was undetermined; the $l = 2$ reflexions were also left out since the anomalous term, F''_{Pb} was too small to define the phase. The method employed was to calculate the phase probability for each one of the Bijvoet pairs individually and to combine these probabilities; two of the angles with a high probability should coincide. The method is essentially that of Blow & Crick (1959) but with no weighting scheme. A typical example of a phase angle determination is illustrated in Fig. 3.

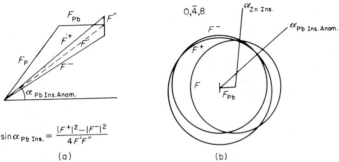

$$\sin \alpha_{\text{Pb Ins.}} = \frac{|F^+|^2 - |F^-|^2}{4\,F'F''}$$

(a)　　　　　　　　(b)

FIG. 3. Diagram illustrating phase derivations for (a) 2Pb insulin from anomalous dispersion relations and (b) 2Zn insulin from 2Pb and 2Zn insulin relations.

4. Discussion of the Maps

Two main series of approximate electron density distributions were then calculated for 2Pb insulin and 2Zn insulin, with terms terminated at 6 Å and 4·5 Å spacing. The lead and zinc insulin maps at each resolution are very similar, except, as would be expected, along the threefold axis. The lead insulin maps show here very large peaks at the expected lead positions. The zinc insulin maps show small peaks at ± 0.2 and ± 0.4 and also a peak at $z = 0$. These may indicate other zinc sites but are more probably a reflection of incomplete breakdown of the symmetry of the Patterson. It is obvious that the maps so far calculated are very imperfect and must contain apparent density of no structural significance. Nevertheless, they do also show many features which are very suggestive and warrant a brief description. These features, which appear in both lead and zinc insulin maps, are as follows. (1) All the maps show very clearly density which repeats through rotations of 180° about axes which lie in the planes $z = 0$ and $\frac{1}{2}$ and at angles of 44° and 104° to a. The twofold repetition of the electron density is best defined near the plane $z = 0$ and in the higher resolution, 4·5 Å, maps. It is illustrated in Fig. 4. The positions of the twofold axes observed in the maps are closely

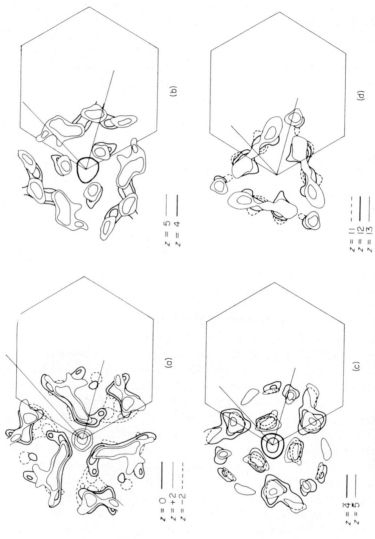

Fig. 4. Sections in electron density map calculated for 2Pb insulin at 5·5 Å resolution; the phasing here included a correction for the zinc contributions. The numbers indicate the *z* level in *c*/24: (a) 2, 0, 2̄; (b) 4, 5; (c) 4̄, 5̄; (d) 11, 12, 13.

those expected from the earlier studies of the intensity distributions in 2Zn insulin. (2) Around the positions of the twofold axes, there is considerable emptiness in the electron density maps. This too is most clear in the higher resolution maps and near the plane $z = 0$. (3) The presence of two insulin molecules in the crystallographic asymmetric unit provides us with a double view of the structure of insulin. Where the similarity of two regions in our maps related by the twofold axes is marked, we feel considerable confidence in the relevance of the electron density observed to the insulin structures. In a few regions, where considerable differences appear, we have more hesitation in accepting the evidence of our present maps, although it is formally quite possible that the conformation of the two insulin molecules is not entirely identical. The degree of twofold symmetry we observe does suggest that a large part of the conformation is the same in both molecules. (4) The regions where there is most obvious similarity between the two molecules appearing in our maps are two chain-like regions. One of these is a short length, about 9 Å long, nearly parallel with the threefold axis, the other, tenuously linked to it, is about 14 Å long, at roughly 10° to the c-plane. At low resolution, in the 6 Å maps, these regions appear as dense continuous chains (cf. Fig. 4(a–c)). At 4·5 Å resolution they are clearly hollow and show density distributions strongly suggestive of α-helices. The main peaks correspond in position to unresolved side-chain masses linked by strands of density following the directions of the peptide chains. A small part of one of these regions is illustrated in Fig. 5, which shows how well the observed density corresponds with part of one of the insulin chains. (5) There is a large region of density in the angle between these chains which is much more incoherent in general form and which also repeats roughly by the twofold axis operation. That there should be a region of this kind, impossible to interpret at low resolution, is very reasonable in relation to the known chemical structure of insulin. (6) At 6 Å resolution the electron density outlined appears to limit the boundary of one insulin hexamer to a region approximately 25 Å from the three-fold axis. Within the hexamer, it is, however, not at present possible to distinguish the insulin dimer that persists in solution. Formally any of the twofold axes of the crystal might be the axis around which the dimer is constructed.

The observations listed above have been assisted by the construction of perspex models illustrating the electron density distributions at 6 Å and 4·5 Å resolution. We have also attempted to build a detailed model of the insulin molecule to fit the known chemical structure of insulin to the electron density outlines. The starting point for this model is the probability that the sections of observed α-helix-like chains are parts of the B chains of insulin and that the amino terminal end of the B chain is likely to be near the trigonal axis to enable the histidine groups to interact with zinc or lead. Although a

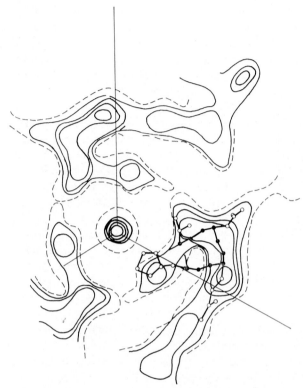

FIG. 5. Electron density map calculated for 2Pb insulin at 4·5 Å resolution: section at $z = 6c/30$. The residues drawn over the contours illustrate the dimensions of the α-helix-like region near the threefold axis.

model built on these lines is plausible, it does not appear worthwhile at present to discuss it in detail. With the accumulation of more data on lead insulin and other insulin derivatives, we hope to obtain clearer evidence on the detailed structure of the insulin molecule.

REFERENCES

Blow, D. M. & Crick, F. H. C. (1959). *Acta cryst.* **12,** 794.

Dodson, E., Harding, M. M., Hodgkin, D. C. & Rossmann, M. G. (1966). *J. molec. Biol.* **16,** 227.

Harding, M. M., Hodgkin, D. C., Kennedy, A. F., O'Connor, A. & Weitzmann, P. D. J. (1966). *J. molec. Biol.* **16,** 212.

Matthews, B. W. (1966). *Acta cryst.* **20,** 230.

Ramachandran, G. N. & Raman, S. (1956). *Current Sci., India,* **25,** 348.

Schlichtkrull, J. (1956). *Acta chem. Scand.* **10,** 1455.

Singh, A. K. & Ramaseshan, S. (1966). *Acta cryst.* **21,** 279.

A Low-resolution Crystallographic Study of Ribonuclease

H. P. Avey, M. O. Boles, C. H. Carlisle, S. A. Evans, S. J. Morris, R. A. Palmer, B. A. Woolhouse

Department of Crystallography, Birkbeck College, London, England

AND

S. Shall

Department of Biochemistry, University of Sussex, England

A low resolution (5·5 Å) electron density map of ribonuclease has been calculated using the multiple isomorphous replacement method for phasing the X-ray reflection. Five metal-substituted crystals were employed for this purpose.

Using the known primary structure of the enzyme, the interpretation of the map reveals a molecule containing a "cleft". Inhibitors have been located in this cleft which identify it as the probable active site of the molecule.

A low resolution electron-density map of crystalline ribonuclease, in which only reflections to a spacing of 5·5 Å were used, has been obtained by using the multiple-isomorphous-replacement technique for phasing the X-ray reflections (Harker, 1956) with five metal-substituted crystals (Dickerson *et al.*, 1961; Cullis *et al.*, 1962). It is not intended, in this article, to describe the X-ray side of the work (see Table 1), but rather to deal briefly with the

TABLE 1. Basic X-ray data

Unit cell dimensions of ribonuclease
$a = 30\cdot31$ Å, $b = 38\cdot26$ Å, $c = 52\cdot91$ Å, $\beta = 105°55'$
Space group $P2_1$
Number of molecules per unit cell $= 2$

results arising from it, as it is this part of the work that will be of more interest to the members of the Symposium than the description of technical detail.

In discussing these results, it should be appreciated that the interpretations of the electron-density map would not have been possible without the knowledge of the amino acid sequence of ribonuclease (Smyth *et al.*, 1963). The

17

molecule is made up of a single polypeptide chain of 124 amino acids, cross-linked by four cystine residues at positions 26 and 84, 40 and 95, 58 and 110, and 65 and 72. For convenience these pairs of linkages are identified by pairs of Roman numerals, I–VI, II–VII, III–VIII and IV–V (see Fig. 1).

Another feature of the enzyme is that the histidine residues at positions 12 and 119 and the lysine at position 41 are in some way collectively responsible for the activity of this enzyme. Any model put forward from a crystallo-

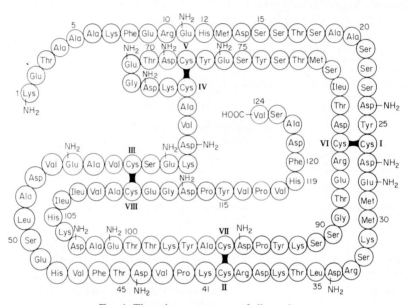

FIG. 1. The primary structure of ribonuclease.

graphic study must therefore show these amino acids, which are situated at such widely different points in the sequence, in sensible relationships to one another in the tertiary structure of the molecule.

Two chemical aspects, both involving inhibitory effects on the enzyme, have played an important part in the elucidation of its broad structure. The first has been the observation that it has been possible to add mercaptide groups to two lysine residues in the molecule. One of these leaves the enzyme in an inactive state and the lysine affected in this case is very probably the one situated at position 41 in the sequence. It has been possible, accordingly, to attach a mercury derivative to this thiolated lysine, and through location of the heavy atom, to identify the approximate position of this lysine residue in the molecule. The other thiolated lysine has not yet been definitely identified, but it is possible that it is either the one at the amino end of the chain or the one at position 7.

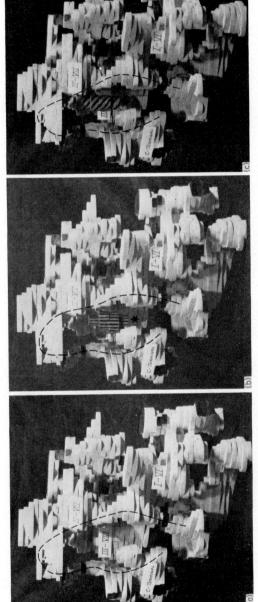

FIG. 2. (a) Solid model of the electron density of ribonuclease, (b) as (a), but including, in the "cleft", the electron density due to the nucleotide (vertical stripes), (c) as (a), but showing, in the "cleft", the electron density due to the mercury atom derivative attached to lysine 41 (diagonal stripes).

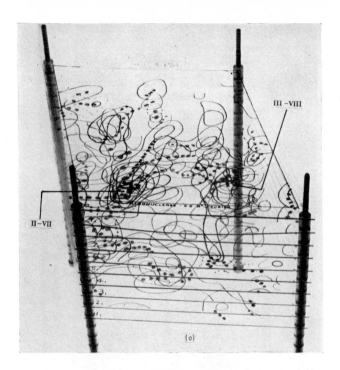

(a)

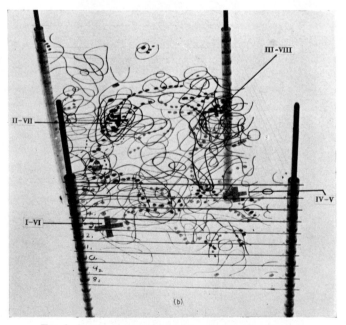

(b)

Fig. 3. Overlapping sections of the electron-density map.

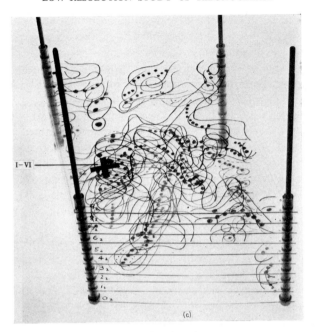

FIG. 3. Continued.

The second point of interest is that the nucleotide 2′-cytidylic acid inhibits the activity of the enzyme, and it is likely that it does so by attaching itself to one or both of the two histidines at the active site. Its location therefore is of considerable importance in the structure analysis, for it would permit the active region of the molecule to be identified.

Figure 2(a) shows a wooden model of the molecule derived from the electron-density map (Fig. 3(a–c)). As such a model shows only the lower levels of electron density, it is not easily interpretable, but it does reveal, by the dashed line, that it contains a cleft in which, as can be seen in Fig. 2(b), the nucleotide inhibitor has been located. It is therefore in this region that the three amino acids responsible for enzyme activity must be found when we come to calculate and interpret the high-resolution 2·0 Å map of this molecule.

An important clue to the interpretation of the electron density map, shown in Fig. 3(a–c) as three separate overlapping regions, came through the location of the mercury–thiolactone of the inactive ribonuclease. This group, as can be seen in Fig. 2(c), was also located in the "cleft" of the molecule. A noticeable feature of the difference Fourier map, which was used to locate this heavy-atom derivative, was the appearance of a column of electron density rising upwards from the mercury-atom position towards a heavy peak, which judging by the sinuous distributions of density emerging from it, could only be a cystine region.

Here was a clue to the interpretation of the electron-density map itself; for if this heavy region was a cystine, it could only be II–VII. It was not a difficult matter to trace the location of another cystine region lying on the far side of the cleft (see Fig. 2(a)) for it was connected to II–VII by two sinuous distributions of electron density. This cystine was identified as III–VIII, because situated near to it, about 15 Å along *a*, was another heavy region that could only be another cystine residue, as judged again by the sinuous distributions of electron density emerging from it. As cystine III–VIII is connected to IV–V by only six amino acid residues (see Fig. 1), it was clear that these two heavy regions of electron density could only be III–VIII and IV–V respectively.

The locations of the remaining cystine residue, I–VI follows naturally from the fact that it is chemically attached to IV–V by a single chain of 11 amino acid residues. Without going into detail, it was not difficult to find a fourth heavy region that was connected to IV–V and also to II–VII, thus completing the link in the chain of cystines.

The four cystine residues, their positions approximately marked by crosses, are found to lie in a crude ring of electron density as seen in Fig 3(b). The normal to this ring system lies approximately perpendicular to ($\overline{3}$04), which set of planes gives rise to one of the strongest X-ray reflections from this crystal.

Although there must be, at this stage of the analysis, some element of uncertainty in the exact conformation of the amino and carboxyl ends of the chain, namely residues 1–25 and 111–124 respectively, there is enough evidence from the electron-density map to support the view that these two ends of the chain tuck in on the same side of the molecule. In fact, the electron-density distribution indicates that these two chains approach each other, and nearly come together, indicating the proximity of histidines 12 and 119 respectively. An interesting observation arising out of this is that these two histidines lie at one end of the cleft and lysine 41 apparently lies at its other end, thus yielding a plausible picture of the spatial relationships of these three amino acids.

Figure 4 shows a wire model of the approximate conformation of the backbone of the polypeptide chain of ribonuclease. Obviously it cannot be accurate in detail, but if the four cystines have been correctly located, then at least the model shows how these residues are connected to form the core of the molecule.

Table 2 shows the heavy atom derivatives used in the phasing of the X-ray reflections, together with a summary of the heavy atom parameters.

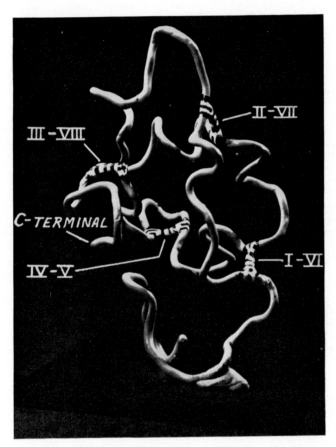

FIG. 4. Wire model showing the approximate conformation of the backbone of the polypeptide chain of ribonuclease.

TABLE 2. Heavy-atom parameters

	x	y	z	B	Z
RNase-*p*-hydroxymercuribenzene-sulphonate	0·957	0·448	0·949	77·8	39·7
	0·317	0·472	0·542	61·4	31·5
	0·922	0·031	0·948	80·1	8·4
	0·188	0·090	0·089	48·3	21·8
RNase-IrCl$_6$	0·786	0·068	0·374	150·0	45·5
	0·018	0·014	0·064	153·9	25·3
	0·929	0·359	0·009	191·8	29·8
RNase-cytidylic acid–uranyl pentafluoride	0·977	0·289	0·011	102·3	68·1
	0·958	0·992	0·072	137·8	66·5
	0·280	0·442	0·919	57·7	15·5
	0·254	0·290	0·521	52·9	18·9
RNase–uranyl pentafluoride	0·971	0·961	0·076	59·9	35·3
	0·950	0·312	0·002	50·3	37·6
	0·155	0·228	0·415	50·4	13·2
Homocysteinyl–RNase(1)†	0·769	0·048	0·965	64·4	47·8

† Homocysteinyl–RNase(2), the inactive derivative, was not used in the calculation of the phases.

x, y, z are the crystallographic co-ordinates of atoms, B is the isotropic thermal vibration parameter, Z is the statistical site occupancy in electrons.

REFERENCES

Cullis, A. F., Muirhead, H., Perutz, M. F., Rossmann, M. G. & North, A. C. T. (1962). *Proc. R. Soc.* **A265**, 15.

Dickerson, R. E., Kendrew, J. C. & Strandberg, B. E. (1961). *In* "Computing Methods and the Phase Problem in X-ray Crystal Analysis", ed. by R. Pepinsky, J. M. Robertson & J. C. Speakman, p. 236. Oxford: Pergamon Press.

Harker, D. (1956). *Acta cryst.* **9**, 1.

Smyth, D. G., Stein, W. H. & Moore, S. (1963). *J. biol. Chem.* **238**, 227.

Addendum

G. KARTHA

Crystallography Center, Roswell Park Memorial Institute, Buffalo, N.Y., U.S.A.

I should like to add a few remarks on some recent results of our study of ribonuclease in the same crystalline form that has been described.

Our investigations on the tertiary structure of the protein ribonuclease were started by Professor David Harker at the Protein Structure Project of the Polytechnic Institute of Brooklyn in 1950 and has continued at the Roswell Park Memorial Institute since 1959. We have been trying to solve the structure of this protein by single crystal X-ray diffraction methods using a combination of isomorphous series and anomalous scattering techniques. During the past four years these studies have resulted in electron density maps of increasing resolution starting with 4 Å. Recently, we have computed a map at 2 Å involving over 7200 protein reflections and data from seven derivative crystals in addition to the free protein. Our aim in these studies has been to depend, as much as possible, on the X-ray data and electron density maps to show the conformation of the molecule. Use was made of aspects of the known amino acid sequence only as check points to confirm the course of the main chains as it is followed up from the amino end, which was clearly visible even in the earlier maps. We believe that this 2 Å map clearly shows the way in which the polypeptide chain is folded up in the molecule and have constructed a model which shows the approximate locations of the successive α-carbon atoms of the chain.

It has been noted from this model that the helical content of the molecule is very low, the only ovbious one being near the amino end. This low helical content is perhaps one of the main reasons for the difficulty encountered in attempting to correctly interpret low resolution electron density maps of this protein. It also suggests that, if the S-peptide obtained by subtilisin modification of ribonuclease is studied in isolation, it will reveal a high helical content (if, as is likely, the conformation of this part of the chain is unaltered by cleavage at residue 20) compared to the low overall helical content of the native ribonuclease. We have located the position of the phosphate group in the crystals from difference electron density comparison between phosphate and arsenate ribonuclease crystals. This group is located in a depression on one side of the molecule, and has one histidine residue 119 near the carboxyl end and another histidine residue 12 near the amino end in close proximity. At somewhat greater distances are the lysines 7 and 41 and histidine 48. Some of these features are in good agreement with chemical information that has accumulated regarding the environment of the active site of this protein. It is hoped to obtain more information regarding the side group interactions and nature of the active site from a more detailed study of the 2 Å electron density maps. This is now in progress.

Chemical Modification of Proteins for X-Ray Investigation†

M. P. VENKATAPPA

*Department of Chemistry, Bangalore University, Central College,
Bangalore, India*

AND

L. K. STEINRAUF

*Department of Biochemistry, Indiana University
Medical School, Indianapolis, Indiana, U.S.A.*

Two heavy atom derivatives of lysozyme: INP (4-iodo-2-nitrophenyl) lysozyme and iodolysozyme, have been prepared and crystallized. The INP lysozyme was prepared by reacting the crystalline protein in buffered medium at neutral pH with the INFB (4-iodo-2-nitrofluorobenzene) reagent, devised and synthesized in our laboratory. Iodolysozyme has been prepared by directly iodinating the crystalline protein at a pH range of 4–5. Both the derivatives have been crystallized in the triclinic and orthorhombic form. These crystals could be used for the study of the three-dimensional structure of lysozyme by X-ray diffraction.

Amino acid analysis of the acid hydrolysate of INP lysozyme in an automatic analyser, and paper electrophoresis at pH 3·6 and pH 6·4 of the tryptic digest of the heat denatured derivative have shown that only the residue No. 13 (which is a lysine) has been attacked by the INFB reagent. Paper electrophoresis of the tryptic digest of the heat denatured iodolysozyme at pH's 3·6 and 6·4 has shown the single histidine in lysozyme has been iodinated.

Biological activity studies on these derivatives have indicated that the particular lysine and the single histidine in lysozyme are not at the active site and so they are not responsible for the biological function.

1. Introduction

The mechanisms by which each protein or an enzyme performs its biological function are obviously of great interest. The biological function of a protein depends not only on its primary structure or the sequence of its amino acids,

† Most of the material for this paper is taken from the thesis of M. P. Venkatappa submitted to the Graduate College of the University of Illinois in partial fulfilment of the requirements for the degree of Doctor of Philosophy, June, 1965.

This work was supported by the grants from the National Institutes of Health, United States Public Health Service and the Heart Research Center of Indiana University Medical School, Indianapolis, Indiana, U.S.A.

but also on its secondary and its tertiary structures. Secondary structure of a polypeptide chain may be either helical or nonhelical or both. Tertiary structure is the three-dimensional arrangement of secondary structure so that the particular amino acid residues that comprise the "active site" are brought into a unique position suitable for biological function.

The problem of primary structure even though a laborious task to the chemist has been solved in many cases, e.g. insulin, ribonuclease, myoglobin, tobacco mosaic virus protein, trypsin, chymotrypsin, lysozyme and a number of others. The determination of secondary and tertiary structure by either chemical or physical means is still a highly difficult task with a low chance of success.

Proteins have been examined by physical methods such as electrophoresis, sedimentation, diffusion, light scattering, osmotic pressure and viscosity to obtain information about their homogeneity, molecular size and shape and also about their conformation in solution. In the last several years, X-ray crystallography has been applied to the problem of solving the three-dimensional structure of crystalline proteins. The method known as the multiple isomorphous replacement technique (MIR technique), which has become the basis for the determination of phases in X-ray crystallography of proteins, requires excellent crystals of the native protein and at least two isomorphous heavy atom derivatives. The only two proteins which have yielded nicely to X-ray investigation are myoglobin and haemoglobin. This is because of their high helix content and the availability of a good series of heavy atom derivatives. Perhaps the most extraordinary fact about the helix in proteins is that it is a highly organized configuration which responds very nicely to X-ray analysis. However, many proteins such as insulin, ribonuclease, trypsin, chymotrypsin and lysozyme are low helix proteins; furthermore, good isomorphous heavy atom derivatives are not always available with these proteins.

Proteins have been modified chemically with reagents which do not contain any heavy atoms. This chemical modification has been investigated for three main purposes: (1) to alter the activity or physical characteristics of proteins in order to render them suitable for medical and industrial use; (2) to determine the nature and number of amino acid residues responsible for biological activity; and (3) to prepare specific protein derivatives for comparative study of the hydrodynamic or biological properties of the unmodified protein. For X-ray crystallography of proteins, however, heavy atom derivatives isomorphous with the native protein are essential. They can be used not only for the solving of phases in the determination of three-dimensional structure of proteins, but also to locate crystallographically as well as chemically, particular amino acids suspected of being responsible for the biological function.

In most of the heavy atom derivatives used for X-ray investigation, the heavy atoms are not covalently linked to the proteins. These are complexes of heavy metal ions, such as Hg^{II} and Au^{III}, with the protein and have not been investigated in a systematic manner. There seems to be little possibility of predicting the site on a protein to which such a complex will be attached. Indeed some complexes seem to have to fit into a void of convenient size and shape near the surface of the protein. Neither any theory of formation of the derivatives nor any systematic approach in their method of preparation have appeared. Only a few heavy atom reagents have been used to modify a protein chemically for the purpose of X-ray investigation. A brief review of the work in progress in various laboratories on the chemical modification of proteins for X-ray diffraction studies would be of some interest here.

The p-chloromercuribenzoate (PCMB) reagent, which is specific for cysteine residue, was used to prepare isomorphous heavy atom derivatives of haemoglobin for the determination of its three-dimensional structure. However, many proteins do not possess free sulfhydryl groups. The use of this reagent is therefore restricted. Attempts are now being made to replace an amino acid residue in a protein by a cysteine thus providing an accessible –SH group for the purpose of attaching a mercury reagent. R. Leberman and K. C. Holmes (private communication) have replaced a tyrosine in the mutant of TMV by a cysteine. Benesch reagent is used by S. Shall (private communication) to introduce a thiol into ribonuclease.

Pipsyl chloride (p-iodobenzene sulfonyl chloride) and pipsyl fluoride have been used to prepare a heavy atom derivative of α-chymotrypsin. This derivative was prepared with a view to locating the active serine residue chemically (Kallos & Rizok, 1964) and crystallographically (Sigler et al., 1964) respectively. Recently p-chloromercuribenzenesulfonyl fluoride (PCMBSF) has also been used to link covalently the active serine residue with a heavy atom, and thus locate the active site crystallographically (Sigler et al., 1965). Because of the variability of relative occupancy, this derivative was considered to be unsuitable for use in structure determination. The pipsyl derivative, however, has been found to give useful phase information. J. Kraut and his collaborators at La Jolla, California, are using similar sulfonyl fluorides to label subtilisin and α-chymotrypsin.

J. Drenth and J. N. Jansonius (private communication) are trying to attach iodo derivative of the Edmund's reagent at specific sites in crystalline papain for X-ray diffraction studies of the protein.

In this study we have prepared and crystallized two heavy atom derivatives of lysozyme: INP (4-iodo-2-nitrophenyl) lysozyme and iodolysozyme. The former was prepared by reacting the crystalline protein with the INFB (4-iodo-2-nitrofluorobenzene) reagent devised and synthesized in our laboratory, and the latter by direct iodination with iodine. The amino acid

residues attacked have been located chemically as well as crystallographically.†
The effect of this chemical modification on the biological activity of the protein
has also been investigated.

2. Materials and Methods

(a) Preparation and purification of lysozyme

Lysozyme required for our research was prepared by us from hen egg-white
as described by Alderton & Fevold (1946) and modified by Steinrauf.
Briefly the method is as follows:

Six dozen egg-whites were strained through a cheesecloth to break up the
membranes, sodium nitrate 5 % by weight was added, and the pH was adjusted
to 10·0 with 1 N sodium hydroxide. The mixture was seeded with crystals
of isoelectric lysozyme and stored in the cold room (4°C) for one week with
stirring at least twice a day. Lysozyme thus precipitated was removed by
centrifugation. This was washed with 5 % sodium nitrate solution whose pH
was adjusted to 9·5 with sodium borate and sodium hydroxide.

Lysozyme was extracted from this precipitate with dilute acetic acid at
pH 4·5. This extract was diluted until the concentration was 1 % and crystallized as triclinic or monoclinic lysozyme with 2 % sodium nitrate and acetate
buffer at pH 4·5, or as orthorhombic lysozyme with 2 % sodium chloride and
borate buffer at pH 10·0. This process of recrystallization was continued until
it was pure.

Lysozyme thus prepared was characterized by standard methods which
gave results that agreed, within the limits of experimental error, with reliable
sources from the literature. The protein had a single peak in the ultracentrifuge, and the value found for $S_{20, w}$ was 1·90 at pH 5·4. The intrinsic
viscosity was found to be 0·025±0·001 at pH 5·4 and 25°C. The ultraviolet
spectrum also agreed with the one reported in the literature.

The value of $E_{1\%}^{280 \, m\mu} = 26·35±0·18$ was used throughout this research
for the calculation of the concentration of lysozyme. A Beckman DU
spectrophotometer was used to measure the optical density of solutions of
lysozyme and its derivatives. The pH's of all solutions used in our research
were measured at 24°C using a Beckman Model G pH meter.

(b) Heavy atom reagents

(i) 4-Iodo-2-nitrofluorobenzene (INFB)

The principle involved in the synthesis of this reagent was to diazotize the
aniline: 4-fluoro-3-nitroaniline (m.p. 96°C), and subsequently to treat the
diazotized aniline with aqueous potassium iodide (Sandmeyer's reaction).

† The crystallographic location of the amino acid residues attacked is being investigated
at the Department of Biochemistry, Indiana University Medical School, Indianapolis,
Indiana, and will be published elsewhere.

In a three-necked flask, 5 g of 4-fluoro-3-nitroaniline was dissolved in 30 ml of conc. sulfuric acid, cooled and then 2·5 g of well-powdered sodium nitrite was added slowly with stirring. The mixture was kept below 5°C. Then 20 ml of 85% phosphoric acid was added to the mixture slowly with stirring in order to liberate nitrous acid from nitrosyl sulfuric acid. During the addition, the temperature was maintained below 10°C. The mixture was stirred until diazotization was complete.

The cold diazonium solution was added gradually with stirring to a cold solution of 7–8 g of potassium iodide in 20 ml of water (with a crystal of copper sulfate). The mixture was allowed to stand for an hour. Afterwards, it was warmed over a water bath until no more gas evolved. The mixture was cooled and any iodine that was present was removed by washing with 5% sodium bisulfite solution. The product was extracted with diethyl ether. The ether extract was dried with anhydrous calcium chloride and the large volume of ether removed in a rotary evaporator.

The product obtained might contain traces of phenol, hence it was purified by chromatography over a column of alumina, being eluted with ether containing increasing amounts of absolute alcohol. The eluent was evaporated to remove all solvent and the material left behind (presumably the product) was a liquid. It was cooled overnight at 4°C. Orange red crystals of the iodo derivative slowly formed and were recrystallized from absolute alcohol.

The melting point of these crystals could not be determined since they were highly hygroscopic. Micro analysis and infrared spectrum agree with those of the desired product: 4-iodo-2-nitrofluorobenzene.

Analysis—Calc. for $C_6H_3FNO_2I$: F, 7·2%; I, 48·1%.

Found: F, 7·78%; I, 48.89%.

This reagent showed specificity for lysine in reactions performed with lysozyme at or slightly above neutral pH. Important features of this reagent were: (1) it is highly selective and hence very useful in protein modification studies. Fluorodinitrobenzene (FDNB) which is analogous to this reagent is very reactive, so it is neither specific nor selective; it attacks histidine, tyrosine and cysteine residues in addition to lysine in proteins (Fraenkel-Conrat et al., 1955); (2) INFB reagent is sensitive to changes in environment and absorbs in a region of the spectrum where the protein is transparent.

The INFB reagent is soluble in acetonitrile, which mixes with water rapidly, and does not denature lysozyme in the proportions used. A 3% solution of this reagent in acetonitrile has been used for nucleophilic aromatic substitution reaction with crystalline lysozyme.

(ii) *Iodine*

Iodine used here was of A.R. grade. It was used without any further purification to iodinate lysozyme in the crystalline form.

A 0·1 N solution of iodine in potassium iodide was used for iodination.

(c) *Preparation and purification of lysozyme derivatives*

(i) *INP (4-iodo-2-nitrophenyl) lysozyme*

Lysozyme contains six lysine residues. Although the pK_a values of these lysines are in the neighborhood of 10·0 (Tanford & Wagner, 1954), it was decided to carry out the reaction with excess of the reagent at lower pH in buffered medium over long periods of time. This was done in order to limit the attack by the reagent to as few lysines as possible. When only a few sites are attacked, interpretation of the diffraction patterns will be easier.

Crystals of lysozyme (approx. 100 mg or 7×10^{-6} mole of triclinic or monoclinic crystals) in 10 ml of mother liquor were mixed with 0·5 ml of 0·1 M phosphate buffer, pH 7·0 and 0·2 ml of 30% sodium nitrate in a crystallizing dish. The pH was finally adjusted to 7·0 with dilute sodium hydroxide or acetic acid. Then 1 ml of 3% solution of INFB reagent in acetonitrile was added ($1·12 \times 10^{-4}$ mole) in small amounts at a time and the mixture shaken gently. The whole reaction mixture was allowed to stand for one week at room temperature.

The mother liquor was decanted, and the reacted crystals were dissolved in very dilute acetic acid ($\sim$pH 4·0) and dialysed for 3–4 days with frequent changes of distilled water. The dialysed solution was filtered using a sintered glass filter and the volume of the solution reduced until the protein concentration was approximately 1%. This pale yellow solution of INP lysozyme was used for crystallization.

This 1% solution of the derivative was crystallized in the triclinic form with 2% sodium nitrate and acetate buffer at pH 4·5, or in the orthorhombic form with 2% sodium chloride and borate buffer at pH 9·0. Excellent yellow colored crystals of both forms were obtained.

Both crystalline forms of INP lysozyme were purified by repeated recrystallization. The crystals obtained were of size suitable for X-ray diffraction studies.

(ii) *Iodolysozyme*

Lysozyme contains only one histidine and three tyrosines. This single histidine in lysozyme is more reactive than in most proteins, and tyrosines very unreactive (Fraenkel-Conrat, 1950). Our interest centered on the reactive histidine residue. The attack by I^+ on this residue or on tyrosines is one of electrophilic aromatic substitution. The imidazole ring must be free of charge for the electrophilic attack. The pK_a value of histidine in lysozyme is in the neighborhood of 7·0 (Tanford & Wagner, 1954). At alkaline pH, I^+ becomes unstable and will not be available for the electrophilic attack on tyrosines. Since we are interested in the histidine only, the pH range between 4 and 5 was chosen, and the iodination reaction carried out with excess reagent over long periods of time.

Crystals of lysozyme (triclinic or monoclinic, approx. 100 mg of 7×10^{-6} mole) in 10 ml of the mother liquor were treated with 0·1 N solution of iodine in potassium iodide in small quantities at a time for a period of one week. The mother liquor was decanted, and the reacted crystals were dissolved in very dilute acetic acid and dialysed for 3–4 days with frequent changes of distilled water. The dialysed solution was filtered using a sintered glass filter and the volume reduced until the concentration was 1%.

This colorless solution of iodolysozyme was crystallized in the triclinic form with 2% sodium nitrate and acetate buffer at pH 4·5, or in the orthorhombic form with 2% sodium chloride and borate buffer at pH 8·6–9·0. Excellent colorless crystals of both the forms were obtained.

Both crystalline forms were purified by repeated recrystallization and the crystals obtained were of appropriate size suitable for X-ray diffraction studies.

The ultraviolet spectra of lysozyme derivatives appeared to be the same as that of the native protein, within the limits of experimental error. This indicated that none of the amino acid residues: tyrosines, tryptophans and phenylalanine which contribute to the spectrum within the range investigated had been attacked by the heavy atom reagents. Therefore, we have used the $E_{1\%}^{280 \, m\mu}$ value of lysozyme to calculate the concentration of its derivatives also.

(d) Electrophoresis

Electrophoresis techniques were used to test the homogeneity and to determine the mobilities of lysozyme derivatives with respect to the native protein. Both paper electrophoresis and starch-gel electrophoresis were used.

The equipment used and the method followed for paper electrophoresis were those of Stong (1962). The cell used was actually constructed in our laboratory. The dye bath consisted of 50 ml of glacial acetic acid, 50 g of zinc sulphate and 0·1 g bromophenol blue dissolved in water to make one liter. Whatman No. 1 filter paper was used. The samples used for investigation consisted of 0·2% solutions of lysozyme or its derivatives, at least twice recrystallized. Electrophoresis of all the samples was carried out on the same strip of paper under identical conditions over a wide range of pH's for 3–6 hours at a constant potential of 200 volts.

Vertical starch-gel electrophoresis developed by Smithies (1959) was used. The apparatus designed by Samuel H. Boyer of the Johns Hopkins Hospital and University and manufactured by Buchler Instruments was used. The starch was purchased from Connaught Medical Research Labs., Toronto, Canada. Borate buffers 0·3 M (pH 8·10) for the wick and electrode chambers and 0·025 M (pH 8·60) for the gel preparations were used. The dye bath consisted of 0·5 g of aniline blue-black in 110 ml of clearing solution (methanol–water–acetic acid = 5 : 5 : 1).

The equipment used for the paper electrophoresis of the tryptic digests of lysozyme and its derivatives and the method followed are the same as before except that the staining reagents, the kind of filter paper, and the buffer systems used here are different. Whatman No. 3 filter paper was used. Volatile buffers such as pyridine–water–glacial acetic acid (10 : 890 : 100) at pH 3·6 and pyridine–water–glacial acetic acid (100 : 900 : 4) at pH 6·4 were used. A 0·25% solution of ninhydrin in acetone was used as the staining solution for most peptides and amino acids. Ehrlich's reagent (1 g of dimethylamino-benzaldehyde in 90 ml of acetone and 10 ml of conc. HCl) was used for tryptophan containing peptides. Ceric ammonium sulphate, sodium arsenite, methylene blue spray (Alexander & Block, 1960) were used to detect the iodinated amino acid residues in certain peptides.

(e) Tryptic digestion

Trypsin, supplied by Worthington Biochemicals, Freehold, New Jersey was used for the digestion of lysozyme and its derivatives. A 0·35% solution of the enzyme in 0·002 M calcium acetate was stored frozen until used.

Tryptic hydrolysis was effected on 3 ml of 1% solution of lysozyme or its derivatives denatured by heat, by 0·1 ml of 0·35% solution of trypsin and 0·5 ml of 0·05 M Na_2HPO_4–HCl buffer pH 7·8 at 37°C for 6 h, 8 h and 24 h. The pH was maintained at 7·8 and the enzyme : substrate ratio at 1 : 100. After the appropriate time interval the enzymic hydrolysis was stopped by bringing down the pH of the hydrolysate to 3·0 with 2 N HCl. The precipitate formed was removed by centrifugation and the supernatant liquid stored frozen for paper electrophoresis. The analysis of the insoluble residue which contain cystine peptides was not undertaken.

(f) Amino acid analysis

Lysozyme and its derivatives were hydrolysed with constant boiling HCl in evacuated sealed tubes at 110°C for 24 h. The HCl was evaporated in vacuum, the dried samples dissolved in citrate buffer at pH 2·2, and aliquots were used for amino acid analysis in an automatic analyser. The amino acid analyser was Beckman/Spinco Model 120, designed by Spackman, Moore and Stein.

(g) Biological activity studies

The method of assay was similar to that of Smolelis & Hartsell (1949). Lytic action on *Micrococcus lysodeikticus* by lysozyme and its derivatives was followed turbidimetrically at pH 6.5 ± 0.1 and at room temperature.

The cell suspension was prepared from the dried cells (*Micrococcus lysodeikticus* strain M2436 supplied by Mann Research Labs., Inc.) in phosphate buffer, 1/15 M, pH 6.5 ± 0.1 prior to the assay. The turbidity of this suspension is adjusted to show 10% light transmission in Beckman DU Spectrophotometer at a wavelength at 540 mμ, and to show 100% transmission with distilled water blank. This suspension of cells in the buffer without lysozyme or its derivative served as the control to indicate autolysis, if any. A sample of 0.1 ml of 0.01% solution of lysozyme or its derivative was added to each of the cuvettes, and per cent transmission of the suspension was read off at 540 mμ at intervals of 5 min for 30 min. During this 30-minute period, per cent transmission of the control was almost constant. The assays of lysozyme and its derivatives were carried out simultaneously under as nearly identical conditions as possible.

3. Results and Discussion

A close study of the paper electropherograms obtained showed that lysozyme and its heavy atom derivatives are homogeneous over the wide range of pH's used. Starch-gel electrophoresis gave similar results.

Lysozyme and its derivatives all migrated towards the cathode, hence they carry a net positive charge. The mobilities of lysozyme derivatives were, however, lower than that of the unmodified protein. This may be due to some of the basic amino acids having reacted with the heavy atom reagents. Therefore, we expected a decrease in the isoelectric point of the protein. This may be the reason why we were able to crystallize the orthorhombic form of INP lysozyme and iodolysozyme at as low a pH as 8.6–9.0.

Amino acid analysis of the acid hydrolysate of INP lysozyme gave one histidine, three tyrosines and only five lysines. This indicated that the INFB reagent had reacted with only one lysine and not with the histidine or tyrosines. Iodolysozyme, however, gave one histidine and three tyrosine residues on amino acid analysis. This was probably due to the deiodination of the iodinated amino acids during acid hydrolysis.

Trypsin, a proteolytic enzyme which splits the peptide bonds involving lysine and arginine only, was used to break down lysozyme and its derivatives. Lysozyme, which contains 11 arginines and six lysines, is an attractive substrate for trypsin. In accordance with our expectation, 10 soluble peptides which could be easily separated by electrophoresis on paper at pH's 3.6 and 6.4, were obtained from the tryptic digestion of heat denatured lysozyme.

Paper electrophoresis is a useful technique in that it not only separates the peptides readily, but also provides information regarding their amino acid composition directly from their distances and direction of migration. The latter task will be easier if the amino acid sequence of the protein under investigation is known (see Fig. 1). The mobilities of the peptides were calculated with respect to arginine equal to $+1$ and are shown in Table 1. The mobilities at pH 6·4 agree closely with those of Jollès-Thaureaux *et al.* (1958) and those at pH 3·6 agree fairly well with those of Canfield (1963). The amino acid composition and sequence of these peptides are shown in Table 2. The naming of the peptides is the same as that of Canfield.

TABLE 1. Electrophoretic behavior of the peptides obtained by the tryptic digestion of heat denatured lysozyme

Peptides	m^a (pH 6·4)	m^a (pH 3·6)
T_1	1·05	1·10
T_4	1·00	1·00
T_5	0·20	0·65
T_7	0·10	0·30
T_{10}	0·70	0·56
T_{12}	1·05	1·10
T_{13}	0·20	0·30
T_{14}	0·75	0·80
T_{16}	0·40	0·50
T_{18}	0·00	0·00

[a] Mobilities of the peptides were calculated with respect to that of arginine taken as $+1$.

TABLE 2. Amino acid composition and sequence of the peptides[a]

Peptides	Amino acid sequence
T_1, T_{12}	Lys
T_4	Arg
	NH$_2$
T_5	His-Gly-Leu-Asp-Asp-Tyr-Arg
	NH$_2$ NH$_2$ NH$_2$ NH$_2$
T_7	Phe-Glu-Ser-Asp-Phe-Asp-Thr-Glu-Ala-Thr-Asp-Arg
T_{10}	Thr-Pro-Gly-Ser-Arg
	NH$_2$
T_{13}	Ile-Val-Ser-Asp-Gly-Asp-Gly-Met-Asp-Ala-Try-Val-Ala-Try-Arg
	NH$_2$
T_{14}	Asp-Arg
	NH$_2$
T_{16}	Gly-Thr-Asp-Val-Glu-Ala-Try-Ile-Arg
T_{18}	Leu

[a] This is from the work of Canfield.

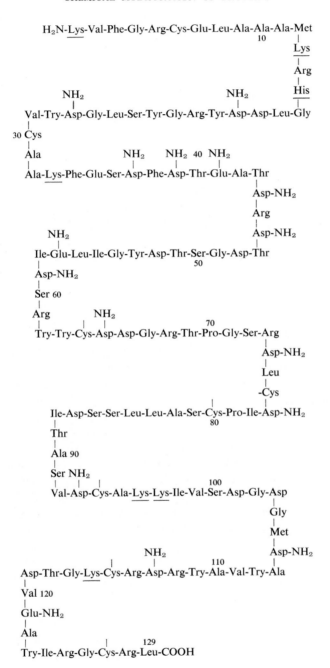

FIG. 1. Amino acid sequence of lysozyme (Canfield).

We are interested in only those peptides which are connected with lysine and histidine. They are: T_1, T_4, T_5, T_7, T_{12}, T_{13} and T_{16}. Of these T_1 and T_{12} are free lysines and T_4 is a free arginine. Lysine and arginine spots on the electrophoresis maps were recognized by running a control of the amino acids concerned simultaneously under identical conditions. T_5 was shown to be a histidine peptide by spraying with Pauly's reagent which turned it yellow. T_{13} and T_{16} were identified by their mobilities and by their reaction with Ehrlich's reagent which turned them purple.

The bonds between T (1+2), T (3+4), T (15+16) and T (17+18) are relatively slowly cleaved by trypsin. Tryptic digestion in our investigation was carried out for 6 h, 8 h and 24 h. We observed, however, little difference in the electrophoresis maps of these digests. This indicates that most of these bonds might have been cleaved in 6 h time. This appears reasonable because the peptide map obtained by Canfield (1963) was produced from a 90 min tryptic digestion of reduced carboxymethylated lysozyme. Since we have digested heat denatured lysozyme with trypsin and we have investigated only the soluble peptides, the peptides T (3+4), T (15+16) and T (17+18) even if formed to some extent have been removed by centrifugation, so the possibility of their appearance on our electrophoresis maps is very remote. T_2 which might have been formed probably overlaps with T_5 at pH 3·6 and with T_{10} at pH 6·4 run.

The electrophoreses of the tryptic digests of lysozyme and its derivatives were carried out under as nearly identical conditions as possible. Now, having recognized and identified those peptides obtained from native lysozyme, we proceeded to identify the peptides from the lysozyme derivatives by way of comparison. Examination of the electrophoresis map of the tryptic digest of INP lysozyme revealed only one peptide (T_4) to be missing. This peptide can only come from the particular part of the sequence -Lys-Arg-His-, in lysozyme. Nowhere else along the sequence can we find such a situation. This can be missed only if the lysine just behind T_4 has been blocked. Therefore, this particular lysine, the residue number 13, has been blocked in INP lysozyme.

The intensity of the lysine spot in the electrophoresis maps of INP lysozyme was found to be less dense than in the case of native lysozyme. Since this spot has been produced from two lysines, 1 and 97, and the reaction conditions we have used are favorable to N–terminal lysine, it is possible that the latter also might have reacted with the INFB reagent. However, amino acid analysis of the acid hydrolysate of INP lysozyme had given five lysine residues only. This perhaps can be resolved by X-ray crystallographic studies of INP lysozyme.

Since the peptides T_7, T_{12}, T_{13} and T_{16} have appeared on the electrophoresis maps of the tryptic digest of INP lysozyme, lysines 33, 96, 97 and 116 have not been attacked by the INFB reagent.

Even though the pK_a values of lysines in lysozyme are in the neighborhood of 10·0 (Tanford & Wagner, 1954), the fact that the residue number 13 has reacted so readily with the INFB reagent shows that it might possess an abnormally low pK_a value. This appears reasonable and justified with regards to its position in the polypeptide chain, and the conditions under which the pK_a values of the various groups in lysozyme were calculated (Tanford & Wagner, 1954; Donovan et al., 1960).

The electrophoresis map of the tryptic digest of iodolysozyme was found to be very similar to that of native lysozyme. This showed that ninhydrin spray could not distinguish the peptide or peptides containing free amino acids from those containing iodinated amino acids. Therefore, ceric ammonium sulphate, sodium arsenite, methylene blue spray (Alexander & Block, 1960), characteristic for iodinated amino acids, were used. Then a blue spot with a yellow-green background was observed at a position where T_5 was found in the case of native lysozyme. This shows that both histidine and tyrosine or only the former in T_5 might have been iodinated. Since the ultraviolet spectrum of iodolysozyme was similar to that of native lysozyme, and since we have used the reaction conditions most favorable to histidine only, it is possible that only the histidine in T_5, and hence in iodolysozyme, might have been iodinated. This, also, should be resolved by means of X-ray crystallographic studies of iodolysozyme.

INP lysozyme and iodolysozyme have been found to be biologically as active as the native lysozyme. These derivatives may therefore be used in X-ray studies with confidence, since we know that the enzymatic activity has not been lost. They have also the same pH optimum of $6·6 \pm 0·1$ for biological activity as the native protein. This shows that lysine number 13 and the single histidine residue are not at the active site, and so they are not essential for enzymic activity. This is in accordance with the observation of Rao & Ramachandran (1962) and Hartdegen & Rupley (1964), who have found out by chemical means that tryptophans are at the active site, but not the single histidine in lysozyme. Johnson & Phillips (1965) have also arrived at the same conclusion as a result of their crystallographic studies on lysozyme—competitive inhibitor complexes.

Lysozyme has the power of rapidly dissolving the cell walls of certain bacteria such as *Micrococcus lysodeikticus*. It breaks the β-glycosidic linkage $(1 \rightarrow 4)$ between *N*-acetylmuramic acid and *N*-acetylglucosamine of mucopolysaccharides which constitute the bacterial cell walls. This cleavage is an acid-catalysed hydrolysis. It is not known whether the tryptophans actually take part in the bond breaking steps of this enzymic mechanism or just aid in the maintenance of the proper conformation near the active site perhaps through hydrophobic linkages. Further, Hartdegen & Rupley (1964) have also found out that only one, out of the six tryptophans present in lysozyme, is essential for the biological function. Therefore, it would be of great interest to locate this tryptophan residue either by chemical means or by crystallographic means, and then explain the mechanism of enzymic action. Since the pK_a value of a tryptophan is very high when compared with the pH optimum for the activity of lysozyme, it appears rather difficult to explain the mechanism of this enzymic action using tryptophan as the only residue involved in the biological function. Therefore it appears that more than one type of residue might be necessary to explain the mechanism.

4. Conclusions

Two heavy atom derivatives of lysozyme: INP lysozyme and iodolysozyme, have been prepared and crystallized. The INP lysozyme was prepared by reacting the crystalline protein in buffered medium at neutral pH with the INFB reagent devised and synthesized in our laboratory. Iodolysozyme has been prepared by directly iodinating the crystalline protein at a pH range of 4–5. Both the derivatives have been crystallized in the triclinic and orthorhombic form. These crystals could be used for the study of the three-dimensional structure of lysozyme by X-ray diffraction.

Amino acid analysis of the acid hydrolyzate of INP lysozyme in an automatic analyser and paper electrophoresis of the tryptic digest of the heat-denatured derivative at pH's 3·6 and 6·4 have shown that the residue No. 13 (which is a lysine) has been attacked by the INFB reagent. Paper electrophoresis of the tryptic digest of the heat-denatured iodolysozyme at pH's 3·6 and 6·4 has shown that the single histidine has been iodinated.

Biological activity studies on these derivatives have indicated that the particular lysine and the single histidine in lysozyme are not at the active site and so they are not responsible for the biological function.

ACKNOWLEDGMENT

Grateful appreciation is expressed to the Department of Biochemistry, Indiana University Medical School, Indianapolis, Indiana, for the provision of laboratory facilities needed for this research.

REFERENCES

Alderton, G. & Fevold, H. L. (1946). *J. biol. Chem.* **164**, 1.
Alexander, P. & Block, R. J. (1960). "A Laboratory Manual of Analytical Methods of Protein Chemistry", Vol. 2, p. 19. Oxford: Pergamon Press.
Canfield, R. E. (1963). *J. biol. Chem.* **238**, 2691.
Donovan, J. W., Laskowski, Jr., M. & Scheraga, H. A. (1960). *J. Am. chem. Soc.* **82**, 2154.
Fraenkel-Conrat, H. (1950). *Arch. Biochem. Biophys.* **27**, 109.

Fraenkel-Conrat, H., Harris, J. I. & Levy, A. L. (1955). "Methods of Biochemical Analysis", Vol. 2, p. 359. New York: Interscience.

Hartdegen, F. J. & Rupley, J. A. (1964). *Biochim. biophys. Acta*, **92**, 625.

Johnson, L. N. & Phillips, D. C. (1965). *Nature, Lond.* **206**, 761.

Jollès-Thaureaux, J., Jollès, P. & Fromageot, C. (1958). *Biochim. biophys. Acta*, **27**, 298.

Kallos, J. & Rizok, D. (1964). *J. molec. Biol.* **9**, 255.

Rao, G. J. S. & Ramachandran, L. K. (1962). *Biochim. biophys. Acta*, **59**, 507.

Sigler, P. B., Skinner, H. C. W., Coulter, C. L., Kallos, J., Braxton, H. & Davies, D. R. (1964). *Proc. natn. Acad. Sci.*, *U.S.A.* **51**, 1146.

Sigler, P. B., Jeffery, B. A., Mathews, B. W. & Blow, D. M. (1966). *J. molec. Biol.* **15**, 175.

Smithies, O. (1959). *Biochem. J.* **71**, 585.

Smolelis, A. N. & Hartsell, S. E. (1949). *J. Bact.* **58**, 731.

Stong, C. L. (1962). *Sci. Am.*, June, p. 171.

Tanford, C. & Wagner, M. L. (1954). *J. Am. chem. Soc.* **76**, 3331.

Calculations of Polypeptide Structures from Amino Acid Sequence†

H. A. Scheraga, R. A. Scott,‡ G. Vanderkooi, S. J. Leach,§
K. D. Gibson, T. Ooi‖

Department of Chemistry, Cornell University, Ithaca
New York, U.S.A.

AND

G. Némethy

Rockefeller University, New York, New York, U.S.A.

This is a report of some of our recent work on the calculation of polypeptide structures from amino acid sequence. Our earlier work, based on a hard-sphere potential, is first summarized. This is followed by a discussion of the various contributions to the free energy of a protein. With the more complete energy function, calculations are given for dipeptide-like and for helical structures. It is shown that the repulsive part of the non-bonded interaction energy (in addition to solvent effects) is one of the most important factors in determining protein conformation. Also, dipole–dipole interactions are shown to play an important role in determining the screw sense of the helix, for some polyamino acids. A hybrid calculation (based partially on a hard-sphere potential and partially on the more complete energy function) of the conformation of gramicidin-S yields a low-energy structure. This structure is being refined further by our newer procedures involving energy minimization. These newer procedures are also being tested on myoglobin and lysozyme.

1. Introduction

It appears that it may be possible to compute the three-dimensional conformation of a protein from a knowledge of the amino acid sequence, the positions of the disulfide bonds, and the nature of the solvent (Anfinsen, 1961; Scheraga, 1964; Scheraga *et al.*, 1965*a,b*,1966). The difficulty of this

† This work was supported by a research grant (GB–4766) from the National Science Foundation and by a research grant (AI–01473) from the National Institute of Allergy and Infectious Diseases of the National Institutes of Health, U.S. Public Health Service.

‡ Present address: Department of Biochemistry and Biophysics, 2538 The Mall, University of Hawaii, Honolulu, Hawaii 96822.

§ Present address: Division of Protein Chemistry, C.S.I.R.O., Parkville N2, Victoria, Australia.

‖ Present address: Department of Physics, Nagoya University, Nagoya, Japan.

task may be appreciated by recalling that the number of available conformations of a polypeptide chain is enormous because of the possibility of rotation (expressed in terms of the angles ϕ and ψ) around the N—C^α and C^α—C′ bonds, respectively, of each amino acid residue (see Fig. 1, which is expressed in terms of a convention recently adopted by Edsall *et al.*, 1966); rotation about the C′—N bond (expressed in terms of the angle ω) is generally severely restricted, and is taken to be so (with the amide group in the planar *trans* configuration) in the work reported here.

Because of the magnitude of the problem, we have approached it by several stages of approximation, each involving simplifying assumptions. In the higher approximations, fewer simplifying assumptions were made, with the hope of ultimately obtaining as exact as possible (or as exact as required) a calculation of the free energy as a function of the coordinates of all the atoms and all the solvent molecules; minimization of the free energy should lead to

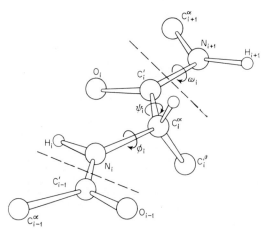

F IG. 1. Perspective drawing of a section of a polypeptide chain representing two peptide units (Edsall *et al.*, 1966).

the most probable conformation. While the three-dimensional conformation of a protein has thus far not yet been computed, much progress has been made, and much information about polypeptide conformation has been obtained since our previous "Progress Report" (Scheraga *et al.*, 1965a); the present paper is a summary of our progress during the past year.

In our initial attempts to compute the conformation of a polypeptide (Némethy & Scheraga, 1965), it was assumed, as a first simplifying approximation, that atoms are hard spheres (an assumption also made by Ramachandran *et al.*, 1963) and that the values of ϕ and ψ are restricted to the positions of the minima of supposed sixfold potential functions for rotation about the N—C^α and C^α—C' single bonds. With these assumptions, it was possible to deduce that a relatively small number of structures satisfied these criteria. More recently, the hard-sphere potential function was abandoned in favor of a Lennard–Jones potential between all pairs of non-bonded atoms, and an improved treatment was provided for the problem of internal rotation about single bonds. In addition, other contributions to the free energy were introduced, viz. hydrogen bonding, hydrophobic bonding, effect of solvent, bond angle bending and bond stretching, and electrostatic interactions.

This paper summarizes the calculations involving all of these contributions to the free energy, and also the use of free-energy minimization procedures. Specifically, we will present our recent results on the conformations of dipeptides, regular structures of hydrocarbons and polyamino acids, the cyclic decapeptide gramicidin-S, and our preliminary results for a generalized protein (e.g., myoglobin, lysozyme, ribonuclease, etc.).

2. Initial Work with Hard-sphere Potential

Before describing our recent results, it will be helpful, as a background, to summarize the earlier ones. Further details can be found in the papers cited.

Using a hard-sphere potential, Ramachandran et al. (1963) computed the sterically allowed ranges of ϕ and ψ for dipeptide-like structures referred to as "Gly-Gly" and "Gly-Ala". (A representation of the sterically allowed regions on a plot of ψ vs. ϕ is known as a "steric map".) Leach et al. (1966a) extended these calculations to various dipeptide-like and tripeptide-like structures, involving all of the amino acids which occur in proteins, thereby assessing the effects of variations in the size and shape of the side-chain groups on the allowed conformations. Their results were represented on steric maps, an example of which is shown in Fig. 2. Steric restrictions, due to the backbone atoms alone, permit the peptide groups adjacent to glycyl residues to assume only about 50% of all conceivable conformations. An alanyl side chain limits these to 16% and, with further side-chain complexity, restrictions increase so that the backbone adjacent to valyl or isoleucyl side chains can take up only about 5% of all possible conformations.

These computations, with a hard-sphere potential, were extended to helical pentapeptide-like and hexapeptide-like structures in order to determine the additional steric restrictions which arise when complete turns of various helical structures are constructed (Leach et al., 1966b). In addition to the steric requirement, Leach et al. (1966b) introduced criteria for the formation of acceptable hydrogen bonds, and examined the influence of amide group geometry on these two properties. A comparison of the steric maps in Figs. 3 and 4 illustrates the additional restrictions in a poly-L-alanine chain, as one passes from a dipeptide-like structure (Fig. 3) to helical structures (Fig. 4).

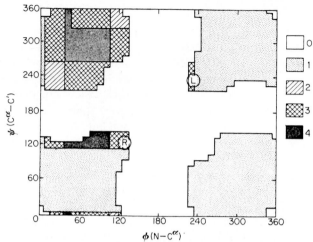

FIG. 2. Allowed areas of the steric map for various dipeptides. In area 0 no conformations are allowed. Conformations in areas 1 to 4 are allowed for glycyl glycine, in areas 2 to 4 for glycyl-L-alanine, in areas 3 to 4 for higher straight chain homologs, while only area 4 is allowed for glycyl-L-valine and glycyl-L-isoleucine. The circles marked R and L indicate the location of the standard right- and left-handed α-helix on the steric map (Némethy *et al.*, 1966).

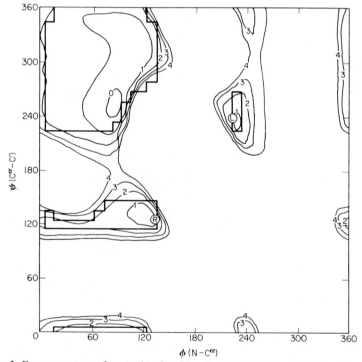

FIG. 3. Energy contours for an alanyl residue (Scott & Scheraga, 1966c). The units of energy are kcal/mole. The circles marked R and L indicate the location of the standard right- and left-handed α-helix. The steric map (Leach *et al.*, 1966a) is superimposed on the energy contours.

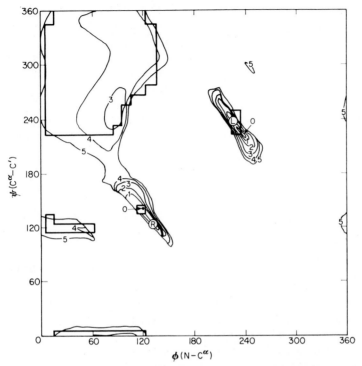

FIG. 4. Energy contours for poly-L-alanine helices (Scott & Scheraga, 1966c). The units of energy are kcal/mole. The circles marked R and L indicate the location of the standard right- and left-handed α-helix. The steric map (Leach *et al.*, 1966b) is superimposed on the energy contours.

The steric maps throw some light on the entropy and enthalpy contributions to helix stability. For example, the greater stability of the poly-L-Ala α-helix compared with the poly-Gly α-helix may be ascribed, in part, to the threefold greater choice of chain conformations (50% compared with 16%) available to poly-Gly when it assumes the non-helical form (Némethy *et al.*, 1966; Leach *et al.*, 1966b). Figure 2 shows (see points R and L) that the backbone rotational angles found as a repeating feature in the right-handed and left-handed α-helices are not always available to dipeptides. This would explain why the α-helical forms of poly-L-Val, poly-L-Ile and poly-L-Thr cannot be made (Blout, 1962; Bloom *et al.*, 1962). However, if *single* residues of this type occur "sandwiched" among other residues in a helical segment of a protein, they do not cause a break in the helix (Kendrew *et al.*, 1961). We have found that the rotation of a bulky side chain by 10–35° out of one of its potential minima is sufficient to admit the right-handed or left-handed α-helices. An estimate of the energy (0·75 kcal/mole) required for this rotation

(Némethy *et al.*, 1966) has provided a measure of the destabilization of the helix in the presence of bulky side chains. The formation of the α-helical form of poly-L-Val is discussed in Section 5.

Using steric maps of the kind shown in Fig. 2, and the assumption that a residue can assume only discrete values of ϕ and ψ (corresponding to the positions of the minima of assumed sixfold rotational potential functions) in the allowed areas, it was possible to compute the conformations of cyclic peptides which satisfied these criteria. The calculations were carried out for a cyclic octapeptide portion of ribonuclease (Némethy & Scheraga, 1965) and for the cyclic decapeptide gramicidin-S (Scheraga *et al.*, 1965a). While the reported structures have been superseded by ones computed with a more complete energy expression (see below), these calculations served to show the great restriction on the number of allowed conformations, imposed simply by the size of the atoms; they also served for the development of computational methods which were later used in the more recent work described below.

3. Contributions to the Free Energy of Polypeptide Structures

With the information gained from the calculations made with the simplifying assumptions described in the previous section, it was possible to extend the computations (to abandon these oversimplified assumptions) and to take into account all the presently known contributions to the free energy of polypeptide structures. Before discussing these computations, we consider first the various contributions to the free energy. All the included contributions to the free energy are energies, except in the case of hydrophobic bonding, where a free energy term is used.

Scott & Scheraga (1965) have presented a discussion of the barriers to internal rotation in ethane-like molecules, making use of the point of view of Pauling (1958,1960) that the barriers are due to exchange interactions between electrons in bonds (e.g. C—H bonds in ethane) adjacent to the bond about which internal rotation occurs, and to non-bonded (van der Waals) interactions. Thus, the total energy U in ethane-like molecules is made up of a torsional term $U_{torsion}$, due to the exchange interactions, and a term $U_{non\text{-}bonded}$, due to the van der Waals interactions.

$$U = U_{torsion} + U_{non\text{-}bonded} \tag{1}$$

In papers on the normal hydrocarbons, Scott & Scheraga (1966a,b) used a threefold cosine term for $U_{torsion}$ and Lennard–Jones terms for $U_{non\text{-}bonded}$. With this approach, the barriers to internal rotation in hydrocarbons, and in model compounds containing atoms other than carbon and hydrogen, were rationalized, thereby providing information about $U_{torsion}$ and $U_{non\text{-}bonded}$ (Scott & Scheraga, 1966c). During the course of these computations, it was possible to calculate the potential energy curves and deduce the conformations

of stable rotational isomers of the normal hydrocarbons. For example, Fig. 5 shows the value of U as a function of ω_3, for rotation about the central single bond, in butane, together with the contributions from $U_{torsion}$ and $U_{non\text{-}bonded}$. For very long aliphatic hydrocarbon molecules ("polyethylene"), calculations carried out with the restriction that the dihedral angle be the same in every residue (i.e. that the structure be helical) yielded the results shown in Fig. 6. The most stable conformation (at $\omega = 180°$) is the all-*trans* one.

On the basis of considerations such as these (including a variety of model compounds) Scott & Scheraga (1966c) selected values of 0·2 kcal/mole and 0·6 kcal/mole for the barriers to internal rotation about the C^α—C' and N—C^α bonds, respectively; these workers also provided some discussion to justify the use of *threefold* potential functions for these rotations. Both of these barriers are considerably smaller than that (~ 3 kcal/mole) for the normal hydrocarbons. For this reason, the earlier assumptions that the barriers were sixfold and that the conformations are restricted to those at potential minima (Némethy & Scheraga, 1965) have been abandoned. The equation for $U_{torsion}$ per residue, i.e. for rotation about the two bonds C^α—C' and N—C^α, is

$$U_{torsion} = \tfrac{1}{2}U_\psi(1-\cos 3\psi)+\tfrac{1}{2}U_\phi(1+\cos 3\phi) \qquad (2)$$

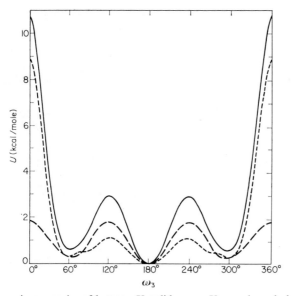

FIG. 5. The various energies of butane: U, solid curve, $U_{torsion}$, long-dashed curve, and $U_{non\text{-}bonded}$, short-dashed curve, plotted as a function of ω_3 (the dihedral angle for rotation about the central C—C bond). Each point on the solid curve was obtained by minimization with respect to the two dihedral angles for rotation about the two terminal C—C bonds (Scott & Scheraga, 1966b).

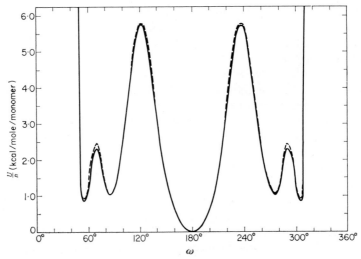

FIG. 6. A plot of the energy per monomer unit, U/n, as a function of ω (the dihedral angle for rotation around a C—C bond), for a hydrocarbon molecule subject to the constraint that ω is the same in every monomer unit. The solid curve is for $n = 15$ and the dashed curve is for $n = 20$ (Scott & Scheraga, 1966*b*).

The non-bonded interactions have been treated in terms of Lennard–Jones pair potentials.

$$U = \frac{d}{r^{12}} - \frac{e}{r^6} \tag{3}$$

where r is the distance between the centers of the two interacting atoms. The values of the constants d and e are given in Table 1.

Brant & Flory (1965*a,b*) have emphasized the importance of including dipole–dipole electrostatic interactions between the polar amide groups in

TABLE 1. Non-bonded potentials (Scott & Scheraga, 1966*c*)

Interacting pair	d (kcal Å^{12} mole^{-1})	e (kcal Å^6 mole^{-1})
C $\cdots$ C	$2 \cdot 86 \times 10^5$	370
C $\cdots$ N	$2 \cdot 16 \times 10^5$	366
C $\cdots$ O	$2 \cdot 05 \times 10^5$	367
C $\cdots$ H	$3 \cdot 80 \times 10^4$	128
N $\cdots$ N	$1 \cdot 61 \times 10^5$	363
N $\cdots$ O	$1 \cdot 53 \times 10^5$	365
N $\cdots$ H	$2 \cdot 70 \times 10^4$	125
O $\cdots$ O	$1 \cdot 45 \times 10^5$	367
O $\cdots$ H	$2 \cdot 51 \times 10^4$	124
H $\cdots$ H	$4 \cdot 46 \times 10^3$	46·7

conformational energy calculations, and assigned a dipole moment of 3·7 D to the amide group. We have selected the partial charges shown in Table 2 to reproduce this dipole moment, and have calculated the electrostatic interaction by Coulomb's law with a dielectric constant of 4·0.

TABLE 2. Partial charges on amide groups (Scott & Scheraga, 1966c)

Atom	Charge (in units of the electronic charge)
H	+0·272
N	−0·305
C′	+0·449
O	−0·416

The potential function for NH $\cdots$ OC hydrogen bonding, used by Scott & Scheraga (1966c) is based on the proposals of Lippincott & Schroeder (1955), Schroeder & Lippincott (1957), and Moulton & Kromhout (1956).

$$U = -D^* \cos^2 \theta_1 \exp\left[-\frac{n^*(R-r-r_0^*)^2}{2(R-r)}\right]$$
$$-D^* \cos^2 \theta_2 \exp\left[-\frac{n^*(R-r-r_0^*)^2}{2(R-r)}\right] + Ae^{-bR} - \tfrac{1}{2}A(R_0/R)^m e^{-bR_0} \quad (4)$$

(See Scott and Scheraga, 1966c, for definitions of the parameters, and the values assigned to them.) This function takes into account the relative orientations of the interacting groups, and is used whenever NH interacts with an O except within each residue (i.e. near-neighbor NH and O atoms); in the latter case, the ordinary N $\cdots$ O and H $\cdots$ O non-bonded potentials are used.

While not yet used in any of our calculations, we have deduced energy expressions to take into account the role of water. These are based on earlier considerations of Némethy & Scheraga (1962) and take into account the effect of water in hydrophobic bonding between non-polar groups and in the hydration of polar groups. Thus, as is well known, the introduction of the role of water would tend, on the average, to force non-polar groups to lie inside the molecule and polar ones to lie outside in contact with water.

Bond angle bending and bond stretching were taken into account (Gibson & Scheraga, 1966) so far only in dipeptide calculations, with the aid of vibrational force constants obtained from the work of Miyazawa et al. (1958), Fukushima et al. (1959), Shimanouchi (1963), and Nakagawa et al. (1965). A listing of the force constants, together with the procedure used, is given by Gibson & Scheraga (1966).

The energies described in this section represent our best estimates to date. In some cases (Scott & Scheraga, 1966c), the parameters have been varied over reasonable ranges of values without appreciable effect on the computed

results. It is, therefore, our belief that the values selected are reasonable ones. Nevertheless, we are at present refining them by adaptation of a computer program of Williams (1965) to the "determination" of the (known) crystal structures of small molecules. An important point to be made here is that the insertion of refined energy parameters into our computer programs for obtaining protein structures is a very simple matter. As long as we can carry out our computations accurately, and in reasonable time, they can easily be repeated with altered energy parameters.

4. Dipeptide-like Structures

While the earlier steric maps (Ramachandran *et al.*, 1963; Leach *et al.*, 1966*a*), of the type shown in Fig. 2, were based on a hard sphere potential, they have now been superseded (Brant & Flory, 1965*a,b*; Liquori, 1966; Gibson & Scheraga, 1966; Scott & Scheraga, 1966*c*) by energy contour diagrams. Figure 3 shows a contour diagram for Gly-Ala, based on torsional energies, non-bonded interactions and dipole–dipole interactions (evaluated in terms of partial charges). In Fig. 3, the steric map for Gly-Ala has been superimposed on the contour diagram. From the similarity of the steric map and the contour diagram, it can be seen that the repulsive parts of the non-bonded interactions play a very important role in determining the energy contours. One interesting difference between the two is that, whereas the steric map is divided into separate regions in the neighborhood of $\phi = 0-150°$ and $\psi = 180°$, the energy contours in these two regions are separated by a relatively low-energy barrier. Since some of the dihedral angles of myoglobin (Watson, 1965) and lysozyme (Phillips, 1965) lie in this region, and would be disallowed on the steric map, it is gratifying that they are allowed on the contour diagrams. Presumably, the energy required to cross this barrier is compensated by other interactions in the protein molecule.

If *all* of the bond angles are allowed to bend, then the region of accessibility (i.e. of low energy) is increased. This can be seen by comparing Fig. 7(a) for a rigid model with Fig. 7(b) for a flexible model (Gibson & Scheraga, 1966). (Small discrepancies between Figs. 3 and 7(a) are due to slightly altered parameters in the case of Fig. 7(a).) This comparison is facilitated in Fig. 7(c), in which the energy is plotted as a function of ϕ for a fixed value of $\psi = 260°$.

5. Homopolymer Helices

Figure 4 illustrates a contour diagram for helical poly-L-alanine. In this diagram, ϕ and ψ have been restricted to being the same in every residue; hence, all points in Fig. 4 correspond to helical structures. Figure 4 is based on torsional energies, non-bonded interactions, hydrogen bonding, and electrostatic interactions. As before, the steric map for poly-L-alanine is superimposed on the contour diagram, and it can again be seen that the

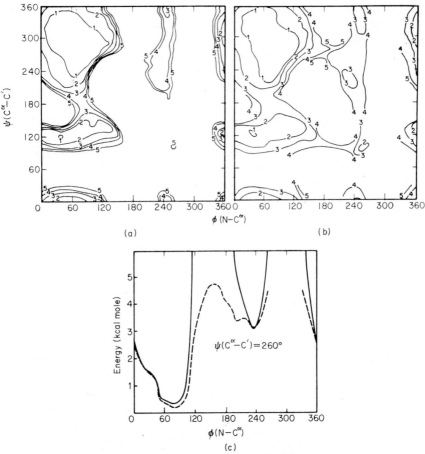

FIG. 7. Energy contours (at intervals of 1 kcal/mole) for glycyl-L-alanine. (a) Rigid model; (b) flexible model; (c) a plot of the energy as a function of ϕ for a fixed value of $\psi = 260°$ (solid curve: rigid model; dashed curve: flexible model) (Gibson & Scheraga, 1966).

repulsive parts of the non-bonded interactions play a very important role in determining the energy contours. The unique positions of the right- and left-handed α-helices may be noted. By carrying out energy minimization calculations within the zero kcal contours, both in the right- and left-handed regions, it was found that the right-handed α-helix was more stable than the left-handed one by a few tenths of a kcal per residue (Scott & Scheraga, 1966c); this energy difference is large enough to favor the right-handed form if the chain were more than 10–20 residues long.

Calculations have recently been performed on several other homopolymer helices (poly-L-valine, poly-β-methyl-L-aspartate, poly-γ-methyl-L-glutamate,

and poly-L-tyrosine) in which rotations about side-chain single bonds must be taken into account (Ooi *et al.*, 1966). A map of the type given in Fig. 4 for poly-L-alanine was obtained for poly-L-valine (Ooi *et al.*, 1967); the energy was minimized with respect to the dihedral angles of the backbone *and* the side chains. The conformation of poly-L-valine of minimum energy is the right-handed α-helix. In agreement with earlier steric calculations (Leach *et al.*, 1966a,b; Némethy *et al.*, 1966), the side-chain group must be rotated around the C^{α}—C^{β} bond by 10–15° out of a torsional energy minimum to make this backbone conformation preferred; the resulting decrease in non-bonded energy more than compensates for the small increase in torsional energy caused by this rotation.†

Poly-β-methyl-L-aspartate and poly-γ-methyl-L-glutamate were studied in the right- and left-handed α-helical regions. Energy minimizations were carried out in these two regions with respect to four single-bond rotations (two backbone and two side-chain) in the aspartate polymer, and with respect to five single-bond rotations (two backbone and three side-chain) in the case of the glutamate polymer. The left-handed α-helix was found to be more stable than the right-handed form for the aspartate polymer, but the reverse was true for the glutamate polymer. The dipole interaction of the ester group with the backbone is the cause of the difference in screw sense; this interaction stabilizes the right-handed form in the glutamate polymer, but destabilizes it in the aspartate polymer. A low dielectric constant ($D \leq 3$) must be used in order for the magnitude of the dipole interaction in aspartate to be great enough to overcome the non-bonded energy, which favors the right-handed form in both polymers. These calculations provide the explanation for the well-known difference in screw-sense between the two polymers.

The right-handed α-helix of poly-L-tyrosine was found to be more stable than the left-handed form. This calculation provides additional evidence, in support of ORD data, that the favored α-helical conformation of this polymer is the right-handed one.

The generalized protein program (described in a later section) has been tested with an α-helix of 20 residues of poly-L-alanine. In this calculation, ϕ and ψ are no longer restricted to being the same in every residue. Starting with a perfect helix, and minimizing the energy by changing the atomic coordinates, the program yielded a structure which was α-helical in the center of the chain and non-α-helical near the ends; its energy was lower than that of the starting perfect helix. These results seem reasonable since the interactions of end residues are different from those of interior residues.

---

† ORD measurements performed in this laboratory (Epand & Scheraga, in preparation) on a block copolymer of the type $(\text{D, L-Lys})_x$-$(\text{L-Val})_x$-$(\text{D, L-Lys})_x$, where $x \sim 40$, have indicated that the L-valine portion exists in a right-handed α-helix form when the polymer is dissolved in 98% aqueous methanol at room temperature.

6. Gramicidin-S

While the ultimate method of computing the structure of a polypeptide of known sequence will involve some kind of energy-minimization procedure (see below), we report here a calculation which is really a hybrid of some of the procedures already described (Vanderkooi *et al.*, 1966). The cyclic decapeptide, gramicidin-S, consisting of two identical pentapeptides joined into a ring by peptide bonds, was selected for the computation; the sequence of this polypeptide is

$$\lceil\text{(L-Val-L-Orn-L-Leu-D-Phe-L-Pro)}_2\rceil$$

As before (Némethy & Scheraga, 1965), only those values of ϕ and ψ, which lie within the allowed regions of the steric map for each amino acid residue, were used in the computation. However, instead of selecting those points within the allowed regions which lie at the positions of the minima of the rotational potential functions, the selection of points was made randomly since the barriers to internal rotation are relatively small. The number of points selected for each amino acid was approximately proportional to the allowed area on the steric map.

Using the above assumption, and regarding the atoms as hard spheres, all sterically allowed conformations of *half* of the backbone of the molecule were generated. The remaining half of the backbone of the molecule was obtained by symmetry, since the gramicidin-S molecule is thought to have a twofold axis of symmetry (Schmidt *et al.*, 1957). Side chains were then added to these backbones; backbone conformations which could not fit side chains were discarded. Also, those conformations, in which the ring closure was imperfect (within an arbitrary tolerance), were discarded. This procedure was repeated twice, with two independent sets of values of ϕ and ψ. In all, 282 allowed conformations were obtained by these criteria.

Having obtained a relatively small number of "allowed" conformations, it was possible to compute the total energy of each conformation. The backbone energies were computed first, based on the values reported in an earlier section for the barriers to internal rotation, the electrostatic energy, the non-bonded interactions, and the hydrogen-bonding interaction. The distribution of energies among these conformations is quite broad (Fig. 8). The backbone conformations with low energies were subjected to minor variations in ϕ and ψ to further lower their energies. All possible sterically allowed combinations of side-chain conformations were then generated on the backbones of low energy, and the energy contributions due to the side chains were calculated. The conformation with the lowest total energy could thus be chosen out of the entire list of sterically allowed conformations (Figs 9 and 10). The energies for this conformation are listed in Table 3.

The energy of the conformation of Figs. 9 and 10 could not be lowered by the variational procedure described above. It therefore probably is near an

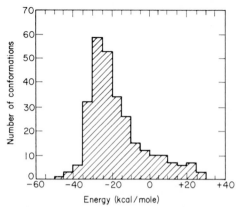

FIG. 8. Distribution of the energies of the sterically acceptable backbones of gramicidin-S which will fit side chains (Vanderkooi *et al.*, 1966).

TABLE 3. Contributions to the energy of the "most-probable" conformation of gramicidin-S

Contribution	Energy (kcal/mole)
Backbone energy[a]	
Torsional	+3·50
Electrostatic	−6·28
Non-bonded	−38·88[b]
Hydrogen bonded[c]	
Non-bonded part	−6·72
Angular-dependent bonded part	−6·11
Total backbone energy	−54·49
Side-chain energy[d]	
Torsional	0·00
Non-bonded	−27·26[e]
Total side-chain energy	−27·26
Total backbone+total side-chain energy	−81·75[f]

[a] "Backbone energy" includes all interactions among the atoms of the backbone, defined to include the C^β atoms and the proline rings, since the positions of these atoms depend solely on the ϕ and ψ values.

[b] −3·10 kcal of this arise from the non-bonded interactions between the non-hydrogen bonded NH and CO groups for which the Lippincott–Schroeder equation was used.

[c] This arises from equal contributions from the two hydrogen bonds.

[d] "Side-chain energy" includes all interactions between the side chains and the backbone, and among the side chains.

[e] As in footnote b, −1·13 kcal arise from the ε–NH_2 groups of ornithine.

[f] After publication of the results for gramicidin-S (Vanderkooi *et al.*, 1966), a minor program error was detected; hence, all of the energies of gramicidin-S reported here should be corrected by the addition of approximately −3·6 kcal/mole; this correction will not change the shape of the distribution curve of Fig. 1, or the choice of the best conformation, or any of the conclusions.

energy minimum. This conformation has two across-the-ring hydrogen bonds, and the dihedral angles shown in Fig. 11. The structure agrees well with the available preliminary X-ray data on gramicidin-S derivatives (Schmidt *et al.*, 1957; Hodgkin & Oughton, 1957; Harding, 1965). These workers state that the atoms tend to be concentrated in layers 4·8 Å apart along the *c*-axis of the crystal, which is at right angles to the molecular symmetry axis; this figure is to be compared with a spacing of 4·5–5·0 Å between the two sides of the ring in the model. According to Harding (1965), the molecule tends to be turned down at the ends; this property can be seen in Fig. 10. Our model is somewhat similar to the structure based on the β-pleated sheet suggested by Hodgkin & Oughton (1957). Infrared dichroism studies by Abbott & Ambrose (1953) on crystals of gramicidin-S derivatives have indicated that the NH and CO bonds principally lie parallel to the *c*-axis, which is the direction of the 4·8 Å spacing. It can be seen from Fig. 9 that 4 NH and 4 CO bonds lie roughly in this direction in the calculated conformation.

This calculation represents the completion of our work making use of hard-sphere potentials. All subsequent work has been, and will be, carried out by energy-minimization procedures.

7. Proteins

At the time of writing, a program has been prepared which incorporates all the energies described above, coordinate transformations, and several energy-minimization procedures. It is still being de-bugged, and has been

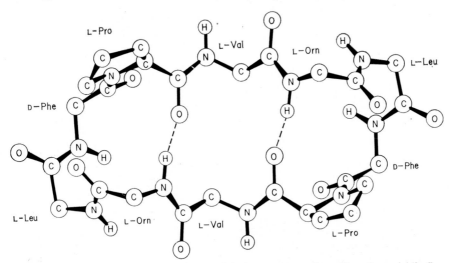

Fig. 9. View down the axis of symmetry of the low-energy conformation of gramicidin-S, with most side-chain atoms omitted (Vanderkooi *et al.*, 1966).

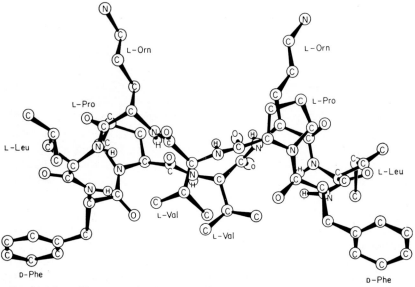

Fig. 10. View of low-energy conformation of gramicidin-S from 80° away from the axis of symmetry, with the side chains included. The apparent asymmetry of the molecule in this figure is due to the angle of observation (Vanderkooi *et al.*, 1966).

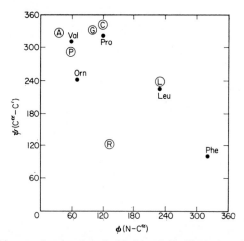

Fig. 11. Dipeptide map showing the relationship of the dihedral angles in the low-energy conformation of gramicidin-S to the angles in various regular structures (Edsall *et al.*, 1966). All of the residues are in the L-configuration except Phe, which is in the D-configuration. While phe falls in a disallowed region for an L-configuration, it falls in the allowed region for a D-configuration (Leach *et al.*, 1966a). R, right-handed α-helix; L, left-handed α-helix; P, parallel chain pleated sheet; A, anti-parallel chain pleated sheet; G, polyglycine II; C, collagen (Vanderkooi *et al.*, 1966).

tried out, in a preliminary way, on homopolymer helices (mentioned in a previous section) and on gramicidin-S. In the latter case, the conformation shown in Figs. 9 and 10 was used as an initial one. Preliminary results indicate that the program makes only minor adjustments in the conformation, suggesting that the structure in Figs. 9 and 10 may be the one which the new program will yield.

Other quite different starting conformations of gramicidin-S (e.g. the fully extended chain) are being fed into the program to see if it will arrive at the structure of Figs. 9 and 10, i.e. to explore the question as to whether our minimization procedures can successfully avoid getting trapped in local minima in the multi-dimensioned energy surface. A problem under investigation in this calculation is the proper procedure for closing loops (i.e. peptide bonds in cyclic peptides, and disulfide-bonded loops in molecules such as lysozyme and ribonuclease).

In addition to the above procedure, we are using an alternative one, which involves the assumption that the chain may be built up (and the energy computed) from the N-terminus. At the time of writing, we are not yet in a position to evaluate the validity of this approach.

8. Conclusions

A considerable amount of stereochemical and thermodynamic information has already been obtained from the calculations described herein. In addition, our approximate methods have already yielded a possible structure for gramicidin-S. Our more exact procedures, involving reasonable energies (which are being refined by calibration with crystallographic data on small molecules), are now incorporated in a computer program. It remains to be seen whether our energy minimization procedures can accomplish the calculation in reasonable computer time, and without being trapped in local energy minima. In addition to gramicidin-S, the program is being tested on myoglobin and lysozyme.

REFERENCES

Abbott, N. B. & Ambrose, E. J. (1953). *Proc. roy. Soc.* **A219**, 17.
Anfinsen, C. B. (1961). *J. Polymer Sci.* **49**, 31.
Bloom S. M., Fasman, G. D., de Loze, C. & Blout, E. R. (1962). *J. Am. chem. Soc.* **84**, 458.
Blout, E. R. (1962). *In* "Polyamino Acids, Polypeptides and Proteins", ed. by M. Stahmann, p. 275. Madison: University of Wisconsin Press.
Brant, D. E. & Flory, P. J. (1965a). *J. Am. chem. Soc.* **87**, 663.
Brant, D. E. & Flory, P. J. (1965b). *J. Am. chem. Soc.* **87**, 2791.
Edsall, J. T., Flory, P. J., Kendrew, J. C., Liquori, A. M., Némethy, G., Ramachandran, G. N. & Scheraga, H. A. (1966). *Biopolymers* **4**, 121; *J. biol. Chem.* **241**, 1004; *J. molec. Biol.* **15**, 399.

Fukushima, K., Onishi, T., Shimanouchi, T. & Mizushima, S. (1959). *Spectrochim. Acta* **15**, 236.

Gibson, K. D. & Scheraga, H. A. (1966). *Biopolymers* **4**, 709.

Harding, M. (1965). Private communication.

Hodgkin, D. C. & Oughton, B. M. (1957). *Biochem. J.* **65**, 752.

Kendrew, J. C., Watson, H. C., Strandberg, B. E., Dickerson, R. E., Phillips, D. C. & Shore, V. C. (1961). *Nature, Lond.* **190**, 666.

Leach, S. J., Némethy, G. & Scheraga, H. A. (1966a). *Biopolymers* **4**, 369.

Leach, S. J., Némethy, G. & Scheraga, H. A. (1966b). *Biopolymers* **4**, 887.

Lippincott, E. R. & Schroeder, R. (1955). *J. chem. Phys.* **23**, 1099.

Liquori, A. M. (1966). *J. Polymer Sci.* Part C, No. 12, 209.

Miyazawa, T., Shimanouchi, T. & Mizushima, S. (1958). *J. chem. Phys.* **29**, 611.

Moulton, W. G. & Kromhout, R. A. (1956). *J. chem. Phys.* **25**, 34.

Nakagawa, I., Hooper, R. J., Walter, J. L. & Lane, T. J. (1965). *Spectrochim. Acta* **21**, 1.

Némethy, G. & Scheraga, H. A. (1962). *J. phys. Chem.* **66**, 1773.

Némethy, G. & Scheraga, H. A. (1965). *Biopolymers* **3**, 155.

Némethy, G., Leach, S. J. & Scheraga, H. A. (1966). *J. phys. Chem.* **70**, 998.

Ooi, T., Scott, R. A., Vanderkooi, G., Epand, R. F. & Scheraga, H. A. (1966). *J. Am. chem. Soc.* **88**, 5680.

Ooi, T., Scott, R. A., Vanderkooi, G. & Scheraga, H. A. (1967). *J. chem. Phys.*, submitted.

Pauling, L. (1958). *Proc. natn. Acad. Sci. U.S.A.* **44**, 211.

Pauling, L. (1960). "The Nature of the Chemical Bond", 3rd ed., p. 130. Ithaca: Cornell University Press.

Phillips, D. C. (1965). Private communication.

Ramachandran, G. N., Ramakrishnan, C. & Sasisekharan, V. (1963). *J. molec. Biol.* **7**, 95.

Scheraga, H. A. (1964). *In* "Molecular Architecture in Cell Physiology", ed. by T. Hayashi and A. G. Szent-Györgyi, p. 39. Englewood Cliffs, New Jersey: Prentice-Hall.

Scheraga, H. A., Leach, S. J., Scott, R. A. & Némethy, G. (1965a). *Disc. Faraday Soc.* **40**, 268.

Scheraga, H. A., Némethy, G., Leach, S. J., Scott, R. A. & Poland, D. C. (1965b). *Fedn Proc. Fedn Am. Socs exp. Biol.* **24**, 413.

Scheraga, H. A., Scott, R. A. & Gibson, K. D. (1966). *Fedn Proc. Fedn Am. Socs exp. Biol.* **25**, 345.

Schmidt, G. M. J., Hodgkin, D. C. & Oughton, B. M. (1957). *Biochem. J.* **65**, 744.

Schroeder, R. & Lippincott, E. R. (1957). *J. phys. Chem.* **61**, 921.

Scott, R. A. & Scheraga, H. A. (1965). *J. chem. Phys.* **42**, 2209.

Scott, R. A. & Scheraga, H. A. (1966a). *Biopolymers* **4**, 237.

Scott, R. A. & Scheraga, H. A. (1966b). *J. chem. Phys.* **44**, 3054.

Scott, R. A. & Scheraga, H. A. (1966c). *J. chem. Phys.* **45**, 2091.

Shimanouchi, T. (1963). *Pure appl. Chem.* **7**, 131.

Vanderkooi, G., Leach, S. J., Némethy, G., Scott, R. A. & Scheraga, H. A. (1966). *Biochemistry*, **5**, 2991.

Watson, H. (1965). Private communication.

Williams, D. E. (1965). *Science, N.Y.* **147**, 605.

A Study of the Conformation of Amino Acids†

A. V. Lakshminarayanan, V. Sasisekharan and
G. N. Ramachandran

Centre of Advanced Study in Biophysics
University of Madras, Madras, India

In this paper, some of the salient conformational features of amino acids and peptides, as observed in the solid state, are presented. The large amount of data available from reported crystal structures have been correlated by referring each molecule to a standard reference plane $NC^\alpha C'$. The parameters ϕ, ψ and χ according to the accepted conventions, have been calculated from the published data and are reported here. The following are among the main conclusions of the analysis of these data. 1. The variations in bond lengths and angles can be, to a good approximation, neglected in the study of the conformational analysis. 2. The "backbone" of the amino acid structure does not show wide variations, though the disposition of the carboxyl group in glycine is different from that in other amino acids. 3. The γ-atom of the side chain occurs in all the three usual staggered positions, though the position *trans* to C' is often preferred. 4. The δ-atom occupies the position *trans* to C^α almost invariably. 5. The rings and planar groups in certain amino acid side chains, such as arginine, glutamic acid, histidine and tyrosine, show deviations from the above rules, but they have also definite types of behaviour. The important result of this study is that there are many common features among the conformations of the amino acid at the molecular level and that the conformation, in general, is independent of the molecular environment, to a large extent.

1. Introduction

In an earlier report from this department (Ramachandran & Lakshminarayanan, 1966) preliminary details regarding the conformation of side groups in amino acids and peptides have been given. A detailed study of the conformation of amino acids and peptides as observed in crystal structures has since been made and an account of the more important conformational features are presented here. A detailed account will be published elsewhere shortly in a series of papers.

In order that the various structures may be grouped and compared together so as to obtain meaningful information about the molecular conformation of amino acids, the nomenclature of atoms, bonds, angles, etc., has been systematized. The notation followed for the description of the entire side chain in all the cases is the same as that proposed at the 1965

† Contribution No. 202 from the Centre of Advanced Study in Biophysics, University of Madras.

Gordon Conference on Proteins (and published recently, Edsall *et al.*, 1966). For convenience, each structure is projected on the NC$^{\alpha}$C′ plane and the backbone is described in terms of the dihedral angles ϕ and ψ conforming to the above conventions. For amino acids, as distinct from peptides, there are two carboxyl oxygens and their disposition will be characterized by two parameters $\psi 1$ and $\psi 2$, $\psi 1$ referring to the oxygen O1 *trans* to the amino nitrogen N and $\psi 2$ to the oxygen O2 *cis* to N in the projection. This is true also for a C-terminal peptide. Fig. 1 explains these

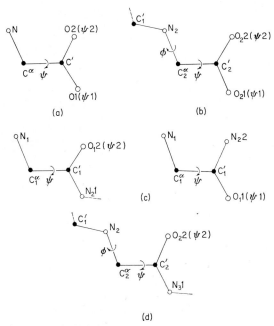

Fig. 1. Schematic diagram showing the parameters (ϕ, ψ) for: (a) an amino acid; (b) a C-terminal residue; (c) an N-terminal residue; and (d) a middle residue.

various conformational parameters for an amino acid and a peptide having a C-terminal, an N-terminal or a middle residue.

In reducing the co-ordinates of a molecule to the standard form for projecting it on the NC$^{\alpha}$C′ plane, the reported co-ordinates were initially converted to a rectangular system with C$^{\alpha}$ as the origin and then transformed to the reference plane through a suitable transformation involving rotations about two different directions. This calculation made use of the usual rotation matrices (e.g. see Jeffreys & Jeffreys, 1946) and was programmed for the IBM 1620.

The investigation revealed two very interesting facts.

(1) The "frame-work" of the amino acid structures, viz. the NC^{x}C' basis, often shows no appreciable differences; the bond lengths and angles at the α-carbon atom correspond very well in different structures, as was reported in our earlier paper. This permitted the gross conformational features to be referred to the backbone NC^{x}C' plane. However, the disposition of the carboxyl group with respect to this frame-work is not the same throughout.

(2) In spite of individual differences in primary valence bond lengths and angles, variations in the degree of accuracy of the structure determinations and widely differing molecular environments, certain conformational features, such as the relative orientation of the γ-atom of the side-chain, follow a general pattern. This observation made clear the fact that the molecule as a whole is more important than its actual environment and justifies our disregarding the finer variations in bond lengths and angles and treating the disparity in the accuracy of the structure determinations on a par with the bond length and angle variations. A study of these finer details will be published elsewhere.

For convenience, the discussion presented in this paper has been divided into two sections: one dealing with glycine conformations and the other with the conformations of amino acids with side groups. Glycine conformation is described in terms of the tilt of the carboxyl group referred to the standard plane, and through the angles ϕ and ψ. The conformation of the other amino acids has been separated into two: the backbone conformation (similar to glycine) and the side-group conformation, mainly concerned with the rotations about the various single bonds in the side chain and described by the set of dihedral angle χ_j. For calculating these torsion angles χ_j, a program written for the IBM 1620 was used.

2. Glycine Conformation

About 60 independent glycine projections have been compared, of which 10 are of glycine and its derivatives, 7 of C-terminal or N-terminal residues of dipeptides, 15 form part of tripeptides and 25 occur in cyclic peptides. The conformational parameters for these are shown in Table 1. (The relevant values of ϕ and ϕ' $(= \psi \pm 180°)$ which were reported earlier from this laboratory (Ramakrishnan & Ramachandran, 1965) are different from the ones given here since the angles are now calculated simply as torsion angles and not by fitting a least squares plane through the atoms involved, as was done previously.)

(a) *Glycine and its derivatives*

The essential conformational features observed in glycine and its derivatives are as follows. In general the tilt of the carboxyl group is characterized by a value for $\psi 2$ that is small, both negative and positive. For a typical case of one form of glycine, viz. α-glycine, this value is 19·2°. Certain peculiar exceptions to this are found for one molecule in each of diglycine HBr and diglycine HCl and one molecule of bisglycino–Cu(II)H$_2$O. For comparison, the projections on the reference plane of α-glycine and the two units of bisglycino–Cu(II)H$_2$O are shown in Fig. 2.

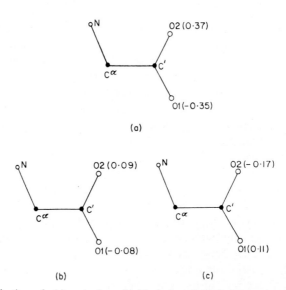

(a)

(b)   (c)

Fig. 2. Projection of: (a) α-glycine; (b) bisglycino–CuH$_2$O (molecule 1); and (c) bis-glycino–CuH$_2$O (molecule 2) on the reference plane NC$^\alpha$C′. (The height of the atoms in Å from the reference plane are given in brackets in this and succeeding Figures.)

(b) *C-Terminal residues*

For C-terminal glycyl residues, the values of ψ2 are in general small. The maximum deviation is in glutathione with ψ2 = 11°. The C-terminal glycyl residues occurring in metal peptide complexes show a somewhat different behaviour. Except for cysteinyl-glycine NaI, the tilt and hence the deviation from planarity is small. The presence of a group of atoms covalently bonded to the peptide nitrogen in these cases appears to produce a tendency in the carboxyl group to be nearly coplanar with the nitrogen. Also, the glycine conformation in the above cases occur in the allowed region of the conformational map of Ramachandran (see Ramakrishnan & Ramachandran, 1965). The most interesting observation is that the carboxyl group and the adjacent peptide plane are either coplanar or perpendicular (as pointed out first by Sasisekharan, 1962, and restated by Freeman *et al.*, 1964*a*). This fact is brought out by the value of φ near 0° or 90°.

(c) *N-Terminal residues*

For N-terminal residues, in general, the amino nitrogen and the peptide nitrogen are *trans* about the C_1^α—C_1' bond, and are characterized by a value of $\psi 2$ near $0°$. For the N-terminal residues of the metal complexes, however, both the *trans* and the *cis* conformations occur. In the latter case, the amino nitrogen and the peptide nitrogen are on the same side of the C_1^α—C_1' bond, as is characterized by $\psi 2$ having a value $\sim 180°$. These two conformations are shown in Fig. 3. It would appear that the *cis* conformation would be a disallowed one (see Ramakrishnan & Ramachandran, 1965), but they occur

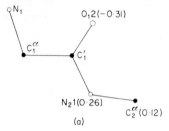

(a)

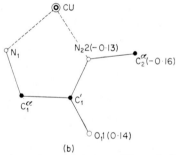

(b)

FIG. 3. Projection of (a) Gly-Gly-Gly CuCl $1\frac{1}{2}H_2O$ (N-terminal) and (b) Na Gly-Gly-Gly Cuprate H_2O (N-terminal) on the reference plane $NC^\alpha C'$.

in the above cases because of the fact that the two nitrogens form the ligands to the metal ion in these structures, thus giving rise to a strong covalent interaction, over-balancing the non-bonded interaction.

(d) *Cyclic peptides*

There are two cases in which glycine forms part of cyclic peptides, viz. cyclohexaglycyl hemihydrate and the hexapeptide Ferrichrome A. In Ferrichrome A, there is only one glycyl residue, and this exhibits the *cis* conformation of the nitrogens about the bond C^α—C', just as in some of the metal complexes cited above. This is shown by a value of $\psi 1 \sim 178°$. At least one such "flip-over" from the usual *trans* configuration appears to be essential

for the formation of a cyclic peptide. This would be clear from the conformational features observed in cyclohexaglycyl hemihydrate structure also.

Quite apart from the glycine conformation that it affords, the structure
of cyclohexaglycyl hemihydrate itself proves interesting, for a six-membered
cyclic peptide cannot be formed if all the peptide units are in plane. The
conformations $\phi = \psi = 0°$ and $\phi = \psi = 180°$ would result only in an
extended chain. A structure with all $\phi = 0°$ and $\psi = 180°$ would result in
severe short contacts between the peptide nitrogens. So also the cycle with
$\phi = 180°$ and $\psi = 0°$ would be ruled out by the oxygen atoms coming up
too close to each other. Of necessity, the ring must be puckered; the puckering
is through the *cis* conformations of the adjacent peptide nitrogens with
reference to the connecting C^α—C' bond as is found in Ferrichrome A.
The "flip-over" is characterized by ψ around 180°, though in the absence of
other stabilizing interactions as in metal peptides, the actual values may be
off by as much as 40° to relieve the steric hindrance. It is this that is found
in the cyclohexaglycyl structure as can be seen from Table 1. For a clearer

TABLE 1. The values of ϕ and ψ for glycine and glycyl residues†

Structure	$\phi(°)$	$\psi1(°)$	$\psi2(°)$	Reference
Glycine				
α-Glycine	—	198·3	19·2	1
β-Glycine	—	203·7	27·3	2
γ-Glycine	—	191·7	15·0	3
Diglycine HBr-1	—	200·8	22·0	4
Diglycine HBr-2	—	182·4	355·8	4
Diglycine HCl-1	—	192·1	16·4	5
Diglycine HCl-2	—	182·5	359·4	5
Bisglycino–Cu-1	—	184·2	4·5	6
Bisglycino–Cu-2	—	173·9	351·7	6
N-Acetylglycine	—	183·0	3·2	7
C-Terminal residues				
β-Gly-Gly	357·7	184·7	0·2	8
Leu-Gly HBr	95·3	176·1	354·6	9
Gly (in Glutathione)	95·6	190·0	10·9	10
Gly-Phe-Gly	264·3	179·3	355·4	11
Leu-Pro-Gly	3·2	180·5	358·1	12
Cys-Gly NaI	207·6	213·1	32·4	13
Gly-Gly-Gly Cu Cl 1½H$_2$O	264·6	175·3	353·2	14
Na Gly-Gly-Gly cuprate	311·2	160·9	342·8	15
2Na Gly-Gly-Gly-Gly cuprate	98·6	179·7	0·4	16
N-Terminal and middle residues				
β-Gly-Gly	—	—	330·8	8
Gly-Asp	—	—	8·0	17
Gly-Try 2H$_2$O	—	—	344·1	18

TABLE 1—*continued*

Structure	$\phi(°)$	$\psi1(°)$	$\psi2(°)$	Reference
Gly-Tyr HCl	—	—	352·3	19
NN′ diglycyl cystine	—	—	24·7	20
Gly-Phe-Gly	—	—	312·6	11
Gly-Gly-Gly Cu Cl 1½H$_2$O	—	—	342·8	14
$\overline{\text{Gly}}$-Gly-Gly Cu Cl 1½H$_2$O	294·2	—	311·0	14
2Na $\overline{\text{Gly}}$-Gly-Gly-Gly cuprate	—	188·6	—	16
2Na $\overline{\text{Gly}}$-Gly-Gly-Gly cuprate	359·6	184·3	—	16
2Na Gly-$\overline{\text{Gly}}$-Gly-Gly cuprate	5·5	179·6	—	16

Cyclic peptides

Structure	$\phi(°)$	$\psi1(°)$	$\psi2(°)$	Reference
Gly (Ferrichrome A)	262·2	178·2	—	21
Cyclohexaglycyl hemihydrate 1	86·0	188·2	—	22
2	110·7	151·3	—	
3	85·3	186·7	—	
4	111·4	150·1	—	
5	87·1	188·3	—	
6	112·2	149·0	—	
7	87·9	184·0	—	
8	111·2	150·4	—	
9	50·1	209·4	—	
10	84·6	183·7	—	
11	48·3	209·5	—	
12	82·5	182·6	—	
13	261·6	186·4	—	
14	90·4	—	336·2	
15	261·8	188·6	—	
16	94·7	—	331·3	
17	289·3	—	312·4	
18	283·8	—	317·7	
19	285·0	—	317·6	
20	290·0	—	312·7	
21	59·0	—	10·0	
22	59·4	—	10·0	
23	65·3	—	2·1	
24	65·7	—	5·4	

† The values of ψ (and ϕ when relevant) given in the table refer to a single molecule in the unit cell for each structure as published. Both (ϕ, ψ) and $(-\phi, -\psi)$ are possible for a glycyl α-carbon atom. In particular, when ϕ is not relevant, the value of ψ in glycine can be both positive and negative.

1. Marsh (1958); 2. Iitaka (1960); 3. Iitaka (1961); 4. Buerger *et al.* (1956); 5. Hahn & Buerger (1957); 6. Freeman *et al.* (1964*b*); 7. Donohue & Marsh (1962); 8. Hughes & Moore (1949); 9. Thyagaraja Rao (1966); 10. Wright (1958); 11. Marsh & Glusker (1961); 12. Leung & Marsh (1958); 13. Dyer (1951); 14. Freeman *et al.* (1964*a*); 15. Freeman *et al.* (1965); 16. Freeman & Taylor (1965); 17. Pasternak *et al.* (1954); 18. Pasternak (1956); 19. Smits & Wiebenga (1953); 20. Yakel & Hughes (1954); 21. Zalkin *et al.* (1966); 22. Karle & Karle (1963).

view, the projection of one of the five cyclohexaglycyl molecules on the least-squares plane through the six α-carbon atoms is shown in Fig. 4 in which the *trans* and *cis* conformations of the nitrogens about the C^α—C' bonds can be clearly seen.

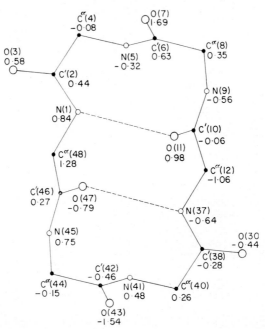

FIG. 4. Projection of one of the cyclohexaglycyl hemihydrate molecules on the least-squares plane through the six α-carbon atoms. Note the nearly *cis* conformation of neighbouring peptide nitrogens at $C^\alpha(4)$ and $C^\alpha(40)$. The intra-hydrogen bonds are shown by broken lines.

3. Amino Acids with Side Groups

(a) *Backbone conformation*

The backbone conformation, as in glycine, is described in terms of the disposition of the carboxyl group with respect to the $NC^\alpha C'$ plane and the relevant ϕ and ψ values are given in Table 2. The most striking observation is that the value of $\psi2$ is small and negative. The actual value is close to 360° as in alanine, for which $\psi2 = 343°$. The projection of alanine is shown in Fig. 5, from which it can be clearly seen that the carboxyl group tips down from the $NC^\alpha C'$ plane. This is in contrast to the general trend observed in glycine where the tilt may be either way. This tendency is observed to be so throughout all the amino acids having side groups, as well as in C- and N-

TABLE 2. Values of ϕ and ψ for amino acids and peptides with side chains

Structure	$\phi(°)$	$\psi1(°)$	$\psi2(°)$	Reference
Amino acids				
Alanine	—	164·7	342·9	1
Alanine	—	161·5	340·7	2
Arginine 2H$_2$O	—	167·9	349·3	3
Arginine 2HI	—	165·5	336·5	4
Arginine HBr H$_2$O (molecule 1)	—	177·2	353·6	5
Arginine HBr H$_2$O (molecule 2)	—	156·1	331·2	5
Arginine HCl H$_2$O (molecule 1)	—	175·0	352·9	6
Arginine HCl H$_2$O (molecule 2)	—	155·3	332·9	6
Arginine HCl (molecule 1)	—	134·3	309·1	7
Arginine HCl (molecule 2)	—	138·3	319·2	7
Asparagine H$_2$O	—	186·2	11·4	8
Aspartic acid HCl	—	22·4	42·3	9
Cysteine HCl	—	174·9	349·1	10
S-Methylcysteine sulphoxide	—	170·2	356·6	11
Cysteine ethyl ester urea	—	179·8	359·0	12
Cystine	—	167·7	345·8	13
Cystine 2HBr	—	180·8	0·7	14
Cystine 2HCl	—	192·6	9·7	15
Glutamic acid	—	147·5	314·2	16
Glutamic acid HCl	—	162·0	342·4	17
Glutamine	—	168·7	340·5	18
Histidine HCl H$_2$O	—	179·5	0·4	19
Di-(histidino)Zn 2H$_2$O	—	170·9	348·2	20
Di-(histidino)Zn 5H$_2$O	—	176·1	356·4	21
Hydroxyproline	—	178·0	356·9	22
Isoleucine HBr	—	159·4	345·7	23
Isoleucine HCl	—	165·7	6·4	23
Leucine HBr	—	170·2	342·5	24
Lysine HCl H$_2$O	—	162·1	340·1	25
α-Methionine	—	149·6	326·3	26
β-Methionine	—	148·4	330·6	26
Norleucine	—	155·6	324·7	27
Phenylalanine HCl	—	177·5	358·1	28
Cu proline 2H$_2$O	—	191·0	11·0	29
Serine	—	181·3	3·8	30
Threonine	—	156·1	333·9	31
Tryptophan HBr	—	201·4	355·8	32
Tyrosine HBr	—	154·7	322·2	33
Tyrosine HCl	—	149·6	323·9	34
Valine HBr	—	165·3	348·4	35
Valine HCl	—	171·2	352·2	36
Valine HCl.H$_2$O	—	174·2	356·3	37

TABLE 2—*continued*

Structure	$\phi(°)$	$\psi 1(°)$	$\psi 2(°)$	Reference
C-Terminal residues				
Gly-Asp	69·2	249·2	63·3	38
Cys (in glutathione)	89·2	174·9	358·7	39
NN'-Diglycylcystine $2H_2O$	20·4	174·9	356·4	40
β-Ala-His Cu $2H_2O$	27·4	174·3	353·6	41
p-Tosyl-Pro-Hypro	137·8	136·4	316·5	42
Thr-Phe-nitrobenzyl ester HBr	66·9	117·9	304·5	43
Gly-Try $2H_2O$	107·1	156·4	326·7	44
Gly-Tyr HCl	93·2	149·1	326·6	45
N-Terminal and middle residues				
Cys-Gly NaI	—	—	349·0	46
γ-Glutamyl (in glutathione)	—	167·5	350·4	39
Leu-Gly HBr	—	—	319·7	47
Leu-Pro-Gly	—	—	329·3	48
p-Tosyl-Pro-Hypro	—	—	353·2	42
Leu-Pro-Gly	111·8	161·9	—	48
Orn2 (Ferrichrome A)	35·6	—	27·2	49
Orn3 (Ferrichrome A)	103·5	131·0	—	49
Orn4 (Ferrichrome A)	75·4	183·6	—	49
Gly-Phe-Gly	53·7	—	314·3	50
Ser5 (Ferrichrome A)	123·0	—	313·3	49
Ser6 (Ferrichrome A)	17·2	—	354·5	49
Thr-Phe-nitrobenzyl ester HBr	—	—	323·1	43

1. Donohue (1951); 2. Simpson & Marsh (1966); 3. Karle & Karle (1964); 4. O. Seely (private comm.); 5. Mazumdar & Srinivasan (1964); 6. Dow & Jensen (private comm.); 7. Mazumdar (1964); 8. Kartha & De Vries (1961); 9. B. Dawson (private comm.); 10. Ramachandra Ayyar & Srinivasan (1965); 11. Hine (1962); 12. Haas (1966); 13. Oughton & Harrison (1959); 14. Peterson *et al.* (1960); 15. Steinrauf *et al.* (1958); 16. Hirokawa (1955); 17. Dawson (1953); 18. Cochran & Penfold (1952); 19. Donohue & Caron (1964); 20. Kretsinger *et al.* (1963); 21. Harding & Cole (1963); 22. Donohue & Trueblood (1952); 23. Trommel & Bijvoet (1954); 24. Subramanian (to be published); 25. Wright & Marsh (1962); 26. Mathieson (1952); 27. Mathieson (1953); 28. Gurskaya (1964); 29. Mathieson & Welsh (1952); 30. Shoemaker *et al.* (1953); 31. Shoemaker *et al.* (1951); 32. R. Ramachandra Ayyar (private comm.); 33. Srinivasan (1959*a*); 34. Srinivasan (1959*b*); 35. Parthasarathy & Chandrasekharan (1966); 36. Parthasarathy (1966); 37. Thyagaraja Rao & Parthasarathy (1965); 38. Pasternak *et al.* (1954); 39. Wright (1958); 40. Yakel & Hughes (1954); 41. H. C. Freeman (private comm.); 42. Fridrichsons & Mathieson (1962); 43. Venkatesan *et al.* (to be published); 44. Pasternak (1956); 45. Smits & Wiebenga (1953); 46. Dyer (1951); 47. Thyagaraja Rao (1966); 48. Leung & Marsh (1958); 49 .Zalkin *et al.* (1966); 50. Marsh & Glusker (1961).

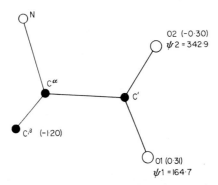

O2 (-0·30)
ψ2 = 342·9

C$^\alpha$

C'

C$^\beta$ (-1·20)

O1 (0·31)
ψ1 = 164·7

FIG. 5. Projection of alanine in DL-alanine on the reference plane NC$^\alpha$C'. The values of ψ are also given.

terminal peptides with side chains. With very few exceptions, such as asparagine H_2O, cystine 2HCl, isoleucine HCl and serine, this is generally true. Another common feature is the following. Of the two C'—O bonds in amino acids, generally one is shorter than the other and this may be considered to be the C=O bond, and the other may be taken as the C—OH bond. (This is not true when the amino acid is in the zwitterion conformation.) It is observed that the shorter bond (C=O) generally takes up the position *cis* to C$^\alpha$—N. This is violated in one or two cases, as for example in aspartic acid HCl, and correspondingly in such cases the angle ψ2 is large (42° in aspartic acid HCl). It is also found, as in glycyl residues, that the N-terminal residues exhibit the *trans* configuration of the nitrogens generally, but a *cis* configuration is observed in two of the ornithine residues in the cyclic peptide Ferrichrome A.

(b) *Side-group conformation*

The discussion of the side-group conformation is divided into two major groups, one dealing with straight side chains and the other with branched side chains. The conformational features are discussed with reference to the various angular parameters χ_j or χ_{ij} in the above two cases. The χ values for all the side chains are listed in Table 3.

(i) *Arginine*

A study on the arginines other than the hydroiodide derivative has been already published (Ramachandran *et al.*, 1966). The conformational parameters for the arginines are summarized in Table 3. The γ-carbon atom is found to occur at all the three staggered configurations, corresponding to $\chi_1 = 60°$, 180° and 300°. The δ- and ε-atoms occur in only one position with χ_2 and χ_3 nearly 180°, the positions being *trans* to C$^\alpha$ and C$^\beta$, respectively.

TABLE 3. Values of χ for amino acid side chains

Structure	χ_1	χ_2	χ_3	χ_4	χ_{51}	χ_{52}
		Straight chains				
Arginine 2HI	60·4	188·4	184·2	191·0	3·6	179·7
Arginine 2H$_2$O	62·2	151·1	175·2	162·0	351·9	171·5
Arginine HCl (molecule A)	170·8	187·4	172·5	188·3	352·9	175·0
Arginine HCl (molecule B)	168·5	166·1	174·8	170·0	5·6	181·4
Arginine HCl.H$_2$O (molecule A)	299·7	195·7	179·5	276·3	11·9	191·0
Arginine HCl.H$_2$O (molecule B)	308·6	172·8	182·2	98·8	344·3	164·8
Arginine HBr.H$_2$O (molecule A)	298·8	197·0	180·4	274·4	9·3	182·9
Arginine HBr.H$_2$O (molecule B)	304·6	168·1	186·3	100·9	342·2	165·3
Cysteine HCl	64·6	—	—	—	—	—
S-Methylcysteine sulphoxide	294·9	—	—	—	—	—
Cysteinylglycine NaI (N-terminal)	64·9	—	—	—	—	—
Cysteinyl (in glutathione)	71·8	—	—	—	—	—
Cysteine ethyl ester HCl-urea	74·9	—	—	—	—	—
Cystine	55·3	81·5	73·8	—	—	—
Cystine 2HBr	70·6	271·1	278·7	—	—	—
Cystine 2HCl	69·1	271·3	280·9	—	—	—
NN'-Diglycyl cystine (C-terminal)	64·0	263·1	281·0	—	—	—
Lysine HCl.H$_2$O	304·2	184·2	188·9	179·0	—	—
α-Methionine	299·9	176·9	80·5	—	—	—
β-Methionine	299·0	183·6	190·4	—	—	—
Norleucine	303·1	182·2	195·2	—	—	—
Ornithine 2 (Ferrichrome A)	55·4	177·1	303·7	—	—	—
Ornithine 3 (Ferrichrome A)	300·7	76·2	45·4	—	—	—
Ornithine 4 (Ferrichrome A)	299·7	149·0	303·8	—	—	—
Serine	69·2	—	—	—	—	—
Serine 5 (Ferrichrome A)	59·5	—	—	—	—	—
Serine 6 (Ferrichrome A)	177·2	—	—	—	—	—
	58·2	—	—	—	—	—

	χ_{11}	χ_{12}	χ_{21}
		Branched at C^β	
Isoleucine HBr	191·7	66·5	68·1
Isoleucine HCl	48·4	287·5	172·1
Threonine	305·2	185·5	—
Threonyl phenylalanine nitro-benzyl ester HBr (N-terminal)	295·6	173·3	—
Valine HBr	195·5	74·0	—
Valine HCl	194·3	64·4	—
Valine HCl.H$_2$O	53·9	289·0	—

TABLE 3—*continued*

Structure	χ_1	χ_2	χ_3	χ_4	χ_{51}	χ_{52}
	χ_1	χ_{21}	χ_{22}			
	Branched at C^γ					
Aspartic acid HCl	296·0	174·1	352·5			
Asparagine H_2O	72·3	183·0	2·7			
Glycylasparagine (C-terminal)	296·6	170·7	352·6			
Histidine HCl·H_2O	71·5	239·5	61·1			
Di-(histidino)Zn $5H_2O$	73·2	317·9	139·8			
Di-(histidino)Zn $2H_2O$	70·9	314·8	134·4			
β-Alanylhistidino Cu $2H_2O$	53·1	244·7	69·6			
Leucine HBr	187·5	182·2	58·4			
Leucylglycine HBr (N-terminal)	292·8	265·6	155·2			
Leucylprolylglycine (N-terminal)	279·4	291·5	170·3			
Phenylalanine HCl	62·1	83·6	262·4			
Threonylphenylalaninenitro-benzyl ester HBr (C-terminal)	172·0	83·6	266·9			
Glycylphenylalanylglycine (middle)	185·3	102·5	278·5			
Tryptophan HBr	65·9	80·7	253·3			
Glycyltryptophan $2H_2O$ (C-terminal)	294·1	60·6	237·7			
Tyrosine HBr	187·3	64·7	250·3			
Tyrosine HCl	185·2	64·3	243·7			
Glycyltyrosine HCl (C-terminal)	189·8	65·3	241·6			
	χ_1	χ_2	χ_{31}	χ_{32}		
	Branched at C^δ					
Glutamic acid	309·9	282·9	204·6	25·0		
Glutamic acid HCl	290·4	188·2	195·9	17·6		
Glutamine	70·6	176·1	164·8	341·6		
γ-Glutamyl (in glutathione)	289·0	291·0	103·3	287·9		

But the atom C^ζ, which forms part of the planar guanidyl group at the end, shows a peculiar behaviour, in that χ_4 takes up a value of either 180° or ±90°. The final rotation about the N^ε—C^ζ bond ends up with a nearly planar configuration for the guanidyl group with respect to the plane of the δ-, ε- and ζ-atoms.

(ii) *Cysteine and cystine*

In these structures the γ-atom is sulphur. In eight out of the nine structures, the atom S^γ occupies only the position with $\chi_1 = 60°$, the smallest angle being 55·3° and the largest 74·9° (see Table 3). The only exception is in *S*-methylcysteine sulphoxide, in which S^γ occurs at $\chi_1 = 300°$. The interesting observation regarding cystine is about the rotations around the C_1^β—S_1^γ and S_1^γ—S_2^γ bonds, i.e. the values of χ_2 and χ_3. In cystine χ_2 is $81°$, whereas in the others it is nearly $270°$. Similarly, χ_3 is $+90°$ for cystine and $-90°$ for the others. The perpendicular positions in arginine and cystine may be due to the fact that the particular single bonds involved do not possess the threefold symmetry the other bonds display.

(iii) *Other unbranched chains*

Lysine exhibits an extended configuration with the γ-atom *trans* to C', the δ-atom *trans* to C^α, and so on, typical of a long-chain carbon compound, as has been observed in many hydrocarbons. This seems to be the most favourable conformation from the point of view of $CH_2 \cdots CH_2$ interactions. There are two forms of methionine and one of norleucine available for comparison. One form of methionine (the α-form) and norleucine follow the pattern of lysine exactly, in that the conformation at each bond is *trans* to a carbon atom. In the β-form of methionine, the atom ε, viz. S^ε takes up a nearly perpendicular position about the C^β—C^γ bond. However, among the three ornithines found in the cyclic hexapeptide Ferrichrome A, the side chains exhibit entirely different conformations. In one case the conformation is $60°$, $180°$, $300°$; in a second $300°$, $60°$, $60°$; and in the third $300°$, $180°$, $60°$. In the three cases of serine, viz. free serine and two residues in Ferrichrome A, the γ-atom, which is an oxygen atom, occurs at $\chi_1 = 60°$. The other position with $\chi_1 = 180°$ for serine 6 in Table 3 refers to the partial occupancy of the atom at the other site reported in the crystal structure.

(c) *Branched side chains*

The following sections describe the salient points of the conformation of side chains in which branching occurs at the β-, γ- and δ-atoms.

(i) *Isoleucine, threonine and valine*

In isoleucine two different conformations are observed in the two structures, viz. the hydrobromide and the hydrochloride derivatives. The two conformers are characterized by $\chi_{11} = 192°$, $\chi_{12} = 60°$ and $\chi_{21} = 172°$ in the first case, and $\chi_{11} = 48°$, $\chi_{12} = 288°$ and $\chi_{21} = 172°$ in the second. Contrasted to the case of isoleucine, the threonine side group as observed in free threonine and in the dipeptide threonylphenylalanine-*p*-nitrobenzyl ester HBr, the hydroxyl group $O^{\gamma 1}$ occurs at $\chi_{11} = 300°$ and the atom $C^{\gamma 2}$ occurs at $\chi_{12} = 180°$. In valine, however, the combination $180°$, $60°$ appears in valine HBr and valine HCl, and the combination $60°$, $300°$ is observed in the hydrated valine HCl. Thus, the same combinations occur in isoleucine and valine, but the third combination 180°, 300° has not been found for the methyl–methyl or the methyl–ethyl pair, although this has been found for the methyl–hydroxyl pair in threonine.

(ii) Aspartic acid, asparagine, glutamic acid and glutamine

The conformations of aspartic acid HCl and glycylasparagine are very similar, with the γ-atom *trans* to C′ and the end planar group in plane with C^{α}. The shorter bond, C–O or C–N, of the side chain end group occurs *cis* to C^{α} in both cases. In asparagine H_2O, the γ-atom occupies the position corresponding to $\chi_1 = 60°$, and the rest of the features are similar to the above cases. It is interesting to compare glutamic acid with the above, though in glutamic acid the branching is at the δ-carbon atom. The position of the γ-atom in glutamic acid, glutamic acid HCl and in glutathione is the same and is the *trans* position with respect to C′ ($\chi_1 \sim 300°$), whereas in glutamine $\chi_1 \sim 60°$. However, the δ-atom of glutamic acid and glutathione is characterized by $\chi_2 \sim 300°$; but in glutamic acid HCl and glutamine it is *trans* to C^{α}. Again, the ε-atom is disposed differently in these cases. In glutathione, the planar group is disposed nearly perpendicular to the $C^{\beta}C^{\gamma}C^{\delta}$ plane, but in the other three cases it is nearly coplanar. Thus, as regards the disposition of the planar group, the amino acids arginine, aspartic acid and glutamic acid are very similar with the plane either nearly coplanar with, or nearly perpendicular to, the plane defined by the preceding three atoms.

(iii) Histidine, phenylalanine, tryptophan and tyrosine

These amino acids all have rings attached to C^{β}. All the three positions of the γ-atom are exhibited by this group. However, all the histidines have $\chi_1 \sim 60°$ and all the tyrosines $\sim 180°$. Tryptophan shows both *gauche* conformations corresponding to $\chi_1 = 60°$ and 300°, and in phenylalanine $\chi_1 = 60°$ or 180°. The δ-atoms would be described by two χ-values differing approximately by 180°, since these form part of a planar ring. The δ-atoms show some peculiarities, as described below. These features are clearly seen from the projections shown in Fig. 6. The χ-values for these structures are drawn up in Table 3.

In histidine HCl H_2O and β-alanylhistidinato Cu, the δ-atoms have a twist of about 240°(60°) around the C^{β}—C^{γ} bond. But in the complexes of histidine with zinc, the δ-atoms take up the position with $\chi_{21} \sim 300°$ ($\chi_{22} \sim 120°$). In phenylalanine, the disposition of the ring is always the same, with the ring nearly perpendicular to the $C^{\alpha}C^{\beta}C^{\gamma}$ plane, though the γ-atoms are differently oriented about the C^{α}—C^{β} bond. The tryptophan side chain in tryptophan HBr and in glycyl tryptophan $2H_2O$ exhibits two different conformations. In the amino acid, C^{γ} occupies the position with $\chi_1 = 60°$, and the ring assumes a perpendicular conformation, as in phenylalanine. But in

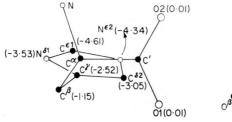

Histidine HCl.H₂O

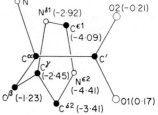

Di – (histidino)Zn.2H₂O

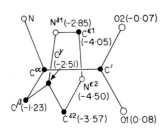

Di – (histidino)Zn.5H₂O

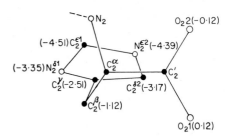

β – Alanylhistidino Cu.2H₂O (C – term)

(a)

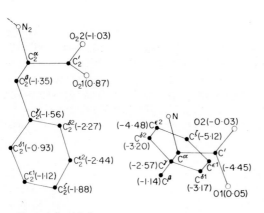

Threonyl phenylalanine
nitrobenzyl ester HBr
(C–term)

Phenylalanine HCl

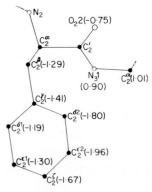

Glycyl phenyl alanyl glycine
(middle)

(b)

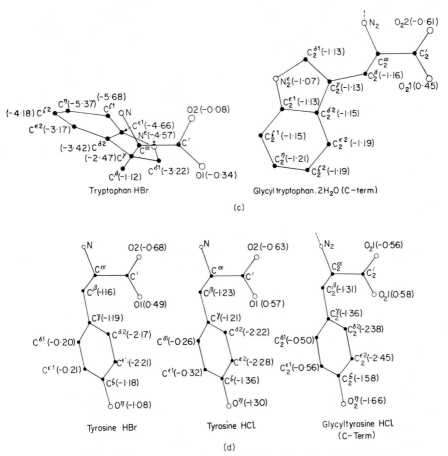

FIG. 6. Projections on the reference plane $NC^{\alpha}C'$ showing the various molecular conformations of (a) histidine, (b) phenylalanine, (c) tryptophan and (d) tyrosine.

the dipeptide, the γ-atom is *trans* to C' and the twist about the C^{β}—C^{γ} bond is 60°. This is like the case of the tyrosine side chain in tyrosine HBr, tyrosine HCl and glycyltyrosine HCl, in which, though the γ-atom occurs at $\chi_1 = 300°$ (*trans* to C'), the δ-atoms are twisted by 60° around the C^{β}—C^{γ} bond. Thus the side chains with rings show very interesting conformations.

(iv) *Leucine*

In leucine, in which the two branches from the γ-atom are methyl groups, two different conformations occur among the three observed structures. The conformations of leucine in the peptides are very similar, as characterized by $\chi_1 \sim 300°$, $\chi_{12} \sim 300°$ and $\chi_{21} \sim 180°$; whereas in the amino acid derivative, the γ-carbon occurs at $\chi_1 \sim 180°$ and the δ-atoms are at $180°$, $60°$. Thus, the combinations $300°$, $180°$ and $180°$, $60°$ occur at the δ-position. Surprisingly, the combination $300°$, $180°$ for the methyl–methyl pair is observed in this case for the δ-atoms in contrast to the case of valine where this combination has not been observed for the same pair as γ-atoms.

(d) *Imino acids*

For proline and hydroxyproline, occurring either as a free imino acid or as part of a peptide, the four atoms, N, C^α, C^β and C^δ, are nearly coplanar. This coplanarity imposes the restriction that this plane be rotated by $120°$ with reference to the $C^\alpha C'N$ plane, since the plane of C', C^α and C^β is at this angle to the reference plane because of the tetrahedral disposition of the bonds at C^α. This would explain why a proline residue must lie close to $\phi = 120°$ on the ϕ–ψ conformational map. However, the disposition of the γ-atom with respect to the plane of the N, C^α, C^β and C^δ atoms is not the same in all the cases (it may be either on one or other side of this plane) and there are two typical conformations for the ring. In fact, in the structure of leucylprolylglycine, both the conformations of the five-membered ring occur with partial probabilities.

4. Conclusion

Thus, the study on the available structures has led to the revelation of certain peculiarities and intricacies of the amino acid conformation. The following are the main interesting facts which emerge from the study:

1. The carboxyl group is oriented in opposite directions with respect to the $NC^\alpha C'$ plane in glycine and in non-glycine amino acids. In glycine, the value of $\psi 2$ is small, both negative and positive. The presence of the β-atom tends to drive the group one way with $\psi 2$ negative. The value of $\psi 2$ is usually small in such instances, being of the order of $-10°$ ($350°$), but under certain circumstances could be as large as $-45°$.

2. In peptides, the conformation of the peptide nitrogens about the C^α—C' bond is usually *trans* (e.g. the nitrogen atoms N_1 and N_2 in Fig. 3(a)). It assumes a *cis* configuration under strong covalent influences, as when a metal ion is bound to the nitrogens (e.g. in Fig. 3(b)).

3. Such "flip-overs" with *cis* configuration as above seem to be key points in the formation of cyclic peptides (see, e.g., Fig. 4).

4. The γ-atom is restricted to three positions. This is shown in Fig. 7(a), in which the projection down the C^α—C^β bond brings out the three possible positions characterized by χ_1 nearly equal to $60°$, $180°$ and $300°$. Leaving out the S and O atoms at the γ-position, the number of cases in which these positions occur are 13, 10 and 21, respectively. It appears from these that the $300°$ position is most favourable, and this is also the position where the

γ-atom is *trans* to C′ and is situated in between N and H (Fig. 7(a)), which are relatively of small size. Based on similar arguments, the position characterized by $\chi_1 = 60°$ would appear to be the most unlikely one; but strangely enough, it is here that the bulky sulphur atom of cysteine and cystine is mostly found.

5. Similarly, the δ-atom would be expected to occupy the three positions shown in Fig. 7(b). Actually, however, it is found to go mostly to the position corresponding to $\chi_2 = 180°$. There are twenty cases in which this happens, but only two with $\chi_2 = 300°$ and only one with $\chi_2 = 60°$. Here again, the simple tendency to occupy a *trans* configuration so as to have a maximum C · · · C distance, and hence have a minimum interaction, is apparent. There are two other cases with $\chi_2 = 60°$, but then there are two δ-atoms in those structures.

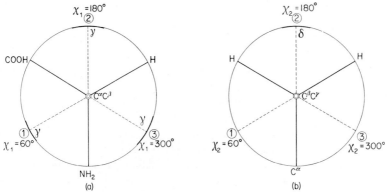

Fig. 7. (a) Positions of the γ-atom, looking down the bond C^α—C^β. (b) Position of the δ-atom, looking down the bond C^β—C^γ.

6. The same trend as above is observed for the position occupied by the ε-atom. When those cases for which the ε-atom forms part of a planar group are excluded, in all the remaining ten cases the ε-atom goes only into the position with $\chi_3 = 180°$. The only case that affords comparison along these lines is arginine. Because of the factors outlined above, it can be seen that, though, in principle, as many as 3^5 conformations are possible, owing to severe restrictions arising from non-bonded interactions the allowed conformations for arginine are very small in number. The distribution of the γ-, δ- and ε-atoms among the various positions is outlined in Table 4.

7. For branched side chains, the possible conformations seem to be restricted, because certain combinations of the positions available for the branched atoms appear to be difficult to realize in practice. The case of valine is worth mentioning here.

TABLE 4. Distribution of χ values

Values around	Number of cases: Without O or S	With O or S	Number of cases with values: > col 1	< col 1
γ-Position				
60	13	11	17	7
180	10	2	8	4
300	21	—	7	14
δ-Position				
60	3	1	3	1
180	20	—	9	11
300	2	—	—	2
90	—	1	—	1
270	—	3	2	1
ε-Position (excluding structures having a planar group at δ)				
60	None	—	—	—
180	10	3	8	5
300	None	—	—	—

8. For those side chains that end with a planar group, such as a carboxyl group or a benzene ring, the orientation of the group is very special. It is either perpendicular to, or coplanar with, the plane defined by the previous adjacent three atoms.

9. This characteristic disposition of the planar groups is observed with the backbone of peptides also, where the carboxyl group and the adjacent peptide group are generally found to be coplanar or perpendicular. These effects seem to be due to π-electron distribution in such cases.

It would appear from these that the gross conformational features of the amino acid are broadly predictable, whether it occurs as a free acid, or a derivative of it, or forms part of a di-, tri- or a cyclic peptide. And, in addition, the conformation of the molecule would appear to be independent of its environment to a large extent. That is to say, the deviations from the ideal values of, e.g. $\chi_1 = 60°$, 180° and 300°, may be due to intermolecular interactions or intra-molecular forces not envisaged in this paper. Recent studies (V. Sasisekharan, unpublished) on the effect of hydrogen bonding on the conformation of the molecule have indicated that the conformation of the groups involved are very nearly the same as dictated by intramolecular interactions. In view of this, an attempt has been made to correlate the distribution of the χ-values with the rotational barrier in order to arrive at the nature of the non-bonded interaction and to obtain an expression for the possible potential function that would explain the optimal conformation and this will be published elsewhere (V. Sasisekharan and A. V. Lakshminarayanan, unpublished).

ACKNOWLEDGMENT

We thank the authors who made available to us details of unpublished structures and the co-ordinates before publication. We also thank the Director of Technical Education, Madras, for the generous offer of computer time on IBM 1620. One of us (A.V.L.) wishes to thank the Council of Scientific and Industrial Research, India, for financial support. This work was partially supported by Research Grant No. AM10905-01 from the United States Public Health Service.

REFERENCES

Buerger, M. J., Barney, E. & Hahn, T. (1956). *Z. Kristallogr.* **108**, 130.

Cochran, W. & Penfold, B. R. (1952). *Acta cryst.* **5**, 644.

Dawson, B. (1953). *Acta cryst.* **6**, 81.

Donohue, J. (1951). *J. Am. chem. Soc.* **72**, 949.

Donohue, J. & Caron, A. (1964). *Acta cryst.* **17**, 1178.

Donohue, J. & Marsh, R. E. (1962). *Acta cryst.* **15**, 941.

Donohue, J. & Trueblood, K. N. (1952). *Acta cryst.* **5**, 419.

Dyer, H. B. (1951). *Acta cryst.* **4**, 42.

Edsall, J. T., Flory, P. J., Kendrew, J. C., Liquori, A. M., Nemethy, G., Rama-chandran, G. N. & Scheraga, H. A. (1966). *J. molec. Biol.* **15**, 339; *J. biol. Chem.* 241; *Biopolymers* **4**, 121.

Freeman, H. C. & Taylor, M. R. (1965). *Acta cryst.* **18**, 939.

Freeman, H. C., Robinson, G. & Schoone, J. C. (1964a). *Acta cryst.* **17**, 719.

Freeman, H. C., Snow, M. R., Nitta, I. & Tomita, K. (1964b). *Acta cryst.* **17**, 1463.

Freeman, H. C., Schoone, J. C. & Sime, J. G. (1965). *Acta cryst.* **18**, 381.

Fridrichsons, J. & Mathieson, A. McL. (1962). *Acta cryst.* **15**, 569.

Gurskaya, G. V. (1964). *Kristallografiya* **9**, 839.

Haas, D. J. (1966). *Acta cryst.* **19**, 860.

Hahn, T. & Buerger, M. J. (1957). *Z. Kristallogr.* **108**, 419.

Harding, M. M. & Cole, S. J. (1963). *Acta cryst.* **16**, 643.

Hine, R. (1962). *Acta cryst.* **15**, 635.

Hirokawa, S. (1955). *Acta cryst.* **8**, 637.

Hughes, E. W. & Moore, W. J. (1949). *J. Am. chem. Soc.* **71**, 2618.

Iitaka, Y. (1960). *Acta cryst.* **13**, 35.

Iitaka, Y. (1961). *Acta cryst.* **14**, 1.

Jeffreys, H. & Jeffreys, B. S. (1946). "Methods of Mathematical Physics", p. 114. Cambridge University Press.

Karle, I. L. & Karle, J. (1963). *Acta cryst.* **16**, 969.

Karle, I. L. & Karle, J. (1964). *Acta cryst.* **17**, 835.

Kartha, G. & DeVries, A. (1961). *Nature, Lond.* **192**, 862.

Kretsinger, R. H., Cotton, F. A. & Bryan, R. F. (1963). *Acta cryst.* **16**, 651.

Leung, Y. C. & Marsh, R. E. (1958). *Acta cryst.* **11**, 17.

Marsh, R. E. (1958). *Acta cryst.* **11**, 654.

Marsh, R. E. & Glusker, J. P. (1961). *Acta cryst.* **14**, 1110.

Mathieson, A. McL. (1952). *Acta cryst.* **5**, 332.

Mathieson, A. McL. (1953). *Acta cryst.* **6**, 399.

Mathieson, A. McL. & Welsh, H. K. (1952). *Acta cryst.* **5**, 599.

Mazumdar, S. K. (1964). Doctoral Thesis, Madras University.

Mazumdar, S. K. & Srinivasan, R. (1964). *Curr. Sci. India*, **33**, 573.

Oughton, B. M. & Harrison, P. M. (1959). *Acta cryst.* **12**, 396.

Parthasarathy, R. (1966). *Acta cryst.* **21,** 422.
Parthasarathy, R. & Chandrasekharan, R. (1966). *Indian J. pure appl. Phys.* **4,** 293.
Pasternak, R. A. (1956). *Acta cryst.* **9,** 341.
Pasternak, R. A., Katz, L. & Corey, R. B. (1954). *Acta cryst.* **7,** 225.
Peterson, J., Steinrauf, L. K. & Jensen, L. H. (1960). *Acta cryst.* **13,** 104.
Ramachandra Ayyar, R. & Srinivasan, R. (1965). *Curr. Sci. India,* **34,** 449.
Ramachandran, G. N. & Lakshminarayanan, A. V. (1966). *Biopolymers* **4,** 495.
Ramachandran, G. N., Mazumdar, S. K., Venkatesan, K. & Lakshminarayanan, A. V. (1966). *J. molec. Biol.* **15,** 232.
Ramakrishnan, C. & Ramachandran, G. N. (1965). *Biophys. J.* **5,** 909.
Sasisekharan, V. (1962). *In* "Collagen" (N. Ramanathan, ed.), p. 39. New York: Wiley.
Shoemaker, D. P., Donohue, J., Shoemaker, V. & Corey, R. B. (1951). *J. Am. chem. Soc.* **72,** 2328.
Shoemaker, D. P., Barieau, R. E. & Donohue, J. (1953). *Acta cryst.* **6,** 241.
Simpson, H. J. & Marsh, R. E. (1966). *Acta cryst.* **20,** 550.
Smits, D. W. & Wiebenga, E. H. (1953). *Acta cryst.* **6,** 531.
Srinivasan, R. (1959*a*). *Proc. Indian Acad. Sci.* **49,** 340.
Srinivasan, R. (1959*b*). *Proc. Indian Acad. Sci.* **50,** 19.
Steinrauf, L. K., Peterson, J. & Jensen, L. H. (1958). *J. Am. chem. Soc.* **80,** 3835.
Thyagaraja Rao, S. (1966). *Crystallography, U.S.S.R.* **11,** 171.
Thyagaraja Rao, S. & Parthasarathy, R. (1965). *Curr. Sci. India,* **34,** 628.
Trommel, J. & Bijvoet, J. M. (1954). *Acta cryst.* **7,** 703.
Wright, W. B. (1958). *Acta cryst.* **11,** 632.
Wright, W. B. & Marsh, R. E. (1962). *Acta cryst.* **15,** 54.
Yakel, H. L., Jr. & Hughes, E. W. (1954). *Acta cryst.* **7,** 291.
Zalkin, A., Forrester, J. D. & Templeton, D. H. (1966). *J. Am. chem. Soc.* **88,** 1810.

Stereochemistry of Polypeptide Chains: Comparison of Different Potential Functions†

C. M. Venkatachalam and G. N. Ramachandran

Centre of Advanced Study in Biophysics, University of Madras, Madras, India

Different types of potential functions, such as those proposed by Liquori and co-workers, Scheraga and co-workers, Brant and Flory, and Kitaigorodskii, were used for calculating the values of potential energy for different conformations of a polypeptide chain. The potential-energy data are given in a schematic form in the ϕ–ψ plane for a pair of linked peptide units and for poly-L-alanine in a helical conformation. The results show that, in general, all the potential functions agree with the broad predictions from contact-distance criteria deduced by Ramachandran and co-workers. All of them show that the right-handed α-helix is more stable than the left-handed, although the exact difference in energy between the two conformations varies with the potential function employed, from 2 kcal/mole per residue to very small values of the order of 0·2 kcal/mole per residue. Further studies are necessary to decide which types of potential functions are best fitted for studies on protein and polypeptide conformations.

1. Introduction

In studying the possible conformations of polypeptide chains, a hard-sphere model has been used quite extensively (Ramachandran *et al.*, 1963; Ramakrishnan & Ramachandran, 1965; Ramachandran *et al.*, 1966a; Némethy & Scheraga, 1965; Leach *et al.*, 1966). A set of contact-distance criteria was chosen after an examination of non-bonded distances observed in crystals whose structures have been determined. Such studies, based on the effect of excluded volume on the conformations that may be permitted for a polypeptide chain, have yielded interesting and useful results. Although this approach cannot be expected to give any definite clue to the most stable conformations of a polypeptide chain, it is extremely useful in rejecting many impossible conformations that contain genuine "bad contacts". However, extreme caution has to be exercised in this method, to avoid rejecting a conformation as untenable just because a single non-bonded distance is slightly less than the allowed value for it. In other words, it is obvious that the stable conformation that is actually realized in a protein is a result of various competing interactions, and a criterion is needed that would give

† Contribution No. 205 from the Centre of Advanced Study in Biophysics, University of Madras, Madras, India.

proper weight to the influence of these competing factors in determining the stability of the polypeptide chain. Such a criterion is found in the potential energy of the chain, where each non-bonded distance would be described by the potential energy of the corresponding interaction, and the most stable conformation would be the one with the least total potential energy.

(a) *Potential functions*†

The application of potential-energy functions to polypeptide chains was first attempted by Liquori and co-workers (De Santis *et al.*, 1965). For this, they used a set of semi-empirical functions to describe the non-bonded interaction energy between different types of atoms. In this way, they obtained potential-energy contours in the (ϕ–ψ) plane ‡ for a helical chain of backbone peptide units (with the β-carbon atom in the L-configuration). This showed that the α-helix is a particularly stable conformation for such a chain and that the right-handed α-helix is more stable than the left-handed one.

More recently, Brant & Flory (1965) worked out a more sophisticated set of potential functions of the "6-exp" type following the method adopted by Scott & Scheraga (1965) for hydrocarbons. They also tried to incorporate electrostatic forces and torsional potentials for rotations about single bonds in calculating the energy. They obtained potential-energy contours for a pair of peptide units, and these were found to be closely similar to the allowed regions calculated from contact-distance criteria by Ramachandran *et al.* (1963). Brant and Flory also found that the results obtained from these functions fitted the observed mean-square unperturbed dimensions of the polypeptide chains. More recently, Ramachandran *et al.* (1966a) have extended the use of these potential functions to calculate potential contours for helices, and they bear out the conclusions of Liquori and co-workers.

In fact, functions with different parameters than the above have also been proposed. Kitaigorodskii (1961,1965) has given a "universal" potential function, with only one variable parameter and has claimed success for this in predicting some crystal structures. More recently, Scott & Scheraga (1966) have renounced their earlier "6-exp" type of functions and have adopted a set of "6–12" functions with suitable parameters.

Thus, there are many different types of potential functions with different parameters proposed in the literature. In fact, it is found that, if graphs of the variation of the potential $V(r)$ with the interatomic distance r are plotted, then the different curves differ appreciably from one another. Two examples

† In this paper, we are restricting ourselves to a study of van der Waals interactions and a comparative study of different potential functions proposed for these. It is not implied that these are the only relevant factors in determining the stability of a polypeptide chain.

‡ We shall use the standard terminology in this field, as was initially developed by Ramachandran *et al.* (1963). In particular, the notation and nomenclature proposed in the recent paper by Edsall *et al.* (1966) will be followed throughout the paper.

are shown in Fig. 1, and it will be seen from this that the maximum value varies by a factor of the order of 3 and that the position of the minimum (i.e. the stable value of r) also differs from one function to the other. It is therefore quite necessary to make a comparative study of these functions and see what differences they have in the predictions given by them regarding the behaviour of polypeptide chains.

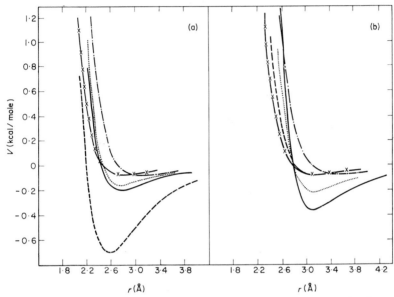

Fig. 1. Potential curves for the interactions (a) N $\cdots$ H and (b) N $\cdots$ N for the various functions: ————, F; – – –, L; – · – · –, K_1; – × – × –, K_2; · · · · ·, S. Note the large differences in shape, apart from difference in absolute values for the different functions.

This is attempted in this paper and some of the results obtained are presented. It is found that in the regions "disallowed" by contact criteria, the potential energy also increases, and this is shown by all the potential functions. Also, if the region is "highly disallowed", i.e. if there are several bad contacts in this region, then all the potential contours indicate a high wall around this region. If the region is only "slightly disallowed", however, i.e. if the short contacts occurring in it are not severe, then there is only a small increase in potential energy (of the order of a few kilocalories) in these regions, but the actual magnitude of this rise is different for the different functions.

In comparing the energies of different stable conformations, such as the right- and left-handed α-helices for poly-L-alanine, it will be noted that the difference in energy between them is appreciably different according to the function used, although, interestingly enough, they all show that the right-handed helix is the more stable one. These and other similar comparative studies are discussed in the sections that follow.

2. Evaluation of Parameters in the Potential Functions

The two most well known potential functions for van der Waals forces are the Buckingham potential, which is of the form "6-exp":

$$V = -A/r^6 + Ce^{-\mu r} \tag{1}$$

and the Lennard–Jones potential of the form "6–12":

$$V = -A/r^6 + B/r^{12}. \tag{2}$$

The problem then reduces to choosing suitable values for the parameters involved in the potential function used. Various values have been used in the literature. Scott & Scheraga (1966) have recently used the Lennard–Jones potential function. The functions with the values of the parameters that they have used is referred to in this paper as "S". Brant & Flory (1965) have used the Buckingham potential function. As mentioned earlier, they estimated the parameters A, μ and C essentially following the method described by Scott & Scheraga (1965). These functions used by Flory and co-workers are referred to here as "F". The actual parameters used are as listed by Ramachandran et al. (1966a). Liquori has adopted a set of semi-empirical potential functions using different types of functions for the various interactions (De Santis et al., 1965). These functions are referred to as "L" in this paper. Kitaigorodskii (1961) has used a potential function that is easily derived from the Bucking-ham potential function. Putting $z = r/r_0$ and $\alpha = \mu r_0$ in equation (1), we obtain:

$$V = \frac{z^{-6} - \dfrac{6}{\alpha}e^{\alpha(1-z)}}{11 \cdot 4 - \dfrac{6}{\alpha}e^{\alpha/3}} V_{2/3} \tag{3}$$

where r_0 is the equilibrium-distance between the atoms at which the potential is required to be a minimum and $V_{2/3}$ is the value of V at $r = \frac{2}{3}r_0$. Kitaigorod-skii assumed that $V_{2/3} = 3 \cdot 5$ kcal/mole and $\alpha = 13$. Using these values, we have:

$$V = 3 \cdot 5\{8600\,e^{-13z} - 0 \cdot 04/z^6\}. \tag{4}$$

This equation is unique in that the value of μ is different according to the value of r_0 chosen for an interaction, whereas Brant and Flory have chosen a constant value of $\mu = 4 \cdot 6$ for all interactions. Moreover, in equation (4) there is only one parameter that characterizes any specific interaction, namely the equilibrium distance r_0. Kitaigorodskii assigned values for r_0 for the interactions C $\cdots$ C, C $\cdots$ H and H $\cdots$ H on the basis of the experimentally observed intermolecular distances in crystals. Dr V. S. R. Rao in this laboratory (private communication) has devised a working rule for finding r_0 that yields values close to those obtained by Kitaigorodskii for the above three interactions. The method is to estimate r_0 by requiring that the potential be zero at a distance of separation equal to the sum of the van der Waals radii of the two atoms. This method has been used to work out the parameters for the other interactions involving also O, N and CH_3 atoms. Table 1 lists all the parameters that were used in this way and the van der Waals radii of the atoms used in these calculations.

TABLE 1. Values of r_0 used in Kitaigorodskii equation†

Interaction	r_0 (Å)	
	K_1	K_2
H $\cdots$ H	2·66	2·4
H $\cdots$ N	3·06	2·75
H $\cdots$ O	3·00	2·7
H $\cdots$ C	3·22	2·9
H $\cdots$ CH$_3$	3·39	3·05
N $\cdots$ N	3·44	3·1
N $\cdots$ O	3·39	3·05
N $\cdots$ C	3·61	3·25
N $\cdots$ CH$_3$	3·78	3·40
O $\cdots$ O	3·33	3·0
O $\cdots$ C	3·56	3·2
O $\cdots$ CH$_3$	3·72	3·35
C $\cdots$ C	3·78	3·4
C $\cdots$ CH$_3$	3·94	3·55
CH$_3$ $\cdots$ CH$_3$	4·11	3·77

† The van der Waals radii used in this calculation are as follows (Å):

$r_H = 1·2$ $r_N = 1·55$ $r_0 = 1·5$
$r_C = 1·7$ $r_{CH_3} = 1·85$

The Kitaigorodskii function with the above parameters are referred to as "K_1" in this paper. The resulting potential curves are found to have their minima slightly shifted from the minima obtained from the functions F. Therefore it was thought useful to derive another variant of the Kitaigorodskii function (referred to as "K_2" here) by requiring that the potential be a minimum at a distance of separation equal to the sum of the van der Waals radii of the two atoms, but otherwise satisfying equation (4). The values of the parameters for the functions K_2 are also listed in Table 1.

These five sets of functions, F, K_1, K_2, L and S, have been used to compute the distribution of potential energy in the ϕ–ψ conformational plane for a pair of linked peptide units, for poly-L-alanine and for polyglycine.

3. Conformation of a Pair of Linked Peptide Units

The conformation of a system of two linked-peptide units is described by a pair of dihedral angles ϕ and ψ that refer to the rotations about the two single bonds passing through the alanyl α-carbon atom at which the two units are linked. Each potential energy map was calculated by varying ϕ and ψ from 0° to 360° at intervals of 10°. These maps, and also the conformational map worked out on the basis of a set of contact-distance criteria that we had previously used are given in Fig. 2(a–f).

(a) *Discussion of the contact diagram*

The broad agreement of the predictions of the contact-distance criteria of Ramachandran *et al.* (1963) with observation was discussed by Ramachandran *et al.* (1966*a*), particularly with reference to the conformational data obtained from myoglobin. Figure 3 gives the results for the protein chain in lysozyme. The diagram was kindly made available to the authors by Dr D. C. Phillips. It will be seen that the conformations in this chain occur mostly within the allowed regions with a crowding near about the regions of the α-helix and the 3_{10}-helix, i.e. about $\phi = 120°$, $\psi = 120°$ to $160°$. It is very

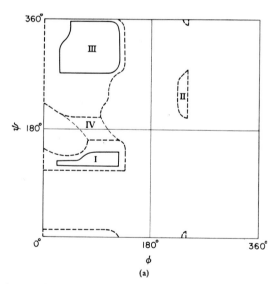

(a)

Fig. 2. (a) ϕ–ψ conformational map for a pair of peptide units linked at an alanyl α-carbon atom: ———, fully allowed; – – –, outer limit.

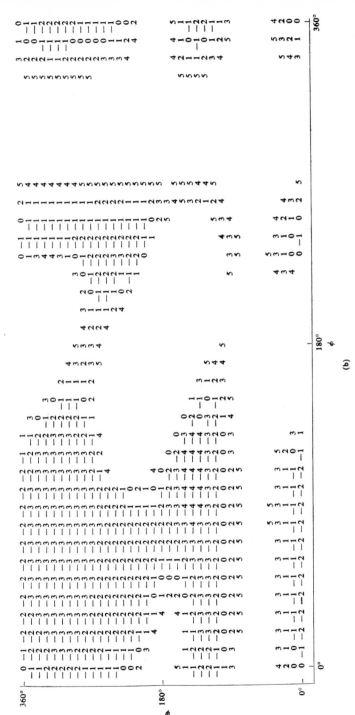

(b)

Fig. 2 continued. (b) The distribution of potential energy in the ϕ–ψ plane for a pair of linked peptide units, according to the Flory functions, F. The value of the potential energy in kcal/mole/residue is rounded off to the nearest integer. Where no number is printed, the potential is large and positive. (See text for explanation.)

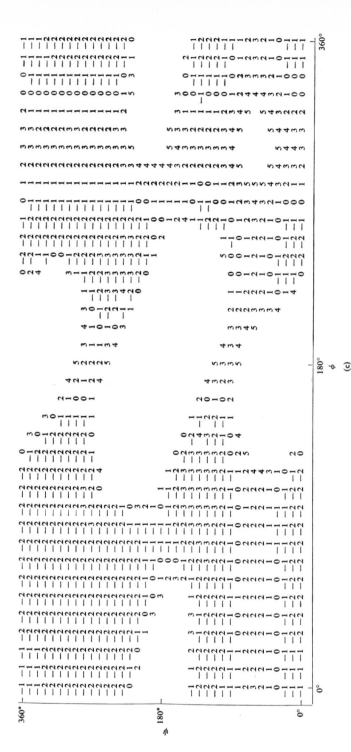

Fig. 2 continued. (c) Same as 2(b), but for the Scheraga functions, S.

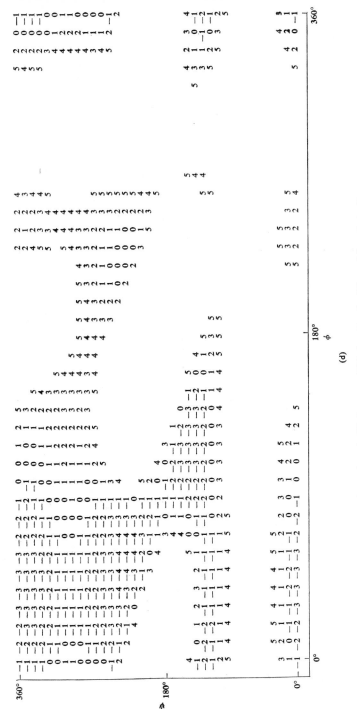

Fig. 2 continued. (d) Same as 2(b), but for the Liquori functions, L.

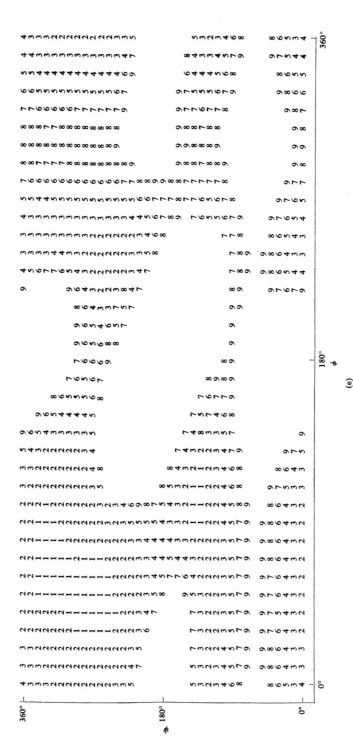

Fig. 2 continued. (e) Same as 2(b), but for the Kitaigorodskii functions, $\mathbf{K}_1$.

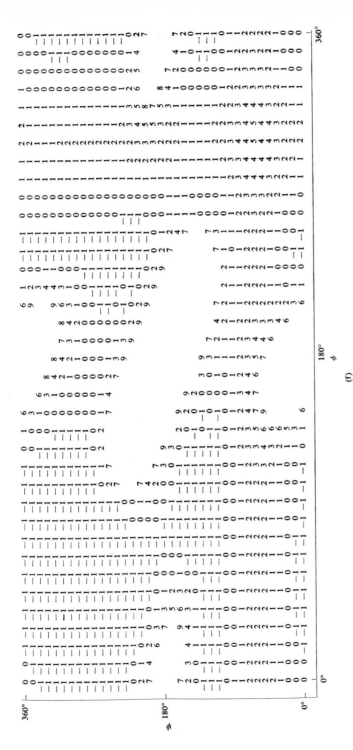

Fig. 2 continued. (f) Same as 2(b), but for the Kitaigorodskii functions, K_2.

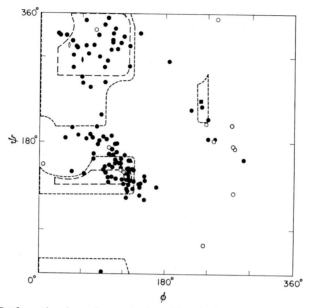

FIG. 3. Conformational map for a pair of peptide units linked at an alanyl α-carbon atom. All observed conformations of the polypeptide chain in the protein lysozyme are also marked. (This figure has kindly been supplied by Dr D. C. Phillips.)

interesting that there is a uniform distribution in the broad, allowed region near about $\psi = 240°$ to $360°$. The only region here that is not well populated is close to $(0°, 0°)$, which corresponds to a fully extended chain. Another feature that is observed is the distribution of points corresponding to $\psi \sim 180°$ and ϕ between $60°$ and $120°$. As already mentioned in the earlier paper (Ramachandran *et al.*, 1966*a*), this region is only slightly disallowed by just two contacts and, as discussed below, all the potential functions show this region to have low potential energy. There are a few conformations, represented by points, in the right-half of the conformational map that do not fall within the allowed regions. It should be interesting to check which of the different potential functions give a low potential energy corresponding to those conformations out of these that do not correspond to a glycyl residue.

(b) *Discussion of the potential maps*

For convenience in presentation, the potential maps have been given in numerical form with the value of the potential rounded off to the nearest integer. This means, for example, that a number 1 may correspond to the potential having a value anywhere between 0.5 and 1.5 kcal/mole per residue.

In comparing the different maps, it is important to remember that the absolute value of the potential is not particularly relevant. What is important is the variation of potential energy over the plane of the map. For example, the Kitaigorodskii functions, in general, give much larger absolute values than the other functions. In order to take care of this, the numbers have been printed on the maps from the lowest value going up to about 8 or 9 kcal above the value in the flat region around (100°, 300°). If no number is printed at any point in the map, it means that the potential is still higher.

It will be noticed that all the potential maps agree broadly with Fig. 2(a), which was obtained from contact-distance criteria (Ramachandran *et al.*, 1966a). They all show minimum energy values in three regions corresponding to the three allowed regions (marked as I, II and III) in the contact map. One is near the right-handed α-helical conformation (120°, 130°) (region I); the second is near the left-handed α-helical conformation (240° 230°) (region II) and the third, a broad minimum around (100°, 300°), i.e. the collagen conformation (region III).

However, the depth of the minimum within the three allowed regions of the contact map is different for the different functions. For example, the Flory function shows minima of about -4, -3 and -3 kcal in the three regions; but, although in all the other maps, regions I and III are joined together by a bridge (marked as IV in Fig. 2(a)) across $\psi = 180°$, the function K_1 exhibits a sharp rise at $\psi = 180°$. In all the other potential maps, the barrier at IV between the regions I and III is small. This would mean that the transformation in a fibre structure from an α-helical conformation to the β-structure can take place readily and reversibly. In other studies made in this laboratory on polysaccharides (Rao *et al.*, 1967), it has been found that the function K_1 yields results in good agreement with observation. However, as regards the 1–2 conformational map, the agreement seems to be rather poor for this potential function.

There is, however, a difference between the potential distribution in region III according to the Liquori function and all the other functions. Although all of the others have only one continuous broad minimum, the function L has one region around (40°, 350°) and another around (60°, 220°) at which the potential drops to a minimum (Table 2(a)). This sort of behaviour is contrary to that found in the distribution of conformations in region III in lysozyme. In particular the minimum around (40°, 350°) is a region that is not occupied by any conformation that is known so far (neither in myoglobin nor in lysozyme). It would appear, therefore, that at least some of Liquori's potential distributions would require revision.

An interesting observation common to all the maps is that the conformation $\phi = 0°$, $\psi = 0°$ has a larger energy than the broad minimum in region III. This would explain the relative absence of conformations around this, which has been mentioned above in relation to Fig. 3.

TABLE 2. Position and value of minima (kcal/mole per residue) in the potential maps for the different functions

	F			K_1			K_2			L			S		
Region	Position	Value		Position	Value		Position	Value		Position	Value		Position	Value	Region
(a) A pair of peptide units															
I	110°, 140°	−4·24		110°, 130°	1·25		110°, 140°	−1·42		130°, 140°	−3·20		110°, 140°	−3·29	I
II	230°, 230°	−2·83		230°, 240°	1·57		230°, 230°	−1·31		230°, 220°	−0·29		240°, 230°	−3·10	II
III	60°, 320°	−3·22		40°, 260°	1·41		60°, 330°	−1·00		40°, 350°	−3·20		100°, 280°	−2·53	III
										60°, 220°	−4·00				
(b) Poly-L-alanine															
I	50°, 120°	−4·68		50°, 120°	1·09		50°, 120°	−1·60		50°, 120°	−3·84		50°, 120°	−3·41	I
	110°, 140°	−6·99		110°, 140°	0·54		110°, 140°	−2·38		120°, 140°	−8·38		110°, 140°	−5·07	
II	230°, 240°	−4·99		230°, 230°	1·02		240°, 230°	−2·19		240°, 220°	−6·20		240°, 230°	−4·55	II
	240°, 300°	−3·83		250°, 290°	1·37		240°, 300°	−1·50		240°, 300°	−0·62		250°, 290°	−3·59	
III	70°, 320°	−3·47		40°, 260°	1·24		70°, 340°	−1·11		40°, 350°	−3·49		110°, 280°	−2·70	III
				80°, 330°	1·12					60°, 220°	−4·34				

4. Helical Conformations of Poly-L-alanine and Polyglycine

The various potential functions were also used for computing the distribution of potential energy in the ϕ–ψ plane for a regular helix of poly-L-alanine and polyglycine. The distribution of potential energy in the ϕ–ψ plane for poly-L-alanine is given in Fig. 4 for all the five functions along with the "contact map". Once again, all the potential maps show a striking resemblance to the contact map. Regions I and II of the 1–2 map are both split into two regions owing to short contacts corresponding to very flat helices (h is small). For instance, corresponding to the area of "disallowed" conformations around $\phi = 90°$, $\psi = 120°$ in the contact map, all the potential maps show very large values for the energy in this region, showing that in these conformations the bad contacts that are present are not compensated by any good contacts.

The positions and values of the various minima occurring in the potential maps for poly-L-alanine are listed in Table 2(b). All the maps consistently show a minimum near $\phi = 110°$, $\psi = 140°$, corresponding to the right-handed α-helix. Similarly, a minimum occurs near $\phi = 240°$, $\psi = 230°$, corresponding to the left-handed α-helix. However, the actual value of this minimum in relation to the broad minimum in region III is different in different cases. The minimum at $(110°, 140°)$ is about 4 kcal below that at $(100°, 300°)$ for function F, and 3 kcal below for function S, but is practically of the same order for functions K_1 and K_2. This minimum is very deep also with function L.

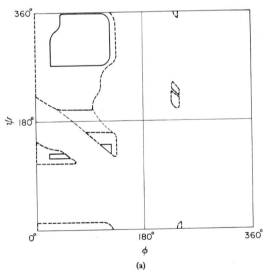

(a)

Fig. 4. (a) ϕ–ψ conformational map for a perfect helix of poly-L-alanine: ———, fully allowed; – – –, outer limit.

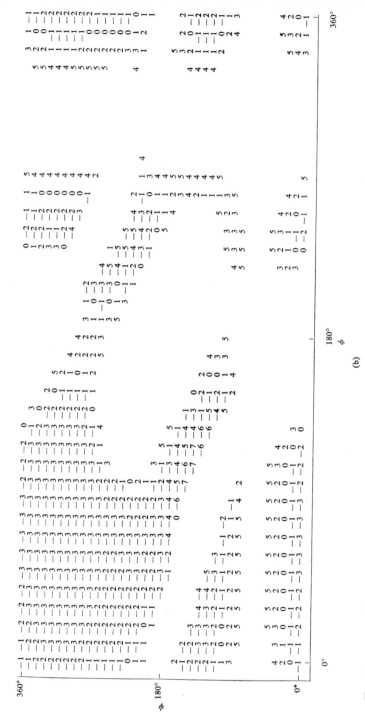

Fig. 4 continued. (b) The distribution of potential energy in the ϕ–ψ plane for a helix of poly-L-alanine, according to the Flory functions, F.

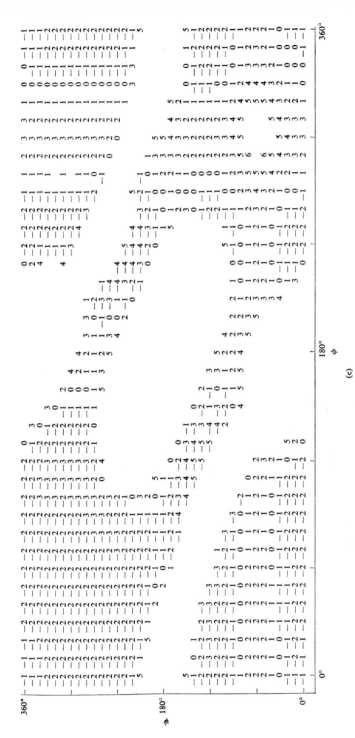

Fig. 4 continued. (c) Same as 4(b), but for the Scheraga functions, S.

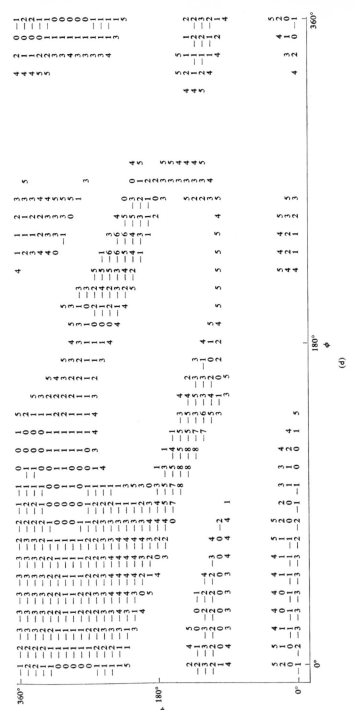

FIG. 4 continued. (d) Same as (4b), but for the Liquori functions, L.

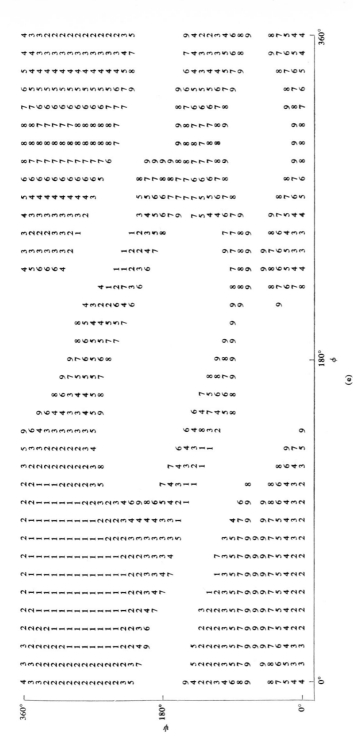

FIG. 4 continued. (e) Same as 4(b), but for the Kitaigorodskii functions, K_1.

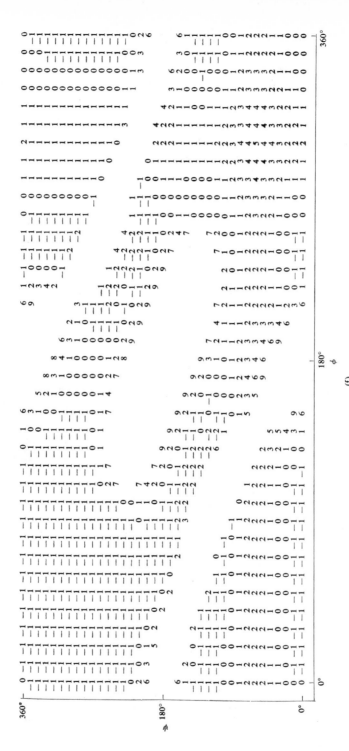

Fig. 4 continued. (f) Same as 4(b), but for the Kitaigorodskii functions, K_2.

Similarly the difference in energy between the right- and left-handed α-helices also varies very much between the different functions, as may be seen from Table 3, in which the data both for polyglycine and for poly-L-alanine are listed. Although it is true that the right-handed α-helix is always

TABLE 3. Potential energy of certain specific conformations

Conformation	$\phi(°)$	$\psi(°)$	Energy (kcal/mole per residue) for function:				
			F	K_1	K_2	L	S
(a) Polyglycine							
α-helix	122	134	−6·60	−1·07	−2·42	−5·30	−4·95
3_{10}-helix	122	158	−3·43	2·38	−1·34	−2·20	−2·40
Polyglycine II	100	230	−12·68	−4·64	−4·73	−11·16	−11·03
(b) Poly-L-alanine							
Right-handed α-helix	122	134	−7·14	0·40	−2·37	−8·45	−5·19
Left-handed α-helix	238	226	−5·15	0·60	−2·19	−6·00	−4·74
Right-handed 3_{10}-helix	122	158	−3·58	3·97	−1·16	−4·07	−2·46
Left-handed 3_{10}-helix	238	202	−2·69	3·74	−1·20	−3·15	−2·37

more stable than the left-handed α-helix for poly-L-alanine, the difference varies with the function adopted. Thus for functions L and F, the right-handed helix is more stable than the left-handed one by a difference of the order of 2 kcal/mole per residue, whereas it is only of the order of 0·2 to 0·4 kcal for functions S, K_1 and K_2. It is not very clear which of these values agrees with experiment, for whereas the left-handed α-helix rarely occurs and has never been found in a protein chain, it is found to occur in poly-β-benzyl-L-aspartate (Bradbury et al., 1962).

The 3_{10}-helix has been shown to be in the allowed region (Ramachandran et al., 1966a) and it is therefore of interest to compare its energy with that of the α-helix. Most of the functions show that the right-handed 3_{10}-helix is much less stable (by of the order 3 to 4 kcal/mole) than the right-handed α-helix. Therefore it is very unlikely that long stretches of the 3_{10}-helix would be observed. However, it is interesting that short stretches of this helix are found to occur in lysozyme (D. C. Phillips, private communication).

It is also of interest to compare the relative stabilities of the α-helix with a polyglycine and a poly-L-alanine chain. With functions F and S, it is found that the polyglycine energy lies almost in between the right- and left-handed α-helices for poly-L-alanine. Thus, on introducing the β-carbon atom, the right-handed α-helix becomes preferentially stabilized. Unfortunately, this behaviour is not found with functions L, K_1 and K_2, for which the polyglycine α-helical chain has an energy lower than either the right- or left-handed poly-L-alanine α-helices.

(a) Packing of polyglycine chains

The α-helical conformation of polyglycine shows a deep minimum in the maps for all functions, and it is strange that polyglycine has been observed only in two forms, neither of which is α-helical, and that all attempts to obtain it in the α-helical form have been unsuccessful. This question prompted a study of intermolecular packing in polyglycine II. Polyglycine chains in this conformation can pack together in the form of a hexagonal lattice, so that all the N—H groups hydrogen bond to a carbonyl oxygen in a neighbouring chain (Crick & Rich, 1955). More recently it has been shown that this structure should be modified to include possible CH · · · O hydrogen bonds (Ramachandran et al., 1966b).† The potential energy of a peptide unit in this three-dimensional structure was computed, taking into account interchain van der Waals interactions. The value of the potential energy for the Flory functions is close to $-12\cdot5$ kcal/mole, which is nearly 6 kcal lower than that of the α-helical conformation. All the other potential functions also show the similar result that the polyglycine II structure has a much lower van der Waals energy than an α-helix made up of polyglycine. Incidentally, polyglycine I, with its three-dimensional structure, was found from the Flory function to have an energy slightly lower than that of polyglycine II. These calculations indicate a probable explanation of the reason why polyglycine does not occur in an α-helical form but mainly in the extended forms as polyglycine I or polyglycine II.

5. Conclusions

The results of the calculations made in the present study show that most of the conclusions drawn from a study of interatomic contacts (Ramachandran et al., 1966a) are mainly supported by the calculations made with all the different potential functions. The potential functions show certain differences in detail, but the main conclusions, such as (a) that there are three broad regions (I, II and III of Fig. 2(a)) of stable conformations for a pair of peptide units, (b) that the right- and left-handed α-helices are particularly stable and (c) that the 3_{10}-helix is less stable than the α-helix, and so on, are supported by the calculations made with all the functions.

The fact that there are minor, but significant, differences in the predictions of the different functions indicates that some of them are superior to the

---

† The existence of such CH · · · O bonds seems to be confirmed by the recent work of Krimm et al. (p. 439).

others. This is a matter for study by the theorist and it is necessary to bring both theoretical approaches as well as methods of comparison with experiment to choose the best parameters for describing the non-bonded interactions between different atoms.

In a similar study made in this laboratory with polysaccharides by using the functions F and K_1 (Rao *et al.*, 1967), function K_1 was found to be slightly superior, in that it gave numerical data in better agreement with experiment. However, in the present study, function K_1 seems to give definitely less satisfactory results than function F. The reason for this is not clear. It may partly reside in the fact that we have neglected other types of interactions, such as torsional potentials and electrostatic interactions. In any case, it is clear that one cannot take any set of functions discussed in this paper to be distinctly superior to others. A more detailed examination of each of them, in relation to available data, is therefore necessary.

ACKNOWLEDGMENT

We thank Dr S. Krimm and Dr V. S. R. Rao for the many valuable discussions we have had with them, and Dr H. A. Scheraga for letting us have a preprint of his article before its publication. We are grateful to Dr D. C. Phillips for kindly making Fig. 3 available to us and for permission to publish it. We also acknowledge the co-operation extended to us by the computer group of the Tata Institute of Fundamental Research, Bombay. This work was partially supported by research grant AM-10905-01 from the U.S. Public Health Service.

REFERENCES

Bradbury, E. M., Brown, L., Downie, A. R., Elliott, A., Fraser, R. D. B. & Hanby, W. E. (1962). *J. molec. Biol.* **5**, 230.

Brant, D. A. & Flory, P. J. (1965). *J. Am. chem. Soc.* **87**, 2791.

Crick, F. H. C. & Rich, A. (1955). *Nature, Lond.* **176**, 780.

De Santis, P., Giglio, E., Liquori, A. M. & Ripamonti, A. (1965). *Nature, Lond.* **206**, 456.

Edsall, J. T., Flory, P. J., Kendrew, J. C., Liquori, A. M., Némethy, G., Ramachandran, G. N. & Scheraga, H. A. (1966). *J. molec. Biol.* **15**, 339.

Kitaigorodskii, A. I. (1961). *Tetrahedron*, **14**, 230.

Kitaigorodskii, A. I. (1965). *Acta cryst.* **18**, 585.

Leach, S. J., Némethy, G. & Scheraga, H. A. (1966). *Biopolymers*, **4**, 369.

Némethy, G. & Scheraga, H. A. (1965). *Biopolymers*, **3**, 155.

Ramachandran, G. N., Ramakrishnan, C. & Sasisekharan, V. (1963). *J. molec. Biol.* **7**, 95.

Ramachandran, G. N., Venkatachalam, C. M. & Krimm, S. (1966a). *Biophys. J.* **6**, 849.

Ramachandran, G. N., Sasisekharan, V. & Ramakrishnan, C. (1966b). *Biochim. biophys. Acta*, **112**, 168.

Ramakrishnan, C. & Ramachandran, G. N. (1965). *Biophys. J.* **5**, 909.

Rao, V. S. R., Sundararajan, P. R., Ramakrishnan, C. & Ramachandran, G. N. (1967). This book, Volume 2, p. 721.

Scott, R. A. & Scheraga, H. A. (1965). *J. chem. Phys.* **42**, 2209.

Scott, R. A. & Scheraga, H. A. (1966). *J. chem. Phys.* **45**, 2091.

PROTEINS AND POLYPEPTIDES

B. Optical Rotation Studies

Optical Rotation and Conformation

Studies on Diamide Models

John A. Schellman and Eigil B. Nielsen

Chemistry Department, University of Oregon
Eugene, Oregon, U.S.A.

Model compounds have been prepared containing two amide groups in which the conformation has been restricted by the enclosure of one or both of the amide groups into closed rings. The conformational limitations of these compounds have been calculated in accordance with the scheme proposed by Ramachandran for handling inter-atomic contacts. Optical rotatory dispersion on six such compounds has been studied down to 190 mμ or to the cut-off limit of the solvent used. In this way, an empirical correlation of rotatory dispersion behaviour as a function of conformation over a rather wide range of conformation has been obtained. The theory of the variation of optical rotation over the amide conformation plane has also been developed.

1. Introduction

These are the results of a series of investigations in which we have been engaged for the past 2 years. It has been, and still is, our hope to obtain experimental information on diamides of controlled, but varied, conformation and to explain the results theoretically insofar as this is possible. Our purpose was twofold: (1) to explore the rotatory behaviour of regions of conformational space that are not normally accessible in studies on proteins and polypeptides; and (2) by using conformation as a variable, to provide a more exacting test of theoretical calculations of optical rotation than is possible with fixed conformations, such as the α-helix. The first part of the investigation has already produced extensive results. We have delayed publication of these results for a considerable length of time in the hope that we could couple them with an adequate theory of the observed phenomena, which are quite complex. This has proved to be a very lengthy task, and we will take the opportunity in this paper to present some of our empirical results without extensive comment, so that they will henceforth be available to others. The general line of attack we have adopted will be indicated by a sketch of the theoretical method and its application to one of the model compounds that has been of particular interest to us.

2. The Conformation of Diamides

The ideal way to conduct an investigation of this kind would be to obtain a series of compounds in which the amide conformations about the α-carbon atom were completely fixed but varied in the series. In general, this is not practicable, except for a few cyclic peptides. By contrast, the diamides† that are readily available are those in which no special restrictions are placed on the amide orientations, other than those inherent in the groups themselves.

Fortunately, diamides have received a very extensive conformational analysis by Ramachandran and co-workers (Ramachandran *et al.*, 1963, 1965) and by Scheraga and co-workers (Leach *et al.*, 1966; Gibson & Scheraga, 1966). The results of these investigations indicate that the two conformational angles ϕ and ψ of diamides (Edsall *et al.*, 1966) are considerably restricted, such that the allowed conformations constitute only

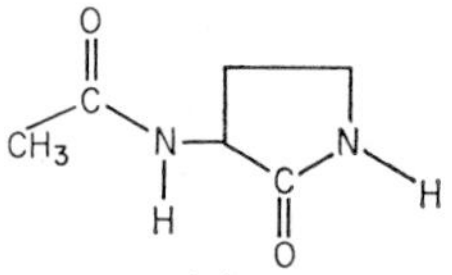

(I)
L–3–Acetamidopyrrolidone

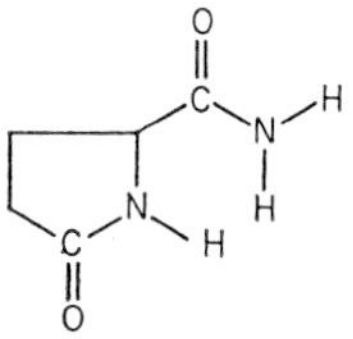

(II)
L–Pyroglutamamide

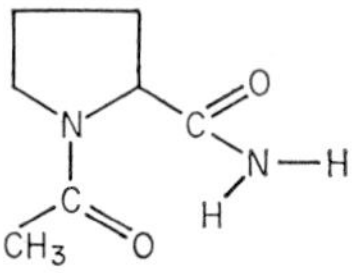

(III)
N–Acetyl–L–prolineamide

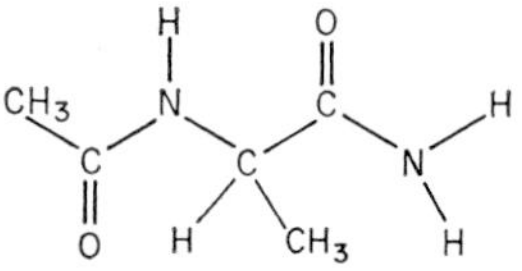

(IV)
N–Acetyl–L–alanineamide

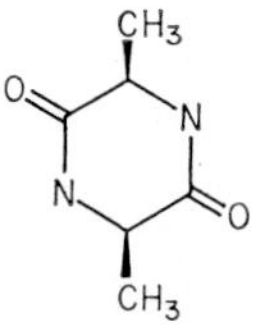

(V)
L–Alanine diketopiperazine
(alanine anhydride)

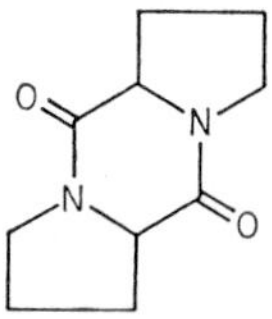

(VI)
L–Proline diketopiperazine

about 20% of the theoretical angular area. This, however, is too much latitude to permit a comparison between theoretical and observed optical rotations or, for that matter, to ascribe a particular feature of the optical-rotation spectra to a given region of the angular plane. Consequently, we attempted

† We use the expression "diamide" rather than "dipeptide", since most of our models will contain a single α-carbon linking two peptide groups. A dipeptide normally contains two amino acids.

to purchase, or to synthesize, compounds in which at least one of the amide groups was fixed into a definite conformation by the presence of a ring. The more important compounds that we have investigated are shown in formulas (I–VI).

The conformational regions of these compounds become lines on the conformational map (the diketopiperazines are represented by points). The conformations are further restricted by inter-atomic repulsions that can be treated in the manner proposed by Ramachandran *et al.* (1963). These calculations must be made afresh for each of the models, since the presence of the closed rings introduces atoms in unwonted positions and presents a different linear conformational problem for each of the molecules. These calculations have been performed by using the partially allowed and fully allowed distances proposed by Ramachandran, with the results shown in Fig. 1. We have not tried to make elaborate calculations involving London

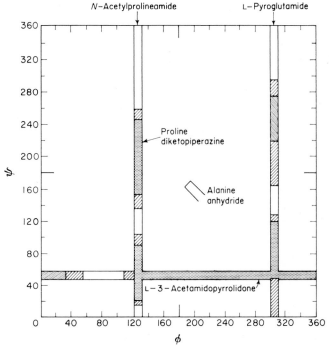

FIG. 1. Allowed regions for models on conformational map. The almost linear regions have been broadened for the purpose of visualization. Within the lines, grey areas indicate forbidden, hatched areas indicate partially allowed and white areas indicate allowed by the Ramachandran criteria. The conformation of alanine anhydride is uncertain. Its optical rotatory behaviour indicates that it is not planar. The location indicated above is based on the plausible assumption that the diketopiperazine ring is folded away from the methyl groups, both of which are on the same side of the ring.

forces or attempted to take into account the restricted rotation about bonds. It is our belief, however, that many of the conformational changes that are observed with variation of solvent are the result of enhanced electrostatic interactions in non-polar solvents. Consequently, electrostatic conformational energies have been calculated for the models in which a point charge model for the peptide group is used. These same electrostatic charges form a part of the optical rotatory theory (Schellman & Oriel, 1962).

It should be remembered in interpreting Fig. 1 that the models represent *trans-trans*, *cis-trans*, *trans-cis* and *cis-cis* conformations of the amide groups. Consequently, a given point on the angular plane has a different interpretation for each type of compound. In addition, the presence of closed rings distorts certain bond angles and lengths. X-Ray diffraction studies on the compounds themselves or closely related substances have permitted the introduction of these variations into the conformational calculations.

3. Theoretical Sketch

A diamide molecule presents virtually all theoretical situations for the generation of optical rotation, even if the problem is restricted to the two lowest absorption bands. In this case, the four excited states are divided up into two electrically allowed and two forbidden, but magnetically allowed, transitions. Energy differences amongst states are small and both inter-group coupling and intra-band mixing can be expected to be large. In general two types of situation may develop. In the first the strong $\pi-\pi^*$ transitions are

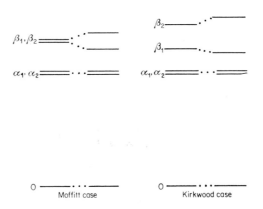

FIG. 2. Energy-level diagrams for diamides. Closely parallel lines indicate degeneracy. In each half of the drawing, the left side indicates the behaviour of separated amides, the right side, interacting amides.

degenerate, or very nearly so. This situation arises, for example, when both groups are secondary amides. In the other case, the amide groups differ in substitution and, consequently, absorb at different wavelengths. The absorption maxima of primary and tertiary amides differ by as much as 25 mμ in cyclohexane. As will be shown in the final section, the interpretation of rotatory dispersion curves indicates that the position of the n–π^* transition is not strongly dependent on the substitution on the nitrogen atom and, as a result, these bands are essentially degenerate in all models. These situations are illustrated in the energy-level diagrams of Fig. 2. The positions of these bands are strongly solvent dependent, and, in particular, the separation between the n–π^* absorption and the nearest π–π^* can be varied considerably by a change in solvent. Such changes in the spacing between bands can have a profound effect on the degree to which the excited states are mixed, and experiment has, in fact, revealed that in certain molecules of fixed conformation there are marked changes in optical rotatory properties with solvent, which apparently are to be ascribed solely to the shifting of energy levels.

The following discussion will develop a very restricted theoretical framework for the interpretation of the Cotton effects of these bands. Configurational interaction with the ground state will be ignored. This will produce small error, since it can be shown that this introduces terms of the order of $(E_2 - E_1)/(E_2 + E_1)$ relative to those which are considered in the calculation. E_1 and E_2 are the energy levels of the two π–π^* transitions in the diamide. In addition, we shall ignore all excited states of the amide group except the two that have been discussed. This is not to be considered as an approximation of general validity, but as a procedure which may be applicable to a limited class. We define this class as follows.

Optical rotatory dispersion measurements are always limited in their penetration into the ultraviolet. As a result of circular dichroism or rotatory dispersion measurement, it is usually possible to assign rotatory strengths to the bands that are within the limits of instrumentation. Two cases can arise: (1) the algebraic sum of the rotatory strengths of the observed bands is approximately equal to zero, relative to the absolute sum; and (2) the sum of the rotatory strengths differs widely from zero. In the second case, clearly any theory that ignores the unobserved bands would be doomed to failure at the beginning. In the first case, however, there is at least the possibility that a large fraction of the observed rotatory strength arises from the interactions amongst the accessible bands. This situation permits a theoretical discussion based entirely on well characterized absorption bands for which we have abundant information on electric and magnetic transition moments and energy levels, as well as approximate wave functions that have evolved from extensive test with experiment. The advantage of a theoretical procedure that contains a minimum of arbitrary assumptions merits a test with experimental observation, and, accordingly, we have proceeded along these lines in our initial attack. The optical-rotation spectra of diamides fall into both classes, sometimes switching from one to the other by a change in solvent. For those falling definitely in the first class, we have had considerable success with the restricted theory.

We consider an excited state of the diamide to be a linear combination of all four of the excited states of the isolated amides, with the following notation:

Symbol	Group	Excited State
α_1	1	$n-\pi^*$
β_1	1	$\pi-\pi^*$
α_2	2	$n-\pi^*$
β_2	2	$\pi-\pi^*$

This leads to a four-by-four secular equation, as shown in Fig. 3, which also demonstrates the significance of the various matrix elements in the framework of the theory of optical rotation. In Fig. 3(a), the only mixing that is occurring is between the α and β transitions of individual groups. This mixing occurs by way of static perturbations from the remaining group, and the secular equation designated by Fig. 3(a) represents a pure application of the theory of Condon, Altar and Eyring transposed to the language of configuration interaction (Schellman, 1966). The secular equation in Fig. 3(b) represents

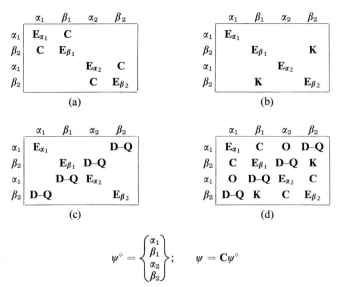

$$\psi^\circ = \left\{ \begin{matrix} \alpha_1 \\ \beta_1 \\ \alpha_2 \\ \beta_2 \end{matrix} \right\}; \qquad \psi = \mathbf{C}\psi^\circ$$

FIG. 3. The secular equation and transformation matrix for the four-state problem. The rows of ψ° are the wave functions for the excited states of isolated amides. The rows of ψ are the mixed excited states of interacting amides.

the terms that arise from the Kirkwood–Moffitt interaction (Kirkwood, 1937; Moffitt, 1956). It is the coupling between the strong transitions in groups 1 and 2. We use a secular equation of this kind rather than first-order perturbation theory because both the degenerate and non-degenerate cases can be handled with the same mathematical apparatus.

We already see that it is inconsistent to separate the Condon and the Kirkwood theories, since the α's are linked to the β's by the first mechanism and the β's to one another by the second. Consequently, all transitions are linked. It would also be inconsistent to leave out certain other terms in this secular equation which were first discussed by Kirkwood (1937) but have since largely been ignored. These are the interactions between the magnetic transition on one group and the electric transition on the other group. The static contribution to the optical-rotation results from the interaction of an atomic quadrupole (the $p_y \rightarrow p_x$ transition quadrupole on the oxygen atom) with the static charge distribution of an adjacent amide group. This static-charge distribution has a dipole moment of about 3·5 debyes. The off-diagonal elements indicated in Fig. 3(c) result from the interaction of the same atomic quadrupole with a transition charge density. The moment of this transition density is about 3 debyes (Hunt & Simpson, 1953). Consequently, one cannot rationally include the off-diagonal elements of Fig. 3(a) and neglect those of Fig. 3(c). The secular equation used in our calculations is given as Fig. 3(d). The remaining blank spaces of the secular equation result from a quadrupole–quadrupole interaction, which we have so far neglected.

We will defer the details of the calculation of the various matrix elements to a later publication. The solution of the secular equation gives us the matrix of coefficients (symbolized by C in Fig. 3) as well as the new energies of the states. The energies of the $n-\pi^*$ states are not much affected, as would be expected from the smallness of dipole–quadrupole interactions. The matrix of coefficients is dependent on the position of the particular diamide on the conformational map.

Once C has been obtained, it is a relatively easy matter to calculate the optical rotatory properties. We define the column vectors $\boldsymbol{\mu}^{\circ}$ and $\mathbf{m}^{\circ}$ as follows:

$$\boldsymbol{\mu}^{\circ} = \begin{pmatrix} \mu_{\alpha_1} \\ \mu_{\beta_1} \\ \mu_{\alpha_2} \\ \mu_{\beta_2} \end{pmatrix} \simeq \begin{pmatrix} 0 \\ \mu_{\beta_1} \\ 0 \\ \mu_{\beta_2} \end{pmatrix} \quad \mathbf{m}^{\circ} = \begin{pmatrix} \mathbf{m}_{\alpha_1} \\ \mathbf{m}_{\beta_1} \\ \mathbf{m}_{\alpha_2} \\ \mathbf{m}_{\beta_2} \end{pmatrix} \simeq \begin{pmatrix} \mathbf{m}_{\alpha_1} \\ \dfrac{i\omega_1}{2}\mathbf{R}_1 \times \mu_{\beta_1} \\ \mathbf{m}_{\alpha_2} \\ \dfrac{i\omega_2}{2}\mathbf{R}_2 \times \mu_{\beta_2} \end{pmatrix}$$

Each of the elements of $\boldsymbol{\mu}^{\circ}$ is the electric transition moment vector associated with one of the four transitions. The orientations of these vectors depend on the position of the conformational plane representing the diamide. In the approximate form of writing we have ignored the electric vector of the $n-\pi^*$ transition that is normal to the amide plane and therefore perpendicular to both the $\pi-\pi^*$ electric moment and the $n-\pi^*$ magnetic moment and is also very small. In the explicit form for $\mathbf{m}^\circ$, we have introduced the experimental fact that the $n-\pi^*$ transition possesses a large intrinsic magnetic moment $\mathbf{m}_\alpha$ derived from the local angular momentum of the transition in the amide group, whereas the $\pi-\pi^*$ transition has vanishing local magnetic moment (provided the local origin is properly chosen) and derives its magnetic moment from the separation of electronic motions in space in the diamide. $\mathbf{R}_1$ and $\mathbf{R}_2$ are the vectors specifying the positions of the transition moments μ_1 and μ_2 and $\bar{\omega}$ is 2π times the frequency of the transition in wave numbers. The electric and magnetic moments of the perturbed system are then given by the equations:

$$\mu = \mathbf{C}\mu^\circ \qquad \mathbf{m} = \mathbf{C}\mathbf{m}^\circ$$

and, finally, the rotatory strength is also represented by a column vector:

$$\mathbf{R} = Im(\mu \cdot \mathbf{m}) = Im(\mathbf{C}\mu^\circ \cdot \mathbf{C}\mathbf{m}^\circ)$$

where the rule of multiplication is the formation of the scalar product between equivalent elements. The four entries of the column vector $\mathbf{R}$ represent the rotatory strengths of the four transitions. The unitary character of C guarantees that the sum of the rotatory strengths of the four transitions must equal zero. A similar expression for the dipole strength indicates that the total absorptive power of the four transitions remains constant under the considered perturbations.

4. The Rotatory Properties of *N*-Acetylprolineamide

The rotatory dispersion curves of *N*-acetylprolineamide in dioxan and in water are shown in Fig. 4. These curves have been fitted by treating the Cotton effects as Kronig–Kramers transforms of Gaussian circularly dichroic bands, in accordance with the procedure outlined by Moscowitz (1960*a*, 1960*b*). We are very grateful to Dr Paul Carver for sending us the computer programme that he developed for this analysis. This programme permits the evaluation of the rotatory strengths, wavelengths and bandwidths associated with observed Cotton effects.

The optical-rotation curve in dioxan is particularly interesting. The tertiary amide associated with the proline residue has a strong absorption band at 201 mμ in water and at 199 mμ in cyclohexane. Solvent shifts of the $\pi-\pi^*$ band are very small for tertiary amides, and it is safe to assume that the

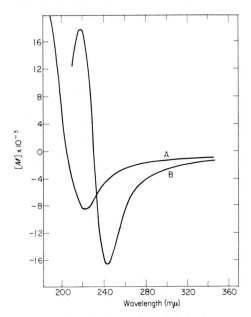

FIG. 4. The molar rotation of N-acetyl-L-prolineamide in A, water and B, dioxan.

absorption band in dioxan is very close to 200 mμ. However, what we are observing in dioxan is an almost pure single $n–\pi^*$ Cotton effect. The computer analysis reveals that the rotatory strength of the $n–\pi^*$ Cotton effect at 230 mμ is −0·22 debye-magneton, whereas the rotatory strength of the $\pi–\pi^*$ band at 200 is only −0·019 debye-magneton. We are thus confronted with an electronic transition that contributes almost nothing to the optical activity and yet is responsible for most of the observed absorption. Moreover, it is known from many other investigations that this transition normally couples very strongly in molecules containing more than one amide group, to give large Cotton effects.

The explanation for this phenomenon comes out of the theoretical calculations. In the first place, the size and sign of the rotatory strength, which is developed from inter-amide coupling, depends in a complex way on the geometry of the pair of amide groups. We illustrate this by considering the optical rotation that is developed on the pure coupling model (Fig. 3(b)). It is possible to calculate the rotatory strength of the lowest electronic transition as a function of the conformational angles ϕ and ψ. Figure 5 illustrates qualitatively the results obtained. The curved lines represent the locus of vanishing rotatory strength on the conformational map. Should any of the model conformations lie very close to one of these nodal lines, the rotatory strength of the 200 mμ band should be very small, as is actually

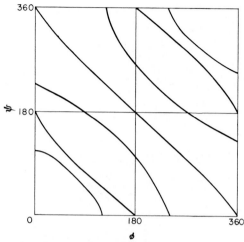

Fɪɢ. 5. The nodal regions for the optical rotation arising from a pure coupling mechanism. (Secular equation in Fig. 3(b).)

observed in dioxan. This cannot be the real explanation, however, since we must also account for the very large $n–\pi^*$ Cotton effect, which presumably arises from interactions with the two $\pi–\pi^*$ bands. What develops from the detailed theory is as follows: there is a strong interaction between the 200 and 230 mµ bands of the tertiary amide. Considered by itself, this gives a large negative Cotton effect at 230 mµ and a large positive Cotton effect at 200 mµ. Simultaneously, there is strong coupling between the primary and tertiary amide bands located at 178 and 200 mµ, respectively. The result is to give a negative Cotton effect to the 200 mµ band. These two opposite contributions virtually cancel, with the result that the band at 200 mµ appears to be almost optically inactive. The conformation at which this cancellation takes place is at $\psi = 230°$. A careful inspection of this conformation reveals that the primary amide group is hydrogen bonded to the oxygen atom of the tertiary amide. Thus, the large Cotton effect that is observed results from the perturbation of the amide group by a hydrogen bond in the upper right quadrant (Schellman, 1966; Schellman & Oriel, 1962). The smallness of the $\pi–\pi^*$ Cotton effect is the result of a fortuitous cancellation characteristic of this conformation. Though in general we have sought only a qualitative correlation of the signs of multiple Cotton effects with regions of the conformation plane, the agreement between experiment and theory in this instance is almost quantitative.

In aqueous solution the rotatory properties are quite different. Analysis of the data reveals a rotatory strength of -0.09 DM at 212 mµ ($n–\pi^*$) and -0.14 DM at 197 mµ. The probable interpretation of this result is as follows:

(1) the molecular conformations are now distributed over a fairly wide range of the available conformational space, so that a relatively small fraction of the molecules possesses internal hydrogen bonds; (2) the $n-\pi^*$ and $\pi-\pi^*$ absorption bands are now only 10 mµ apart, and thus mix very strongly when properly perturbed. As a result, the small population of internally hydrogen-bonded molecules still contributes a fairly large negative $n-\pi^*$ Cotton effect; and (3) there is a region of conformation space between $\psi = 170°$ and $240°$ in which the $\pi-\pi^*$ Cotton effect is predicted to be extremely large and negative ($R \sim -0.6$ to -0.8). As is shown in Fig. 6, this region is disallowed only because of the approach of the NH proton to the carbonyl oxygen atom, but is favoured strongly electrostatically. Evidently, the fraction of the population falling in this region is sufficiently great to oppose the smaller positive rotatory strengths that result from regions near $\psi = 120°$ and $330°$.

More recent work on this problem by Vincent Madison of this laboratory has revealed completely different optical-rotation spectra in other solvents, such as trimethylphosphate, trifluroethanol and alcohols.

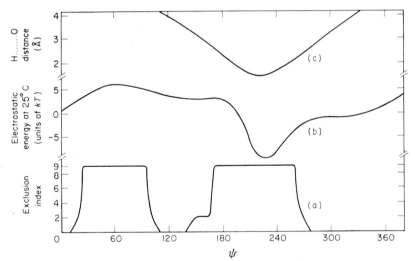

FIG. 6. Details of conformational calculation on N-acetyl-L-prolineamide. (a) Ramachandran exclusion diagram. The computer program enumerates the number of contacts in the partially allowed region. This is the ordinate. Non-allowed regions are recorded as 9. All atoms of the molecule are included in this calculation. (b) the electrostatic energy as a function of conformation. (c) the O $\cdots$ H distance as a function of conformation.

Taken together these figures indicate that conformations which bring the NH proton and oxygen together are favoured even though they would be normally rejected by an uncritical use of the table of allowed distances. Ramachandran and co-workers have recently come to similar conclusions (Ramachandran et al., 1966). The minima in the energy and O $\cdots$ H distance graphs correspond to the formation of a hydrogen bond.

5. Survey of Results with Other Models

Figure 7 illustrates the variety of experimental results that may be obtained as the conformation of the diamide is varied over angular space. (The results on proline diketopiperazine are taken from a subsequent investigation by P. Bayley and S. Rogers of this department, and are included for the purpose

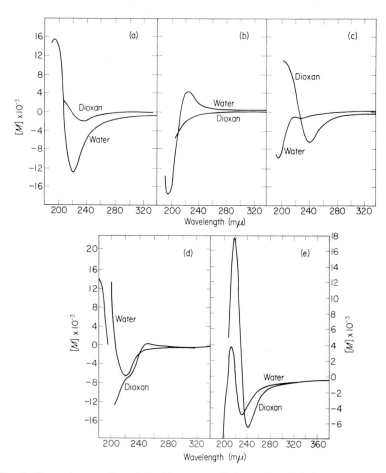

FIG. 7. The molar rotation of model compounds in aqueous solution and in dioxan: (a) L-3-acetamidopyrrolidone, (b) L-pyroglutamide, (c) N-acetyl-L-alanine amide, (d) L-alanine anhydride (the short part on the extreme left refers to [M] for the water curve, rising from 20,000 to 36,000 on a different vertical scale), (e) proline diketopiperazine. Diketopiperazines have also been recently studied by Balasubramanian & Wetlaufer (1966). An unpublished addendum by the same authors brings the results on alanine anhydride into closer agreement with our results (D. B. Wetlaufer, private communication).

of comparison. The initial investigations on alanine anhydride were by S. Zimmerman, who prepared the compound.) Our theoretical investigations have led to an explanation of several of the features of these curves, but the work is not yet complete. We shall content ourselves here with a few empirical statements. (1) the $n–\pi^*$ transition of amides is in the neighbourhood of 230 mμ in dioxan and 212 mμ in aqueous solution, regardless of the nature of the substituents on the nitrogen atom. (2) Well developed $n–\pi^*$ Cotton effects are a common feature of the rotatory dispersion of diamides. Contrary to the situation with acetylprolineamide, the $n–\pi^*$ Cotton effect is more marked in aqueous solution than it is in dioxan for pyroglutamamide and acetamidopyrrolidone, where it is either absent or very small. This is partially the result of a conformational change, but also stems from the fact that the $n–\pi^*$ and $\pi–\pi^*$ bands are closer to one another in aqueous solution, so that mixing is stronger for a given conformation. (3) The two diketopiperazines display solvent effects that are probably exclusively the result of the shift in energy levels, since it is unlikely that there is a significant dependence of conformation on solvent with these molecules. (4) The rotatory behaviour of acetyl-L-alanine amide in aqueous solution is not drastically different from that of a random polypeptide chain. However, in dioxan there is an $n–\pi^*$ Cotton effect of considerable size. Since there are no special constraints on the conformation of this molecule, this is evidence that segments of a polypeptide chain can develop strong $n–\pi^*$ Cotton effects in a non-polar environment in the absence of any long-range structure. This could well have application to many of the interior peptide groups of an essentially non-helical protein. It is to be observed that, in dioxan at any rate, this band has a trough above 240 mμ, whereas most proteins have their troughs at 232 mμ if they are helical to some extent, and lower if they are not. (5) Those substances in which the $\pi–\pi^*$ bands are degenerate (pyroglutamamide, acetamidopyrrolidone, alanine anhydride and proline diketopiperazine) display in their rotatory behaviour a classical exciton splitting. In some instances, the long wavelength branch has the positive rotatory strength. In others, it is negative. It is interesting that the doublet rotations of alanine anhydride and proline diketopiperazine are of the same sign, even though conformational calculations indicate that the folding of the diketopiperazine ring is reversed in the two cases. (6) An asymmetric hydrogen bond produces very large $n–\pi^*$ Cotton effects.

Finally, it should be remarked that there is a possibility that some of the optical-rotation changes in dioxan result from the association of the molecules by hydrogen bonds. In several instances it has been shown that such association has very little effect on the general features of the optical rotatory curves, but the possibility of optical-rotation changes induced by association has not always been excluded.

ACKNOWLEDGMENT

This work was supported by grants from the National Science Foundation and the National Institutes of Health (Cancer Institute Ca-4216). Theoretical calculations were performed through the courtesy of the Western Data Processing Center, Los Angeles.

REFERENCES

Balasubramanian, D. B. & Wetlaufer, D. B. (1966). *J. Am. chem. Soc.* **88,** 3449.

Edsall, J. T., Flory, P. J., Kendrew, J. C., Liquori, A. M., Nemethy, G., Ramachandran, G. N. & Scheraga, H. A. (1966). *Biopolymers*, **4,** 121.

Gibson, K. D. & Scheraga, H. A. (1966). *Biopolymers*, **4,** 607.

Hunt, H. D. & Simpson, W. T. (1953). *J. Am. chem. Soc.* **75,** 4540.

Kirkwood, J. G. (1937). *J. chem. Phys.* **5,** 479.

Leach, S. J., Nemethy, G. & Scheraga, H. A. (1966). *Biopolymers*, **4,** 369.

Moffitt, W. (1956). *J. chem. Phys.* **25,** 467.

Moscowitz, A. (1960*a*). *In* "Optical Rotatory Dispersion", ed. by C. Djerassi, p. 150. New York: McGraw-Hill.

Moscowitz, A. (1960*b*). *Rev. mod. Phys.* **32,** 440.

Ramachandran, G. N., Ramakrishnan, C. & Sasisekharan, V. (1963). *J. molec. Biol.* **7,** 95.

Ramachandran, G. N., Ramakrishnan, C. & Venkatachalam, C. M. (1965). *Biopolymers*, **3,** 591.

Ramachandran, G. N., Venkatachalam, C. M. & Krimm, S. (1966). *Biophys. J.* **6,** 849.

Schellman, J. (1966). *J. chem. Phys.* **44,** 55.

Schellman, J. & Oriel, P. (1962). *J. chem. Phys.* **37,** 2114.

The Optical Activity of the Disulfide Bond in Some Cystine-containing Cyclic Peptides and Synthetic Polypeptides†

D. L. Coleman‡ and E. R. Blout

*Department of Biological Chemistry, Harvard Medical School
Boston, Massachusetts, U.S.A.*

It is recognized that cystine residues play an important role in maintaining the specific molecular conformations of proteins. Previous work from this laboratory has described the results of investigations of the rotatory properties of the disulfide bond in cystine and some derivatives of cystine. It was found that the most significant contributions to the observed optical rotatory dispersion and circular dichroism curves of these compounds are associated with a strong transition of the disulfide bond found near 200 mμ and a weaker transition around 260 mμ. We report here the results of an extension of these investigations to disulfide-containing peptides. The rotatory properties of the cyclic disulfide-containing peptides, arginine vasotocin and 8-L-ornithine vasopressin, are dominated primarily by contributions associated with the disulfide group in which the optical activity of the S–S transition near 200 mμ is similar in magnitude, sign and position to that observed with the model compound NN'-diacetyl-L-cystinebismethylamide. Investigations of the rotatory properties of three high molecular weight copolypeptides of L-glutamic acid and L-cystine are also reported. In only one case was evidence observed of a disulfide contribution at 200 mμ. A suggestion is offered for the failure to observe this transition in these polypeptides. In all of the high molecular weight cystine-containing polypeptides, however, a contribution to the circular dichroism due to a 260 mμ disulfide transition was observed. The implications of the results of these investigations in assessing helix contents of proteins by means of optical rotatory dispersion are considered.

1. Introduction

With the results of numerous investigations of the far ultraviolet optical activity of various proteins now available, it has become increasingly evident that chromophores other than the peptide group may make significant contributions to observed optical rotatory dispersion (ORD) or circular dichroism (CD) curves. The implications of these findings are twofold: on the one hand, evaluation of the secondary structure and, particularly, the estimation of helix content in these molecules may be complicated by the

---

† Taken in part from the dissertation of D. L. C., Harvard University, 1966.
‡ Present address: Carlsberg Laboratory, Copenhagen, Denmark.

presence of other optically active transitions in the same region. On the other hand, it must be recognized that there is available in the data additional, supplementary information about the architecture of the protein molecule which may reflect the existence of highly specific interactions involving side-chain chromophores or prosthetic groups.

The analysis of ORD curves has reached a high level of development with the increasing use of computers to resolve complex dispersion curves by means of non-linear least squares analyses (Moscowitz, 1960; Carver et al., 1966a; King & Schellman, 1966). But even with the use of computers, the resolution of dispersion curves of proteins into their component Cotton effects presents a formidable problem which can best be overcome through the investigation and analysis of both CD and ORD curves, in order to take advantage of the complementary nature of the two properties.

The interpretation of the rotatory properties (both CD and ORD) of proteins rests heavily on the use of model compounds to characterize the optical activity of individual chromophores. Most of our knowledge of the rotatory properties† of the peptide bond has come from the investigations of model polypeptides (Carver et al., 1966a; Blout, 1960; Holzwarth & Doty, 1965). More recently, investigations of the optical activity of some amino acid side-chain chromophores have been reported (Hooker & Tanford, 1964; Moscowitz et al., 1965; Iizuka & Yang, 1964).

In a forthcoming communication (Coleman & Blout, 1967), we report the results of investigations of the rotatory properties of the disulfide bond in cystine and some derivatives of cystine. It has been found that the most significant contribution to the observed ORD and CD curves of these compounds was associated with a transition of the disulfide bond found near 186 mμ with cystine, and at 199 mμ with the model compound, NN'-diacetyl-L-cystinebismethylamide (DACMA). The rotational strength of this transition approaches the magnitude predicted by Moscowitz (1961) for an inherently asymmetric chromophore, and has been found to be more than an order of magnitude greater than the rotational strength of the long wavelength disulfide transition at 260 mμ. The rotatory properties of the S—S group evaluated from the ORD and CD of DACMA were used to predict the magnitude of the disulfide contribution to the optical activity of proteins, and to evaluate its significance.

In this communication, we report the results of an extension of these investigations to disulfide-containing peptides. In Section 2, the rotatory properties of the disulfide-containing cyclic peptides, arginine vasotocin (AVT) and 8-L-ornithine vasopressin (OVP) are reported and compared with the properties of some homodetic cyclic hexapeptides. In Section 3,

---

† Although the term refers to optical rotation, we use it here in a broader sense to refer to both manifestations of optical activity, ORD and CD.

investigations of the rotatory properties of synthetic polypeptides containing disulfide bonds are reported. Finally, the results are compared with those predicted on the basis of the optical activity of the S—S group of DACMA.

Materials

Arginine vasotocin and 8-L-ornithine vasopressin were synthesized (Bodanszky *et al.*, 1964) and provided by Dr Miklos Bodanszky. Cycloglycyl-L-tyrosyldiglycyl-L-histidylglycyl, cycloglycyl-L-tyrosyldiglycyl-N^{im}-benzyl-L-histidylglycyl, and L-tyrosyltriglycyl-N^{im}-benzyl-L-histidylglycine were synthesized (Kopple & Nitecki, 1962) and provided by Dr K. D. Kopple of the University of Chicago. Copoly-α-(γ-benzyl-L-glutamate-S-carbobenzoxy-L-cysteine) was synthesized by Dr D. B. Wetlaufer by the copolymerization of the *N*-carboxyanhydrides (NCA's). The initial ratio of NCA's in the polymerization reaction was 9 : 1 :: Glu : Cys, and the anhydride-initiator ratio was 400.

NN'-di-(poly-α-benzyl-L-glutamate)-L-cystine dimethyl ester was synthesized by initiating polymerization of γ-benzyl-L-glutamate NCA with L-cystine dimethyl ester in dry, purified dimethylformamide (Lundberg & Doty, 1957). Progress of the reaction was followed by observing the disappearance of the characteristic NCA bands in the infrared spectrum. The polymers were precipitated with isopropanol, collected by centrifugation, and washed in isopropanol. They were then dissolved in benzene, filtered, and lyophilized.

Removal of the benzyl groups, and simultaneous removal of both benzyl and carbobenzoxy groups in the case of the copolymer, was carried out by treatment with anhydrous hydrogen bromide in benzene (Idelson & Blout, 1958; Wetlaufer & Blout, 1961) with vigorous stirring until the product would dissolve readily in 0·1 N NaOH. In some cases, the reaction took up to 72 h.

Reduction of disulfide bonds was achieved by incubation with a 100-fold excess of β-mercaptoethanol at pH 8–9 overnight under a nitrogen atmosphere. The polypeptides were precipitated by the addition of acid, centrifuged, and washed several times to remove the bulk of the β-mercaptoethanol. The –SH groups were alkylated by reaction with sodium iodoacetate (10-fold excess) at pH 8–9 for 1–2 h. Excess iodoacetate was removed by precipitating the polypeptide with acid, and washing thoroughly. The polypeptides were then dissolved by addition of 0·1 N NaOH until the pH was 7·0, and the solutions were filtered and lyophilized. With the copolymer the debenzylated product was first dissolved in the 0·1 N NaOH in the presence of a 100-fold excess of β-mercaptoethanol to ensure that all disulfide bonds were reduced. One fraction was precipitated, washed, and alkylated as described above and the other was washed free of mercaptoethanol, dissolved, and brought to a final concentration of approximately 0·04% at pH 9. It was left open to the air and stirred vigorously overnight. Both the oxidized and alkylated polymers were checked for the presence of unreacted –SH groups by titrating with p-chloromercuribenzoate (Benesch & Benesch, 1962). They were precipitated, washed, and lyophilized as described above.

Methods and Calculations

Reduction of the disulfide bond of AVT was carried out in an electrolytic desalter (Research Specialties Co., Berkeley, California) according to the general procedure of Benesch and Benesch (1957). Concentration of the reduced solution was determined on the basis of the optical density at 275 mμ using the optical density of the unreduced solution to determine ε_{275}.

Amino acid analyses were carried out on a Beckman Analyzer. Samples were prepared according to the method of Moore & Stein (1963).

Ultraviolet spectra were obtained with a Cary 15 Recording Spectro-photometer. Optical rotatory dispersion measurements were made on a Cary 60 Recording Spectropolarimeter, as well as with a JASCO UV/ORD-5 Optical Rotatory Dispersion Recorder equipped with a circular dichroism attachment. Circular dichroism measurements were made on the latter instrument. Cell path-lengths varying from 5·00 cm to 0·01 cm were used for measurements of both CD and ORD. Calculations were carried out as previously described (Coleman & Blout, 1967), except that mean residue weights were used rather than molecular weights in order to calculate mean residue rotations [R] and reduced mean residue rotations [R']. With AVT the CD data are expressed as molar ellipticities $[\theta]_\lambda$; the actual molecular weight of the compound was used in the calculations. With the synthetic polypeptides, the CD data are expressed as reduced mean residue ellip-ticities $[\theta']_\lambda$.

Helix content estimates were calculated as noted in footnotes c and d of Table 2, p. 137

2. The Rotatory Properties of Arginine Vasotocin and 8-L-Ornithine Vasopressin

The formation of intramolecular disulfide bonds in proteins results in the introduction of loops into the peptide backbone. Of particular interest are the relatively small loops which are occasionally observed, such as that in the A-chain of insulin (Sanger, 1956) or the loop resulting from the disulfide bridge between residues 65 and 72 of bovine pancreatic ribonuclease (Smyth et al., 1963). Such loops may be relatively rigid and have well-defined conformations which could be related to the biological activity of the pro-tein, and which may be distinguished from other types of secondary structure by ORD studies. Since the specific residues which make up these loops vary from one protein to another, it would not be predicted that the loop conformations would be identical, but that they might have general points of similarity as a result of the limitations on the range of possible conformations imposed both by their annular nature and by the geometry of the disulfide bridge. Apart from the conformation of the loop as a whole, these structures are of interest because it is conceivable that the Cotton effects of the disulfide bond might be considerably altered in small ring structures, either as a result of perturbations associated with neighboring residues, or because the dihedral angle might be distorted from the normal value of approximately 90°.

The cyclic disulfide-containing neurohypophyseal hormones, oxytocin and vasopressin, contain the type of loop which we have been discussing, from which a three amino acid residue "tail" extends. Although the ring portion alone has little biological activity (Ressler, 1956), the integrity of the ring is essential for activity in the complete hormone (duVigneaud *et al.*, 1960). It appears that the overall ring conformation, or at least the relative orientation between two or more specific residues stabilized by the ring, is essential to the activity of the hormone.

As shown in Fig. 1, the ORD curves of two derivatives of oxytocin and vasopressin, 8-L-orinthine vasopressin (OVP) and arginine vasotocin (AVT), are generally quite similar in the far ultraviolet spectral region. Of particular

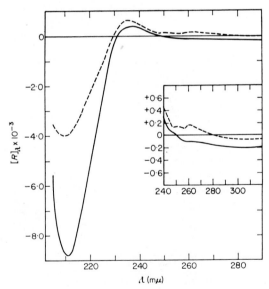

FIG. 1. Ultraviolet ORD of 8-L-ornithine vasopressin (————) and arginine vasotocin (— — —), pH ca 3.

interest is the large trough exhibited in each curve near 210 mμ. Since this is the position at which a large trough associated with a disulfide Cotton effect was observed (Coleman & Blout, 1967) with the model compound, NN'-diacetyl-L-cystinebismethylamide (DACMA), as well as with oxidized glutathione, it is of interest to know whether the trough observed with OVT and AVT is disulfide in origin. To this end, a number of additional studies were carried out. However, no attempt has been made to carry out a non-linear least squares analysis of the ORD such as was used with DACMA because these cyclic peptides have a multiplicity of chromophores in the far ultraviolet region for which model studies on optical activity are not available.

Cleavage of the disulfide bond of AVT by electrolytic reduction (10 V, 0·05 A, for 20 min) results in a marked decrease in the rotations in the region near 210 mμ relative to those of AVT as well as other changes at higher wavelengths (Fig. 2). These results indicate that the disulfide bond has a strong influence on the ORD of AVT either directly, as a result of disulfide Cotton effects, or indirectly, through conformational limitations imposed upon the molecule by the S—S bridge or by means of perturbations of other chromophores. To distinguish between these different possibilities, the CD and absorption spectra of AVT were investigated, as well as the effect of pH on the spectral properties of AVT.

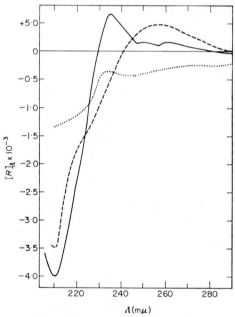

FIG. 2. Ultraviolet ORD of arginine vasotocin at pH 0·1 (————) and pH 12 (— — —), and reduced arginine vasotocin at pH 0·1 (. . . . .).

The CD curves of AVT and reduced AVT are given in Fig. 3. In addition to the strong negative band located near 200 mμ with AVT, a positive band of moderate size is found near 227 mμ. In contrast, the curve for reduced AVT reveals a weak positive band at 227 mμ. The negative band of reduced AVT located below 220 mμ appears to be a fraction of the size of the band observed with AVT in this region. In the region near 260 mμ, a weak positive band is observed as a shoulder on the much larger 227 mμ band of AVT. This band, whose strength is of the same order of magnitude as the disulfide band observed at 260 mμ with DACMA (Coleman & Blout, 1967) does not appear to be present with reduced AVT, and is probably associated with the disulfide transition found in this region.

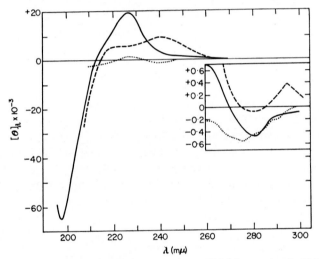

FIG. 3. Ultraviolet ellipticity of arginine vasotocin at pH 0·1 (————) and pH 12 (— — — and reduced arginine vasotocin at pH 0·1 (·········).

The nature of the 227 mμ positive band of AVT is revealed from the ORD and CD curves for AVT in 0·1 N NaOH (Figs. 2 and 3, respectively). Under these conditions, the CD band is split into two components, a peak at 240 mμ and a shoulder in the vicinity of 220 mμ. We also find that the weak negative CD band found near 280 mμ for AVT at neutral pH is replaced by a positive band at 295 mμ for the CD in alkaline solution. Finally, the 260 mμ band is no longer observed as a distinct shoulder on the 240 mμ band, and does not appear to change its position at high pH.

The changes in the ORD curve corresponding to those observed in the CD measurements primarily involve the 232 mμ peak, which is shifted to

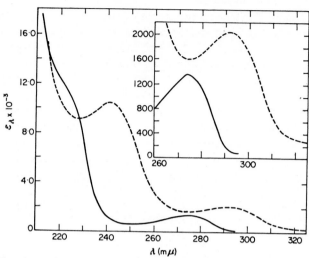

Fig. 4. Ultraviolet absorption spectrum of arginine vasotocin at pH 3 (————) and pH 12 (— — —).

255 mμ at alkaline pH. This shift is accompanied by the appearance of a shoulder at 225 mμ. The deep trough at 210 mμ, however, is only slightly reduced in size, and the extremum shifted a few mμ to the red.

The u.v. absorption spectrum of AVT at neutral pH (Fig. 4) includes a shoulder near 225 mμ and a weak maximum near 275 mμ both of which are shifted when the pH is raised. At pH 13, a maximum at 242 mμ is found in place of the shoulder, while the weak, long wavelength band is shifted to 292 mμ.

H–Cys-Tyr-Phe   H–Cys-Tyr-Ile
| | | |
Cys-Asn-Gln   Cys-Asn-Gln
| |
Pro-Orn-Gly-NH$_2$ Pro-Arg-Gly-NH$_2$

8-L-Ornithine vasopressin   Arginine vasotocin
(OVP)   (AVT)

A result of raising the pH of the AVT solution is the ionization of the phenolic group of the tyrosine residue. The changes observed in the u.v. spectrum are those which have been found with tyrosine as well as proteins containing tyrosine (Beaven & Holiday, 1952). The corresponding shifts in the CD curves with pH show that the positive band at 227 mμ (neutral pH) is associated with the tyrosine residue, as is the much smaller band at 280 mμ. Legrand & Viennet (1964) have reported the presence of similar bands in the CD curve for L-tyrosine, which are likewise shifted at high pH,

However, they found that the 225 mμ band changed sign at high pH, while the 280 mμ band remained positive whereas in the case of AVT, the 227 mμ band of AVT does not change sign but the 280 mμ band does. These differences in the pH dependence of the aromatic CD bands of tyrosine and the tyrosyl residue undoubtedly are related to the differences in the perturbing groups responsible for the optical activity of the phenolic group, and probably involve both the orientation and the electrostatic properties of the groups.

Since the rotatory properties of reduced AVT were not investigated at high pH, we cannot be certain whether the small positive band found at 228 mμ with reduced AVT is a tyrosyl band or not. However, it is clear that the reduction of the disulfide bond has resulted in the loss of most, if not all, of the tyrosine optical activity.

The insensitivity of the 200 mμ transition of AVT to increased pH, as reflected by both CD and ORD measurements, leads us to conclude that this transition is not associated with the tyrosine residue. However, the question of whether this band is disulfide or peptide in origin cannot be so easily resolved. Although the marked effect of cleaving the disulfide bond on the ORD of AVT in the region of the 210 mμ trough would seem to support the interpretation that a disulfide Cotton effect is responsible for these changes, the possibility of changes in contributions from the peptide transitions should be considered. We have not attempted to differentiate between these two possibilities by use of solvent perturbations or by other means. It may be noted, however, that with the reduced peptide, we do *not* observe peptide contributions of the magnitude which might be expected on the basis of studies on oligopeptides by Goodman & Rosen (1964) and by Oriel & Blout (1966), or those on polypeptides, such as poly-α-L-glutamate (Carver et al., 1966a; Holzwarth & Doty, 1965), in the random conformation. The reason for this is not clear and must await further studies on the rotatory properties of small peptides, particularly those which are composed of a number of different amino acid residues,.

When the size of the 210 mμ ORD trough of AVT is compared with that which might be expected on the basis of the study of model disulfides (Coleman & Blout, 1967), we find that the expected disulfide contribution to the mean residue rotation (-2.82×10^3 degrees) is about 72% of the magnitude of the observed trough. The expected disulfide contribution to mean residue ellipticity of AVT in the region of 200 mμ is about 65% of the observed value of $[\theta]_{200}$. It is clear that the contribution responsible for the 200 mμ CD band of AVT or the 210 mμ trough in the ORD is very similar to the characteristics of the disulfide bond as found with DACMA and oxidized glutathione (GSSG). We cannot conclude that peptide contributions are not in part responsible for the observed rotatory properties of AVT and OVP, only that the 210 mμ trough is probably not associated with a peptide Cotton effect of the type found with model polypeptides in the random conformation. Indeed, the vague shoulder on the short wave-length side of the 227 mμ CD band of AVT which becomes more pronounced at high pH where the main band is red-shifted may well be a peptide band similar to the amide band was observed with DACMA and oxidized glutathione in the same region—and the residual rotations found with reduced AVT in the region below 225 mμ may well be part of a peptide Cotton effect. But on the basis of the considerations discussed above, we conclude that it is a disulfide Cotton effect which is directly responsible for the 210 mμ ORD trough of AVT and OVP, and for the disappearance of that trough upon reduction of the disulfide bond.

Finally, the interesting observation of the 260 mμ shoulder in the CD curve of AVT deserves comment. If, as seems likely, this is a disulfide band, it is of the opposite sign from the corresponding bands observed with cystine, DACMA and other cystine derivatives (Coleman & Blout, 1967). It is possible that this reversal is indicative of a change in the average disulfide configuration from one diastereoisomer to the other. However, in interpreting this finding, it is necessary to note that the short wavelength disulfide CD band (or Cotton effect) does not appear to have changed sign. On the basis of the magnitude of the rotational strengths of the two disulfide transitions of DACMA, we concluded (Coleman & Blout, 1967) that the optical activity of the shorter wavelength transition probably reflects the inherent asymmetry of the chromophore whereas the weak optical activity of the 260 mμ disulfide transition might arise primarily from environmental perturbations. Thus the change in sign of the 260 mμ disulfide CD band of AVT is probably not associated with a change in disulfide configuration, but rather is an environmental effect.

In conjunction with the studies on AVT and OVP which we have been discussing, ORD curves for two homodetic cyclic hexapeptides were obtained. These compounds, cycloglycyl-L-tyrosyldiglycyl-L-histidylglycyl (I) and cyclo-glycyl-L-tyrosyldiglycyl-N^{im}-benzyl-L-histidylglycyl (II) as well as the linear hexapeptide, L-tyrosyltriglycyl-N^{im}-benzyl-L-histidylglycine (III) had been synthesized (Kopple & Nitecki, 1962; Kopple et al., 1963) as models for use in investigations of possible imidazole–hydroxyphenyl interactions. We have investigated the optical activity of these compounds as models for the tyrosine residue in linear and cyclic peptides. The ORD of (I), the cyclic hexapeptide, is given in Fig. 5. The rotations are expressed on a mean residue basis, but it should be noted that a more realistic expression for the observed rotations might be $[\phi]/2$, where $[\phi]$ is the molar rotation, since the four glycyl residues presumably contribute little to the rotatory properties of the molecule. The ORD consists of a relatively symmetric negative Cotton effect similar to those which we have observed for N-acetyl-L-cysteine methylamide and

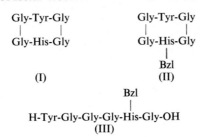

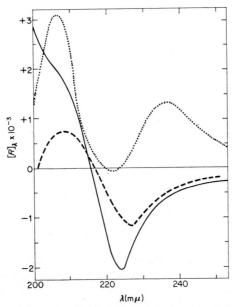

FIG. 5. Ultraviolet ORD of cyclo-Gly-L-Tyr-Gly-Gly-N^{1m}-benzyl-L-His-Gly (———),
cyclo-Gly-L-Tyr-Gly-Gly-L-His-Gly (— — —), and L-Tyr-Gly-Gly-Gly-N^{1m}-benzyl-L-His-
Gly (··········).

reduced glutathione (Coleman & Blout, 1967). The midpoint of this Cotton
effect appears to be near 217 mμ, a position which makes it unlikely that it
is an aromatic Cotton effect. With the benzylated cyclic hexapeptide (II),
the ORD is similar (Fig. 5) except that there seems to be a prominent positive
background contribution so that only a shoulder is found near 208 mμ where
a peak was observed with the ORD of (I). Also, the magnitude of the 217 mμ
Cotton effect is somewhat greater with II relative to I. On the other hand, the
ORD of the benzylated linear hexapeptide (III) is significantly different from
the curves observed for the cyclic compounds. For example, the peak found at
236 was not found with either cyclic peptide. A qualitative determination of the
effect of raising the pH of the solution on the ORD and CD of (III) (Fig. 6)

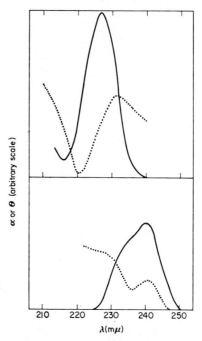

Fɪɢ. 6. Effect of high pH on observed ultraviolet ORD (. . . . .) and ellipticity (———)
of ʟ-Tyr-(Gly)₃-N^{im}-benzyl-ʟ-His-Gly: upper panel, pH 7; lower panel, pH 12.

shows clearly that the new peak is the result of an additional Cotton effect
rather than being the product of the negative 217 mμ Cotton effect combined
with a positive background curve. The CD measurements reveal a band
near 227 mμ at neutral pH which is shifted to near 240 mμ when the pH is
raised to ca 12. The peak and trough of the corresponding Cotton effect
undergo a similar shift with pH. These shifts appeared to be accompanied
by similar shifts in the region of the weak, long-wavelength aromatic transitions, although the pH effect is discerned more clearly in the case of the more
prominent band at 227 mμ. We conclude that the aromatic transition associated with the absorption band near 227 mμ is optically active in the case of
the linear hexapeptide but not with the cyclic peptides. These results suggest
that the optical activity of AVT associated with the aromatic transitions is
not primarily related to the ring structure *per se*, but is dependent upon the
presence of specific residues. It is not clear whether the effect of cleaving
the disulfide bond on the optical activity of the aromatic group is indicative
of a specific interaction between the disulfide and the adjacent phenolic
group, or a consequence of the loss of some other interaction which is stabilized by the ring structure.

3. Investigations of the Rotatory Properties of Synthetic Polypeptides Containing Disulfide Bonds

In the preceding section, we found that the rotatory properties of the disulfide-containing nonapeptides, AVT and OVP, included a prominent contribution near 200 mμ which was attributed to the optical activity of the disulfide group. The characteristics of this contribution were similar to those which had been observed with the model disulfide, DACMA. In this section, we describe the results of some experiments with larger polypeptide systems which are used as models for both *inter*chain and *intra*chain disulfide bonds in proteins. In the latter case, the polypeptide contained multiple disulfide bonds whereas the interchain models had only one S—S bond linking two polypeptide chains.

The ORD and CD spectra of these compounds were investigated and compared with the properties of the corresponding derivatives, in which the disulfide bonds had been reduced and the resulting sulfhydryl groups alkylated. The polypeptide dimers linked by a single intermolecular S—S bond were made by initiating polymerization of γ-benzyl-L-glutamate-N-carboxyanhydride (NCA) with L-cystine dimethylester with subsequent removal of the benzyl groups. The intrachain disulfide model consisted of a copolymer of γ-benzyl-L-glutamate and S-carbobenzoxy-L-cysteine in which all protective groups were removed and the sulfhydryl groups oxidized under dilute conditions which favored the formation of intrachain disulfide bonds.

In addition to finding whether the disulfide contributions to the observed curves could be distinguished as discrete bands or extrema, it was of interest to determine whether the presence of the disulfide contribution would interfere with the estimation of helix content on the basis of the rotatory properties of the polypeptide, e.g. $[R']_{233}$, $[R']_{198}$, or the values of H_{225} and H_{193} (the estimated helix contents) calculated from the modified two-term Drude equation (MTTDE) (Shechter & Blout, 1964). In particular, it was of interest to see whether the values of H_{225} and H_{193} calculated from the MTTDE would be in agreement for polypeptides containing disulfide bonds since it had been suggested that the presence of Cotton effects other than those for peptide transitions in the α-helix and random coil conformations would lead to discrepancies between the two values. Lacking a sensitive, independent means of determining helix content, the interpretation of the data was made primarily on the basis of internal consistency among the various helix content parameters. In addition, comparison of the data for the disulfide-containing polypeptides with those for the corresponding reduced-alkylated derivatives at the same pH served as a second method for estimating the extent of any deviation introduced by the contribution of the disulfide group. Table 1 includes a list of the poly-

TABLE 1. Physical characteristics of polypeptides investigated
A. disulfide-containing(cystine) polypeptides

Code	Name	A/I	Half-cystine : Glu ratio[a, b]
PGA-Cys I	Poly-α-L-glutamate-L-Cys-OMe | Poly-α-L-glutamate-L-Cys-OMe	33	0·030[c]
PGA-Cys II	Poly-α-L-glutamate-L-Cys-OMe | Poly-α-L-glutamate-L-Cys-OMe	20	0·043
Copoly-(Glu-Cys)	Copoly-α-(L-glutamate-L-Cystine)	400	0·10

B. reduced-alkylated cysteine polypeptides

Code	Derived from	CM-cysteine : Glu ratio[a]	Half-cystine : Glu ratio[a, b]
PGA-CM Cys I	PGA-Cys I	0·02	0·008
PGA-CM Cys II	PGA-Cys II	0·013	0·005
Copoly-(Glu-CM Cys)	Copoly-(Glu-Cys)	0·105	0·008

[a] Ratios determined by amino acid analysis.
[b] Includes cysteic acid.
[c] Theoretical—amino acid analysis not available.

peptides investigated as well as results of amino acid analyses which were used to estimate sulfur contents. The analyses for the reduced-alkylated polypeptides indicate that a minimum of 71% of the disulfide bonds were cleaved and alkylated.

The estimates of helix content for the various polypeptides are given in Table 2. As noted, the lowest pH listed for each polypeptide is the pH where the solubility became limiting in each case. Since this pH value varies in each case between the disulfide-containing polypeptide and the associated reduced-alkylated derivative, it is clear that the two polypeptide forms do not have completely identical physical properties. It is not clear whether this is wholly due to the presence of the disulfide bonds or represents an inadvertent fractionation of the polypeptide in the course of the reduction and alkylation procedures. In the results given in Table 2, the agreement between H_{225} and H_{193} is generally excellent, the difference between the two values being less than or equal to the estimated accuracy of the method, five percentage points, in all but one case. The agreement between the helix content estimates determined through the use of the MTTDE and those based on the magnitudes of rotations in the far u.v. ($[R']_{233}$ and $[R']_{198}$) is not as close as might have been expected, but we see that the agreement

TABLE 2. Percent helix content estimates (H_λ) for polypeptides
containing cystine or carboxymethylcysteine (CM Cys)

Polypeptide[a]	pH[b]	H_{225}[c]	H_{193}[c]	H_{233}[d]	H_{198}[d]
PGA-Cys I	5·5	33	28	35	—
	6·1	31	30	28	31
	9·8	17	12	10	7
PGA-CM Cys I	4·5	66	74	63	79
	8·9	14	10	7	4
PGA-Cys II	5·8	16	16	12	14
PGA-CM Cys II	5·5	29	31	28	—
	5·8	20	22	15	18
Copoly-(Glu-Cys)	4·2	67	67	73	75
	4·8	66	65	65	69
	7·0	11	6	3	—
Copoly-(Glu-CM Cys)	4·8	59	61	63	71
	7·0	11	6	4	—

[a] For abbreviations see Table 1.

[b] For each polypeptide, the lowest pH given represents the limit of solubility.

[c] These helix content estimates were calculated using the modified two-term Drude equation (MTTDE) as described by Shechter & Blout (1964).

[d] These helix content estimates were calculated from values of $[R']_{233}$ and $[R']_{198}$ using the standard values of 0% and 100% helix given by Carver et al. (1966b).

is no better with the reduced-alkylated polypeptides than with the disulfide-containing forms. Thus, these differences cannot be the result of the presence of the disulfide bond. Although some differences are observed between the averages of the helix content estimates for the disulfide-containing polypeptides and those for the associated reduced-alkalyted derivatives at the same pH, they do not appear to be significant in consideration of the variations among the values within any single set of measurements. With the Glu-Cys and the Glu-CM Cys copolymers at pH 7, the ORD curves were identical in the visible region of the spectrum. Whereas a difference in $[R']_{589}$ of 22° would be expected on the basis of our analysis of model disulfides (Coleman & Blout, 1967), the observed values of $[R']_{589}$ were exactly the same. Thus, we can find no evidence in the *visible ORD* curves of these disulfide-containing polypeptides for a contribution associated with the disulfide group.

The far ultraviolet ORD and CD curves for these compounds were found to be intermediate in form between the curve for the α-helix and that of the random coil (Carver et al., 1966a), depending on the pH of the solution. With copoly-(Glu-Cys) the ORD curve at pH 4·2 (Fig. 7) is that of a polypeptide with a high helix content. When this curve is compared with the curve for copoly-(Glu-CM Cys) at pH 4·8 the differences are consistent with the difference in pH and cannot be attributed to the presence of an additional

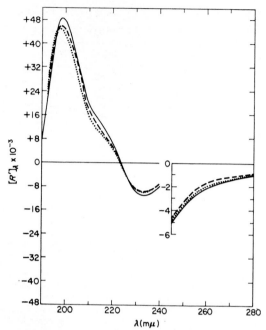

Fig. 7. Ultraviolet ORD of copoly-(Glu-Cys) at pH 4·2 (———) and pH 4·8 (···········), and copoly-(Glu-CM Cys) at pH 4·8 (— — —).

Cotton effect. Similarly, discrepancies between estimates of helix content based on $[R']_{233}$ and $[R']_{198}$ and those obtained from the MTTDE (see Table 2) seem to be no more pronounced in the case of the disulfide polypeptide than with the reduced-alkylated form. With the corresponding CD curves (Fig. 8), the differences in the far ultraviolet region are associated with the peptide transitions rather than with the presence of a new band near 200 mμ.

Although we have not included them in a figure, the ORD and CD curves for copoly-(Glu-Cys) and copoly-(Glu-CM Cys) at pH 7 could be characterized in the same manner. As shown in Table 2, the helix content estimates based on $[R']_{233}$ were identical for the disulfide-containing and reduced-alkylated polypeptides, as were those obtained from the MTTDE.

With PGA-Cys II at pH 5·8, the ORD curve (Fig. 9) has a trough near 210 mμ which is similar in appearance to the disulfide trough found in the same region with the cyclic disulfides, AVT and OVP, and previously observed with DACMA and oxidized glutathione. In the case of the polypeptide, however, we see that reduction of the S—S bond does not result in the disappearance of the trough: the ORD of PGA-CM Cys II at the same pH is quite similar. In particular, it should be noted that the decrease in the size

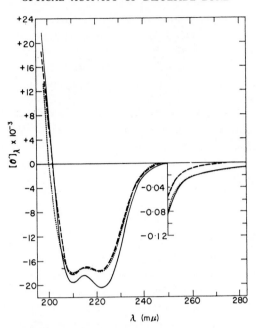

FIG. 8. Ultraviolet ellipticity of copoly-(Glu-Cys) at pH 4·2 (———)and pH 4·8 (..........) and copoly-(Glu-CM Cys) at pH 4·8 (— — —).

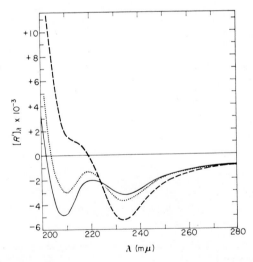

FIG. 9. Ultraviolet ORD of PGA-Cys II at pH 5·8 (———), and PGA-CM Cys II at pH 5·5 (— — —) and pH 5·8 (..........).

of the 210 mμ trough with PGA-CM Cys II is accompanied by an increase in the 233 mμ trough. Thus, the differences between the two curves are undoubtedly the result of differences in the helix contents rather than being related to the presence of a disulfide Cotton effect. For comparison, we have calculated ORD curves for a hypothetical polypeptide having helix contents of 20, 30 and 40% using the Cotton effect parameters reported by Carver *et al.* (1966*a*) and the assumption that the rotational strengths of the helix Cotton effects are proportional to percent helix while those of the random coil are proportional to (100 − % helix).† These curves (Fig. 12) show the reciprocal relationship between the 210 mμ trough and the 233 mμ trough, and indicate the isorotational point at 225 mμ. This isorotational point is also observed with PGA Cys II and PGA CM Cys I, providing further evidence that there is no significant "extra" contribution to the ORD in this region. As with copoly-(Glu-Cys) and its alkylated derivative, the differences in the CD curves of PGA-Cys II and PGA-CM Cys II in the far ultraviolet (Fig. 10) can be accounted for by changes in the peptide contributions associated with conformational changes.

In contrast to the results in the far ultraviolet, all of the CD curves of the disulfide-containing polypeptides were found to deviate from those of the reduced-alkylated derivatives in the region between 250 and 280 mμ (Figs. 8, 10 and 11). These differences were independent of pH and indicate

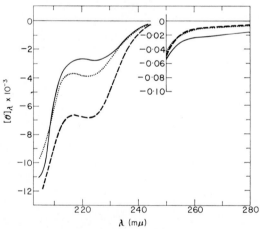

Fɪɢ. 10. Ultraviolet ellipticity of PGA-Cys II at pH 5·8 (————), and PGA-CM Cys II at pH 5·5 (— — —) and pH 5·8(..........).

† This assumption has been made in all methods for estimating helix content from the ORD or CD of polypeptides and proteins. For a critical discussion of this and other assumptions implicit in the analysis of the ORD and CD of proteins and polypeptides, see Carver *et al.* (1966*b*).

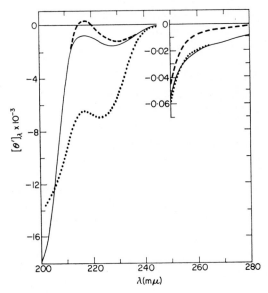

Fɪɢ. 11. Ultraviolet ellipticity of PGA-Cys I at pH 9·8 (————) and pH 6·1 (············)
and PGA–CM Cys I at pH 8·9 (— — —).

the presence of an additional negative CD band in this region. In Figs 8
and 11, it is shown that changing the pH of the disulfide-containing polypeptide results in variations in the CD curves below 250 mμ, while the
curves in the 250 and 280 mμ region remain constant. As indicated in Fig. 10,
the effect of varying the pH of a reduced-alkylated polypeptide is similar.
Thus, this additional band at ~ 260 mμ is not sensitive to changes of the
polypeptide conformation. From the size and location of this band it is
clear that this is a contribution associated with the 260 mμ disulfide transition. That there should be no indication of the associated Cotton effect in
the ORD curves of the disulfide-containing polypeptides is not surprising
in view of the fact that even with DACMA and oxidized glutathione this
Cotton effect is almost completely obscured due to the overlapping effect
of much stronger Cotton effects at shorter wavelengths. Thus, with one
exception (see below), these investigations provided no evidence for the
presence of any disulfide contribution to the ORD and CD curves in the
far ultraviolet spectral region. On the other hand, all of the CD curves of
disulfide-containing polypeptides revealed the presence of the 260 mμ
disulfide CD band.

   The exception referred to above was found in the ORD and CD measurements of copoly-(Glu-Cys) at pH 4·8, shown in Figs 7 and 8 respectively.
This solution differed from the others in that it was made by adjusting the

pH of the original pH 4·2 solution of copoly-(Glu-Cys) several days after it had been made up. All other measurements had been made with freshly prepared solutions. In Fig. 7, we see that the magnitude of the 233 mμ trough is slightly larger for copoly-(Glu-Cys) at pH 4·8 than for copoly-(Glu-CM Cys) at the same pH. Accordingly, below the isorotational point at 225 mμ, the curve for copoly-(Glu-Cys) would be expected to be slightly more positive. In fact, the curve for the disulfide-containing polypeptide deviates significantly in a negative direction from the expected values in the region between 225 and 197 mμ. Below 197 mμ, this deviation appears to become positive. With the CD measurements a consistent picture is obtained: the curve of copoly-(Glu-Cys) at pH 4·8 (Fig. 8) is very close to that of copoly-(Glu-CM Cys) at the same pH in the region of the peptide bands but deviates from it below 210 mμ, the direction of the deviation being negative.

In Fig. 12, we show the predicted disulfide contribution to the value of [R'] in the far u.v. for a polypeptide containing two S—S bonds per hundred residues based on the analysis of the ORD of DACMA. It is clear that the presence of a disulfide Cotton effect such as this will not be marked by the

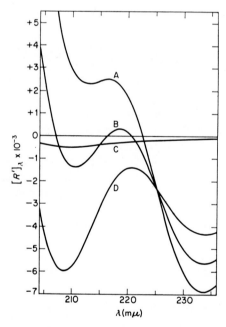

FIG. 12. Ultraviolet ORD curves for a hypothetical polypeptide with A, 40% helix content; B, 30% helix content; and D, 20% helix content. Curve C shows the calculated disulfide contribution to the ultraviolet ORD of a hypothetical polypeptide having 2 disulfide bonds per hundred residues.

presence of a distinct extremum, but will only produce a gently varying deviation in the overall curve. Thus, the deviations observed in the ORD of copoly-(Glu-Cys) at pH 4·8 are exactly the sort which would be expected to arise from the presence of a negative Cotton effect or CD band located near 200 mμ and indicate the presence of the predicted disulfide contribution in the rotatory properties of this polypeptide solution. The observed deviation in the ORD in the region near 210 mμ is approximately -2×10^3 degrees. The predicted value for a polypeptide having five disulfide bonds per hundred residues is $-1·2 \times 10^3$ degrees.

A possible explanation for our failure to observe any evidence of a 200 mμ Cotton effect or CD band in cystine-containing polypeptides, which also is consistent with the exception which we have been discussing, is based on our previous suggestion that the optical activity of the 200 mμ disulfide transition is related to the inherent asymmetry of the chromophore whereas that of the 260 mμ transition results primarily from asymmetric environmental influences. Thus, in systems where there is no preferred configuration of the disulfide bond, the net contribution from the 200 mμ disulfide transition would become negligible due to extensive cancellations of the contributions associated with the two isomeric forms. The 260 mμ transition would still be observed, not being markedly affected by this averaging process.

With the particular polypeptide system which we have investigated the disulfide bonds may be termed *non-equivalent*. In the case of the Glu-Cys copolymer, both the incorporation of *S*-carbobenzoxycysteinyl residues into the chain and the subsequent pairing of sulfhydryl groups in the oxidation step are assumed to be random processes. It is reasonable to expect that the constraints imposed on the configuration of the disulfide bond by the long polypeptide chains will result in a random distribution of disulfide isomers with extensive cancellation of the optical activity associated with the asymmetry of the chromophore. Even with the disulfide-linked polypeptide dimers, where the local environment of the disulfide group is more uniform, any differences in energy of the two disulfide isomers would be more than offset by the adverse change in entropy which would accompany the assumption of the favored disulfide configuration.

With copoly-(Glu-Cys) at pH 4·8, it is not inconceivable that the appearance of a disulfide contribution is the result of a slow relaxation process where, by means such as disulfide interchange, the polypeptide system approaches a final equilibrium state. The relatively large number of disulfide bonds per polypeptide chain, an average of 20, and the rigidity associated with the 65–70% helix content could substantially reduce random fluctuations in the molecule which tend to reduce any unequal distribution of disulfide isomers. However, under conditions favoring a random coil conformation, such fluctuations would be expected to effectively overcome any preference toward a particular disulfide isomer, resulting in the disappearance of the optical activity associated with the asymmetry of the disulfide chromophore.

A situation similar to that which we have been discussing might also be expected with unfolded or denatured proteins where the polypeptide chains may assume a wide range of conformations. On the other hand, with proteins in their native conformations, the disulfide bonds become *equivalent*. Any particular S—S bond in a native protein is expected to have the same configuration over the entire population of molecules. Since the number of disulfide bonds is relatively small for most proteins, the resultant optical activity of the 200 mμ disulfide transition could vary considerably from one protein to another depending on the particular distribution of disulfide configurations. Although complete cancellation is possible, as was noted by Beychok (1965), it would occur only for the case when there were equal numbers of both disulfide isomers.

The significance of these findings is that unfolding of a protein can lead to the loss of a major portion of the net optical activity of the 200 mμ disulfide transition, even in cases where there is only one disulfide bond in the molecule. Subsequent cleavage of the S—S bonds would therefore lead to little additional change in the ORD related to the 200 mμ disulfide contribution. On the other hand, the smaller contribution from the 260 mμ transition would be predicted to be less affected by the unfolding process and thus could give rise to an observable change upon cleavage of the disulfide bonds. This means that the significance of the disulfide contribution must be considered when changes in the ORD accompanying protein denaturation are investigated in contrast to earlier suggestions (Wurz & Haurowitz, 1961; Turner *et al.*, 1959) that the disulfide contribution must be taken into account when the disulfide bonds of a protein are cleaved. In either case, the question may be somewhat academic since the presence of a 200 mμ disulfide contribution of the predicted magnitude in the case of copoly-(Glu-Cys) at pH 4·8 did not appear to introduce any significant inconsistencies into the estimation of the helix content by four independent parameters.

4. Conclusions

The rotatory properties of the cyclic disulfide-containing peptides, arginine vasotocin and 8-L-ornithine vasopressin are dominated primarily by contributions associated with the disulfide group in which the optical activity of the S—S transition near 200 mμ is similar in magnitude, sign, and position to that observed with the model compound, diacetyl-L-cystinebismethylamide. The apparent reversal of the sign of the 260 mμ disulfide CD band of arginine vasotocin is not considered to carry any implications regarding the geometry of the disulfide bond, but rather to reflect the particular molecular environment of the disulfide bond in this cyclic peptide. Apart from the contributions of the S—S group, the bulk of the optical activity of these compounds is associated with optically active transitions of the tyrosine group which are dependent upon the integrity of the ring structure. However, this dependency appears to involve the stabilization of a specific interaction of the tyrosyl residue with some other group, rather than with the peptide ring. The characterization of the optical activity of arginine vasotocin in terms of contributions from specific residues may be useful in future investigations of the interaction of the hormone with its receptor molecule.

In our investigation of the rotatory properties of disulfide-containing polypeptides, a contribution to the CD spectra of all these compounds was observed which was associated with the 260 mμ disulfide transition. It is suggested that the optical activity of this transition is primarily a result of asymmetric environmental influences and not the asymmetry of the disulfide bond. With these disulfide-containing polypeptides the failure to observe evidence of the predicted disulfide contribution at 200 mμ (except in one case) is attributed to the non-equivalence of the disulfide bonds whereby extensive cancellation of contributions from the 200 mμ disulfide transition takes place as a result of the randomization of the configurations of the S—S bond.

Since the unfolding or denaturation of a disulfide-containing protein involves the conversion of one or more equivalent disulfide bonds into a population of non-equivalent S—S bonds, we conclude that the net disulfide optical activity associated with the 200 mμ transition will be lost in the denaturation step, rather than in the process of cleaving the disulfide bonds of a denatured protein.

With the one polypeptide in which far ultraviolet disulfide optical activity of the magnitude predicted from small cystine peptides was observed, no discernible inconsistencies were found in estimates of helix content from four different parameters of the ORD curve. Thus, the presence of disulfide Cotton effects may not be an important component in assessing helix contents of proteins by means of optical rotatory dispersion. However, this conclusion should not be considered firm until model linear polypeptides containing small cystine peptide rings are investigated.

ACKNOWLEDGEMENTS

We wish to thank Dr M. Bodanszky, formerly of the Squibb Institute for Medical Research, for the generous gift of the arginine vasotocin and 8-L-ornithine vasopressin used in this work. We are also indebted to Dr K. D. Kopple of the University of Chicago who generously provided the samples of cycloglycyl-L-tyrosyldiglycyl-L-histidylglycyl, cycloglycyl-L-tyrosyldiglycyl-N^{im}-benzyl-L-histidylglycyl, and L-tyrosyltriglycyl-N^{im}-benzyl-L-histidyldiglycine. We are grateful to Dr D. B.

Wetlaufer for synthesizing the copoly-α-(γ-benzyl-L-glutamate-S-carbobenzoxy-L-cysteine). We wish to thank Mrs Kay (Shaw) Brown and Miss Mary Jane Becherer for indispensable technical assistance.

We are pleased to acknowledge the support provided by the National Institutes of Health in the form of a Predoctoral Fellowship to D. L. C. and by National Institutes of Health Research Grant No. AM 07300–03.

REFERENCES

Beaven, G. H. & Holiday, E. R. (1952). *Adv. Protein Chem.* **7**, 319.

Benesch, R. E. & Benesch, R. (1957). *Biochim. biophys. Acta*, **23**, 658.

Benesch, R. & Benesch, R. E. (1962). *Methods biochem. Analysis*, **10**, 43.

Beychok, S. (1965). *Proc. natn. Acad. Sci. U.S.A.* **53**, 999.

Blout, E. R. (1960). *In* "Optical Rotatory Dispersion", ed. by C. Djerassi, p. 238. New York: McGraw-Hill; see also references contained therein.

Bodanszky, M., Ondetti, M. A., Birkhimer, C. A. & Thomas, P. L. (1964). *J. Am. chem. Soc.* **86**, 4452.

Carver, J. P., Shechter, E. & Blout, E. R. (1966a). *J. Am. chem. Soc.* **88**, 2550.

Carver, J. P., Shechter, E. & Blout, E. R. (1966b). *J. Am. chem. Soc.* **88**, 2562.

Coleman, D. L. & Blout, E. R. (1967). In press.

duVigneaud, V., Winestock, G., Murti, V. V. S., Hope, D. B. & Kimbrough, R. D., Jr. (1960). *J. biol. Chem.* **235**, 64.

Goodman, M. & Rosen, I. G. (1964). *Biopolymers*, **2**, 537.

Holzwarth, G. & Doty, P. (1965). *J. Am. chem. Soc.* **87**, 218.

Hooker, T. M., Jr. & Tanford, C. (1964). *J. Am. chem. Soc.* **86**, 4989.

Idelson, M. & Blout, E. R. (1958). *J. Am. chem. Soc.* **80**, 4631.

Iizuka, E. & Yang, J. T. (1964). *Biochemistry*, **3**, 1519.

King, T. E. & Schellman, J. A. (1966). *Fedn Proc. Fedn Am. Socs exp. Biol.* **25**, 411.

Kopple, K. D. & Nitecki, D. E. (1962). *J. Am. chem. Soc.* **84**, 4457.

Kopple, K. D., Jarabak, R. R. & Lal Bhatia, P. (1963). *Biochemistry*, **2**, 958.

Legrand, M. & Viennet, R. (1964). *Bull. Soc. chim. Fr.* **259**, 4277.

Lundberg, R. D. & Doty, P. (1957). *J. Am. chem. Soc.* **79**, 3961.

Moore, S. & Stein, W. H. (1963). *In* "Methods in Enzymology", ed. by S. P. Colowick and N. O. Kaplan, Vol. 6, p. 827. New York: Academic Press.

Moscowitz, A. (1960). *In* "Optical Rotatory Dispersion", ed. by C. Djerassi, p. 150. New York: McGraw-Hill.

Moscowitz, A. (1961). *Tetrahedron*, **13**, 48.

Moscowitz, A., Rosenberg, A., & Hansen, A. E. (1965). *J. Am. chem. Soc.* **87**, 1813.

Oriel, P. J. & Blout, E. R. (1966). *J. Am. chem. Soc.* **88**, 2041.

Ressler, C. (1956). *Proc. Soc. exp. Biol. Med.* **92**, 725.

Sanger, F. (1956). *In* "Currents in Biochemical Research", ed. by D. E. Green, p. 434. New York: Wiley.

Shechter, E. & Blout, E. R. (1964). *Proc. natn. Acad. Sci. U.S.A.* **51**, 695.

Smyth, D. K., Stein, W. H. & Moore, S. (1963). *J. biol. Chem.* **238**, 227.

Turner, J. E., Kennedy, M. B. & Haurowitz, F. (1959). *In* "Symposium on Sulfur in Proteins", ed. by R. Benesch, R. E. Benesch, P. D. Boyer, I. M. Klotz, W. R. Middlebrook, A. G. Szent-Györgyi and D. R. Schwarz. New York: Academic Press.

Wetlaufer, D. B. & Blout, E. R. (1961). *Abstr. 5th Int. Cong. Biochemistry*, Moscow, 1961, p. 4. Oxford: Pergamon Press.

Würz, H. & Haurowitz, F. (1961). *J. Am. chem. Soc.* **83**, 280.

Optical Properties of Cyclic Peptides

Prototypic Helix Systems

D. Balasubramanian† and D. B. Wetlaufer

Department of Biochemistry, Medical School, University of Minnesota, Minneapolis, Minnesota, U.S.A.

The optical rotatory dispersion, circular dichroism, ultraviolet and infrared spectra of amino acid diketopiperazines and a cyclic tetrapeptide have been investigated. The optical rotatory dispersion of the diketopiperazines show the presence of at least two Cotton effects in the peptide absorption region, a negative one at about 210 mμ, and a positive one below 194 mμ assigned to the π–π*. The dispersion of the tetrapeptide is consistent with three Cotton effects, a negative one of the n–π*, and two Cotton effects, a longer wavelength negative effect and a shorter wavelength positive one, assigned to a split π–π* peptide band. Circular dichroism studies supplement these conclusions for the tetrapeptide; the dichroism of the diketopiperazines also suggest that even here, split π–π* Cotton effects may exist, besides the n–π* Cotton effect. These results on the cyclic systems closely parallel those of the right-handed α-helix, and are in accord with the predictions of Schellman & Oriel and Litman that local rigidity of conformation and proper vicinal atom orientation will promote the n–π* Cotton effect; and also the prediction of Kauzmann that a proper disposition of identical chromophores in a simpler system than a helix may produce exciton effects. These cyclic systems are thus to be considered as prototypes of helical polypeptide structures insofar as their optical properties are concerned.

1. Introduction

The optical rotatory dispersion (ORD), circular dichroism (CD), ultraviolet spectrum of the peptide chromophore and the infrared spectral characteristics of the various common conformations of the polypeptide chains have been investigated in detail both theoretically and by experimental methods. It has become possible to detect the presence and estimate the amount of any ordered conformation of the polypeptide chain with reasonable confidence, with a wise combination of the above-mentioned techniques. An excellent review on this general topic has been presented by Schellman & Schellman (1964). Apart from their intrinsic interest pertaining to the synthetic homo-polypeptide systems, these spectral studies have been of considerable value

† Present address: Department of Chemistry, Indian Institute of Technology, Kanpur, India.

in the study of chain conformations of proteins. ORD has been of particular significance in this connection. The dispersion parameters b_0 and a_0 of Moffitt & Yang (1956), and also the sign, spectral location and the magnitudes of the Cotton effects due to the transitions of the peptide chromophore have been repeatedly used in the detection of conformations such as the α-helix and the β-forms in proteins (Schellman & Schellman, 1964; also Iizuka & Yang, 1966).

A point of particular interest here is the Cotton effects due to the $n-\pi^*$ and the $\pi-\pi^*$ transitions of the peptide chromophore. Recent investigations of the rotatory properties of α-helical polypeptides and proteins have revealed the presence of three Cotton effects in the range 230–190 mμ. The first is negative, centred around 222 mμ; the second is another negative Cotton effect around 206 mμ; and finally there is a positive one centred around 190 mμ. The latter two correspond fairly well with the positions of the two peaks of the split $\pi-\pi^*$ absorption band of the peptide group. The splitting of the normally degenerate $\pi-\pi^*$ peptide group was predicted by Moffitt (1956), who treated the α-helix as an array of identical peptide chromophores displaying exciton interactions. He also predicted that these exciton-split $\pi-\pi^*$ bands should give rise to a longer-wavelength negative Cotton effect at about 206 mμ, and a positive Cotton effect at 190 mμ. Experimental confirmation of this splitting has come both from u.v. spectral work (Gratzer et al., 1961) and ORD work (Holzwarth & Doty, 1965). In contrast to this exciton behaviour of the α-helix, the ORD and CD characteristics of the disordered conformation of the polypeptide chain reveals only one negative rotatory band at 198 mμ, assigned to the $\pi-\pi^*$ transition (Holzwarth & Doty, 1965, and also Schechter et al., 1966). Thus, in the disordered form, the exciton effects are lost, presumably owing to loss of the required geometric disposition of the chromophores that is necessary for their collective interaction. Further, the negative Cotton effect at 222 mμ associated with the $n-\pi^*$ band and seen in the α-helix (Woody, 1962; Schellman & Oriel, 1962) is almost totally lost in the random coil. This again suggests that in order to realize the $n-\pi^*$ and the $\pi-\pi^*$ Cotton effects in peptide systems, a certain typical geometry of the chain conformation, such as the α-helix, is necessary. Until recently, the $n-\pi^*$ Cotton effect was not observed in systems simpler than polypeptides and proteins. However, recent illuminating experiments by Litman & Schellman (1965) have revealed this Cotton effect in a model system, L-3-aminopyrrolid-2-one. They have suggested that this $n-\pi^*$ Cotton effect of the peptide group is a spectral feature that is brought out by molecular rigidity, properly distributed vicinal atoms and a low dielectric constant; one is thereby brought to wonder whether or not the $n-\pi^*$ Cotton effect can be induced in the peptide links in regions of a protein that are not helical in the usual sense of the word.

Recent investigations in these laboratories have been concerned with the optical properties of amino acid diketopiperazines. These model systems possess a twofold advantage: (1) there is local rigidity in the molecule, which would be expected to promote the $n-\pi^*$ Cotton effect under appropriate conditions; and (2) there are two peptide links in these molecules—if the piperazine ring becomes nonplanar, thereby allowing the overlap of the orbitals of the two chromophores, one may see aspects of rudimentary exciton effects. Studies on L-alanyl-L-serine diketopiperazine (LALSDKP) have indeed shown part of these predictions to be true (Balasubramanian & Wetlaufer, 1966). Additional information on some more of these systems, and also on a higher homologue, cyclic tetra-L-alanine, are presented in this paper.

2. Materials and Methods

(a) *Solvents*

Spectroquality dioxan, acetonitrile and trifluoroethanol were redistilled and used. Ethanol and water were doubly distilled as well, for all the spectral measurements.

(b) *Compounds*

All the diketopiperazines were bought from Cyclo Chemical Corp., Los Angeles, and had the right elemental analyses. They were all ninhydrin negative, and thus cyclic peptides. However, the commercial sample of L-alanyl-L-alanine diketopiperazine that was investigated and reported in the previous publication (Balasubramanian & Wetlaufer, 1966) turned out not to be a diketopiperazine at all, but a cyclic tetrapeptide of L-alanine. Hence the results presented therein on what was inadvertently called L-alanyl-L-alanine diketopiperazine refer to cyclotetra-L-alanine. A brief report on this situation was presented before the 152nd national meeting of the American Chemical Society in New York, on 13 September 1966. The tetra-alanine was characterized as follows. The commercial sample of "L-alanyl-L-alanine diketopiperazine" was run through a LH20 Sephadex column with ethanol as the solvent and the major peak was isolated, and its i.r. spectra and molecular weight determined. The molecular-weight determinations were made in ethanol by Dr. Neumeyer of the 3M Co., St Paul, Minnesota, using a vapour-pressure osmometer, and was determined to be 282, corresponding to the cyclotetraalanine. Infrared spectrum of this fraction in Nujol mull revealed the presence of *trans*-peptide links and no similarity whatever to that of diketopiperazines. The minor peak from the Sephadex column constituted less than a few per cent by weight, and its i.r. spectrum coincided with that of an authentic sample of L-alanyl-L-alanine diketopiperazine.

We are in great debt to our colleague, Mr. Dorr Dearborn, for the painstaking process of isolation and characterization of the tetrapeptide. We also thank Drs. F. A. Bovey and S. Feinleib of the Bell Telephone Laboratories, Murray Hill, New Jersey, for access to their spectropolarimeter, and for pointing out the false identity of the commercial sample of "L-alanyl-L-alanine diketopiperazine". The laboratory synthesis of L-alanyl-L-alanine diketopiperazine was made according to the following scheme:

N-CBZ-L-Ala-L-Ala methyl ester $\xrightarrow[\text{H}_2/\text{Pd in methanol}]{}$ L-Ala-L-Ala methyl ester

L-Ala-L-Ala methyl ester $\xrightarrow[\text{methanol/ammonia, overnight}]{}$ L-Ala-L-Ala diketopiperazine

The concentration of the precursor in each step of the synthesis should be about 0·1–1·0 M, otherwise higher peptides result. The molecular weight, i.r. spectra, ninhydrin test, Sephadex elution, and spectral data of the recrystallized product established the authenticity of the sample as the diketopiperazine.

The other diketopiperazines reported in this paper were also characterized by the above criteria, and established to be the authentic cyclic dipeptides.

(c) Optical rotatory dispersion

All the ORD measurements were done in a Cary model 60 spectropolarimeter, at an ambient temperature of $27° \pm 1°C$. Cells of path lengths from 0·5 mm to 1·0 dm were used. The normal concentration range of investigation was 10^{-4} to 2×10^{-3} M. Each run was repeated several times, with different path lengths and concentrations, and the reproducibility was usually within 1%. Some ORD data was also obtained with the Jasco–Durrum ORD/CD/UV-5 spectropolarimeter at the Bell Telephone Laboratories, Murray Hill, New Jersey.

Circular dichroism (CD) studies are under way on these samples. The instruments used for the preliminary CD work were the Jasco–Durrum, and the Cary prototype CD attachment for the model 60 spectropolarimeter.

(d) Infrared spectra

The infrared spectral measurements were made with a Perkin–Elmer model 521 spectrophotometer, and the Unicam IR spectrophotometer. Most of the measurements were run in Nujol mull, and some solution measurements were also made in dioxan, acetonitrile and ethanol.

(e) Association of these compounds in solution

Intermolecular association of amide molecules is a well-known phenomenon. Evidence for this association in the solution state is exemplified by the work of Mizushima (1954). However, Litman and Schellman (1965)

find negligible association of L-3-aminopyrrolid-2-one in dioxan and aceto-nitrile solutions, in the concentration range of from 5×10^{-3} to $1 \cdot 5 \times 10^{-2}$ M. In any case, even if association occurs in nonpolar solvents in the concentration range of this study, it can be safely concluded that diketopiperazines and similar amides are essentially monomeric in hydroxylic solvents, such as ethanol, trifluoroethanol and water (cf. Franzen & Stephens, 1963).

The concentration range of all the investigations reported here is 10^{-4}–2×10^{-3} M.

3. Results

The u.v. absorption spectra of these diketopiperazines fail to reveal a discernible shoulder in the 200–230 mμ region. Thus the n–π^* absorption of the peptide group is apparently totally masked by the broad, very high absorption of the π–π^* peptide transition centred at 187 mμ. It is also worth pointing out that these cyclic peptides show residue molar extinction co-efficients greater than 8000 at their π–π^* band, and thus are much more highly absorbing than an isolated peptide or a disordered polypeptide chain. There is no hypochromism of the π–π^* band, as occurs in the helical polypeptide cases (Gratzer *et al.*, 1961). The molar extinction coefficient of the residue at 225 mμ is less than 500.

The i.r. spectra (in Nujol mull and in films) of the diketopiperazines show the amide I peak at about 1685 cm^{-1}. These compounds being *cis*-peptides, show no absorption in the 1550 cm^{-1} region. Instead, the amide II band occurs around 1450 cm^{-1}. These results are in accord with the experimental observations of Lenormant (1950), and the normal mode calculations of Fukushima *et al.* (1965). The i.r. spectrum in Nujol mull of the cyclic tetra-L-alanine, however, is very different. This cyclic peptide seems to exist in the *trans*-peptide configuration. Molecular models show that in cyclic peptides of less than four units, the amide bonds are forced into the *cis*-configuration, but the tetramer accommodates a *trans*-peptide form. The absorption bands in the amide I region of the cyclic tetra-L-alanine occur at 1680 cm^{-1} (med) and 1650 cm^{-1} (strong), and the amide II peak occurs at 1545 cm^{-1}. This i.r. spectrum is directly comparable to that of the α-helix, which shows an amide I peak at 1650 cm^{-1} and the amide II peak at 1546 cm^{-1} (Schellman & Schellman, 1964). One turn of the α-helix contains 3·7 residues and the axial translation of the helix is 1·5 Å, whereas the cyclic tetramer has four residues to the cycle. This may seem to be relevant in the parallel infrared behaviour in the amide I and II region.

The small discrepancies between the amide I and II absorption frequencies of the substituted diketopiperazines and the unsubstituted glycyl-glycine diketopiperazine that Fukushima *et al.* (1965) have calculated could be due to the fact that the side-chain substitution perturbs the skeletal absorption, and also that whereas the glycyl-glycine diketopiperazine ring is planar (Corey, 1938), substitution leads to deviation from planarity.

The ORD of L-alanyl-L-serine diketopiperazine and what was inadvertently called the L-alanyl-L-alanine diketopiperazine, but later identified as the cyclic tetra-L-alanine, have been published (Balasubramanian & Wetlaufer, 1966). Focusing attention on the cyclic tetra-L-alanine, one sees the presence of at least two Cotton effects. There is a trough at about 230 mμ with [M] of about $-1000°$. This trough shifts to the red and increases in magnitude with decreasing solvent dielectric constant, thereby suggesting its origin as the $n-\pi^*$ transition of the peptide (Litman & Schellman, 1965; Bayliss, 1950). Further down in the u.v., there is another trough around 208 mμ and a peak at 194 mμ, both of which are tentatively assigned to the split $\pi-\pi^*$ band of the peptide chromophore. The sign of the 230 mμ trough is negative, confirming the quadrant-rule predictions of Litman & Schellman (1965). Thus the cyclic tetrapeptide resembles the α-helix in the formal shape of its rotatory dispersion curve: a negative $n-\pi^*$ Cotton effect, a longer wavelength negative and a shorter wavelength positive Cotton effect of the $\pi-\pi^*$ absorption. The geometry of the tetrapeptide seems to satisfy the requirements of local rigidity and the proper disposition of the two chromophores for interaction to give the ORD behaviour that had been so far seen as unique in the α-helix.

Figure 1 shows the rotatory dispersion of L-alanyl-L-serine, L-alanyl-L-alanine and L-alanyl-L-phenylalanine diketopiperazines in trifluoroethanol. All these curves look formally alike, with a negative trough around 220–225 mμ and a positive peak around 194 mμ. The peak height is much larger than the trough depth, suggesting the existence of at least two Cotton effects that are responsible for this ORD profile. The negative trough around 220–225 mμ shifts slightly to the red with decreasing solvent dielectric constant. The data in Fig. 1 are consistent with the formulation of two Cotton effects. It is also to be noted that repeated experiments on the L-alanyl-L-phenylalanine diketopiperazine under various conditions fail to reveal any Cotton effect in the aromatic absorption band around 260 mμ of the phenylalanyl side chain, in ORD measurements. Experiments are under way on L-phenylalanyl-L-phenylalanine diketopiperazine and will be reported shortly.

Circular dichroism studies have also been undertaken on these systems. CD measurements on the cyclic systems are necessarily difficult owing to their high absorption in the far ultraviolet and their low rotations. The main absorption peak occurs at about 187 mμ, in which region the noise in the CD instrument is already high. In that sense, ORD studies are relatively more informative, since the extremes of the Cotton effects occur at longer

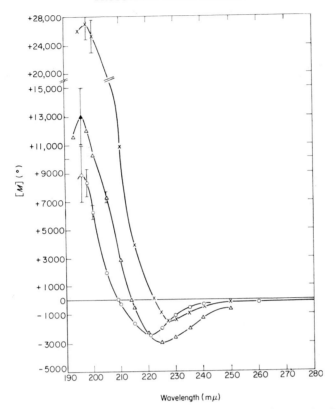

FIG. 1. Optical rotatory dispersion in trifluoroethanol solution of: ○, L-alanyl-L-alanine diketopiperazine; △, L-alanyl-L-serine diketopiperazine; and ×, L-alanyl-L-phenylalanine diketopiperazine. All measurements at ambient temp. $27 \pm 1°C$. The rotations are expressed as residue molar rotations. No refractive-index correction has been made.

wavelengths in the ORD curves than in the CD curves. Preliminary CD measurements show in the cyclotetra-L-alanine, a negative CD band centred around 222 mμ, followed by another negative CD band centred around 198 mμ. The noise level of the present CD measurements becomes high below 200 mμ, with the result that CD bands at lower wavelengths could not be determined with high confidence. However, the asymmetry of the ORD profile in the 210–190 mμ region suggests the presence of a longer wavelength negative and a shorter wavelength positive Cotton effect in this range. The negative CD band at 222 mμ shows the solvent-dependence characteristic of the $n–\pi^*$ absorption.

CD measurements on a few of the diketopiperazines show dichroic behaviour similar to the tetrapeptide case in the formal shape of the curve. Although their ORD is consistent with two Cotton effects, as Fig. 1 shows, the CD spectrum reveals a negative CD band at 210 mμ, and another CD band below 200 mμ. These combined ORD and CD results seem to suggest that even in these simple systems, there might be three Cotton effects in the peptide-absorption region. It is worth noting that Bovey & Hood (personal communication) have detected three CD bands in L-prolyl-L-proline diketopiperazine, which suggests that their origin is due to the $n-\pi^*$ and the split $\pi-\pi^*$ peptide bands. The CD spectrum of L-alanyl-L-alanine diketopiperazine also reveals a small and reproducible positive CD band at 236 mμ, the origin of which is not yet clearly established. Thanks are due Drs. Bovey and Feinleib for first pointing this out.

4. Discussion

The results described above confirm the prediction of Litman & Schellman (1965), that the $n-\pi^*$ Cotton effect is a spectral feature realizable in systems simpler than the α-helix geometry under proper conditions. The diketopiperazines and the cyclic tetramer seem to satisfy the requirements of local rigidity of structure and the proper disposition of vicinal perturbing atoms. Thus, the negative Cotton effect around 225 mμ that Ruttenberg et al. (1965) have reported in cyclic Tyrocidine B and in Gramicidin S-A might also be due to satisfaction of the same conditions. It should also be pointed out that situations may arise in the folding of protein molecules where cyclization and local rigidity imposed by, e.g., disulphide bridges or hydrophobic interactions, will produce $n-\pi^*$ Cotton effects. This phenomenon will therefore cast doubts on the usual estimates of α-helical structure based on the values of the Cotton effect minimum at about 233 mμ.

The second point of interest here is that a simple system, such as the cyclotetra-alanine, and indeed quite likely some diketopiperazines as well, also satisfy conditions required for exciton interactions among peptide groups giving rise to split $\pi-\pi^*$ bands and Cotton effects. Kauzmann (1957) has pointed out that exciton effects can arise in simple systems where the proper geometric disposition of identical chromophores is realized. Thus the results reported here demonstrate that neither the $n-\pi^*$ Cotton effect nor the exciton split of the degenerate $\pi-\pi^*$ transition of the peptide chromophore is unique to the α-helix, but can be displayed if the proper molecular rigidity, orientation of perturbing atoms and the required disposition of the identical groups are realized. Figure 2 is a comparative graph of the rotatory dispersion behaviour of a cyclic "monopeptide", a cyclic dipeptide, i.e. diketopiperazine, a cyclic tetrapeptide and the α-helix. The monopeptide displays a positive Cotton effect, and is reproduced from the work of Litman & Schellman (1965). Since there is only one peptide link in this molecule, exciton effects will not occur. The ORD curves of the diketopiperazine, and the tetramer are also presented, and these are to be compared with that of the α-helix

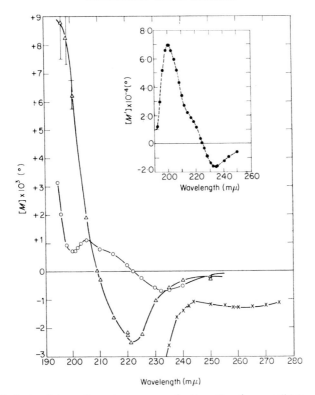

FIG. 2. Optical rotatory dispersion curves of: ×, L-3-aminopyrrolid-2-one in aceto-nitrile; △, L-alanyl-L-alanine diketopiperazine in trifluoroethanol; and ○, cyclic tetra-L-alanine in trifluoroethanol. Insert: the rotatory dispersion curve of the α-helix in methanol: water (9 : 1) mixture. The ordinates are in residue molar rotations, and refractive-index corrections have only been made for the α-helix.

which is shown in the insert. The sizes of the Cotton effects in the cyclic cases are smaller than those of the helix. But the graph is a reiteration of the point that multiple Cotton effects, and exciton behaviour are no longer unique to the helical polypeptide case. The conventional interpretation of the optical properties of proteins and polypeptides, and the estimation of the ordered polypeptide conformations thereby should be viewed with caution.

ACKNOWLEDGMENT

This investigation has been aided by grants from the Jane Coffin Childs Memorial Fund for Medical Research and the U.S. Public Health Service Grant No. GM 10900. D. B. is grateful to the Jane Coffin Childs Memorial Fund for a research fellowship.

REFERENCES

Balasubramanian, D. & Wetlaufer, D. B. (1966). *J. Am. chem. Soc.* **88,** 3449.
Bayliss, N. S. (1950). *J. chem. Phys.* **18,** 292; (1954) *J. phys. Chem.* **58,** 1002.
Corey, R. B. (1938). *J. Am. chem. Soc.* **60,** 1598.
Franzen, J. S. & Stephens, R. E. (1963). *Biochemistry,* **2,** 1321.
Fukushima, K., Ideguchi, Y. & Miyazawa, T. (1965). *Mem. Inst. Protein Res. Osaka Univ.* **7,** 16.
Gratzer, W. B., Holzwarth, G. & Doty, P. (1961). *Proc. natn. Acad. Sci. U.S.A.* **47,** 1785.
Holzwarth, G. & Doty, P. (1965). *J. Am. chem. Soc.* **87,** 218.
Iizuka, E. & Yang, J. T. (1966). *Proc. natn. Acad. Sci. U.S.A.* **55,** 1175.
Kauzmann, W. (1957). *A. Rev. phys. Chem.* **8,** 413.
Lenormant, H. (1950). *Annls Chim.* (12), **5,** 459.
Litman, B. J. & Schellman, J. A. (1965). *J. phys. Chem.* **69,** 978.
Mizushima, S. (1954). *In* "Structure of Molecules and Internal Rotation". New York: Academic Press.
Moffitt, W. (1956). *Proc. natn. Acad. Sci. U.S.A.* **42,** 736.
Moffitt, W. & Yang, J. T. (1956). *Proc. natn. Acad. Sci. U.S.A.* **42,** 596.
Ruttenberg, M. A., King, T. P. & Craig, L. C. (1965). *J. Am. chem. Soc.* **87,** 4196.
Schechter, E., Carver, J. P. & Blout, E. R. (1966). *J. Am. chem. Soc.* **88,** 2550.
Schellman, J. A. & Oriel, P. (1962). *J. chem. Phys.* **37,** 2114.
Schellman, J. A. & Schellman, C. (1964). *In* "The Proteins", ed. by H. Neurath, 2nd Ed. New York: Academic Press.
Woody, R. W. (1962). Dissertation, University of California, Berkeley, Calif.

Optical Activity of the α, β and Coiled Conformations in Polypeptides and Proteins

JEN TSI YANG

Cardiovascular Research Institute, and Department of Biochemistry
University of California San Francisco Medical Center
San Francisco, California, U.S.A.

The development of the Moffitt equation, expressed in terms of wavelength, is briefly described, and the known Cotton effects and circular dichroism of the α, β and coiled conformations are summarized. The aggregation of the α-helices will not only increase the magnitude of the dichroic bands and the 232–233 mμ trough but also cause a small red shift of the extrema. Synthetic polypeptide ions in the coiled conformation are shown to behave as polyelectrolytes, unlike the corresponding disordered portion in a protein molecule. These complications, however, do not significantly alter the b_0 of the Moffitt equation. The recently discovered Cotton effects of the β-form are also complicated by the formation of aggregates. However, the helical form usually dominates the rotatory contributions, when the helical and β-forms co-exist in a molecule. Evidence suggests that the b_0 method based on visible rotatory dispersion is still the best one to meet the requirement for estimating the helical content in protein molecules.

1. Introduction

During the past decade, optical rotatory dispersion (ORD) has become a useful physical method for characterizing the conformations of biopolymers, especially proteins. In 1955, our first ORD measurements were taken with a crude polarimeter, visual type, using a sodium lamp and a mercury lamp with green and blue filters. From this crude experiment, we observed dextro-rotations for poly-γ-benzyl-L-glutamate in chloroform, a helix-promoting solvent, and were convinced of the presence of an anomalous dispersion for a helical polypeptide. Soon after that we acquired a spectropolarimeter (manual type) and were able to accumulate a large amount of experimental data in a relatively short period (Doty & Yang, 1956; Yang & Doty, 1957). Today we are able to measure ORD in the absorption bands of proteins and polypeptides down to about 185 mμ, and the current recording spectro-polarimeters make them almost too easy to work with. (One cannot help admiring the early pioneers, who succeeded in measuring both ultraviolet and infrared rotatory dispersion through ingenious devices such as the use of a fluorescent screen or a photographic method and a thermocouple.) We

have now begun to complement ORD studies with corresponding measurements of circular dichroism (CD). In this communication, we will briefly
describe the optical activity of the α-, β- and coiled conformations, and discuss
some of the problems that remain unsolved.

2. α-Conformation

(a) Visible rotatory dispersion

In general, proteins become more levorotatory in the visible region upon
denaturation and their specific rotations change toward -90 to $110°$ at the
sodium D line. Like many others, I used $[\alpha]_D$ to study the conformational
changes of proteins in solution, but knew little about the protein structures
responsible for the experimental observations. In 1951, however, Pauling and
Corey's α-helix provided an attractive answer to the problem. If the helix of
one screw sense prevails in a protein molecule and it has a dextrorotation at
the sodium D line, its disruption in the protein molecule by a denaturing
agent can account nicely for the increase in levorotation upon denaturation.
The crucial test would then be to measure the ORD of some model polypeptides, since their conformations are well characterized by other physical
methods. In the summer of 1954, I went to work in Professor P. Doty's laboratory, where the helix–coil transitions of poly-γ-benzyl-L-glutamate and poly-
L-glutamic acid (PGA) in solution were soon established (Doty & Yang,
1956; Doty et al., 1957). These provided an ideal test of the rotatory contributions of the α-helix (Yang & Doty, 1957). However, Cohen (1955) was
the first to put this explanation into writing. From the beginning we realized
that only ORD, rather than rotations at any single wavelength, can give any
quantitative analyses with reasonable confidence. Since I was quite unaware
of the theoretical work then in progress (Fitts & Kirkwood, 1956; Moffitt,
1956), I used a two-term Drude equation for the ORD data of the helical
polypeptides (Yang & Doty, 1957):

$$[\alpha] = k_1/(\lambda^2 - \lambda_1^2) + k_2/(\lambda^2 - \lambda_2^2). \tag{1}$$

One term represented the rotations of the helical backbone and the other
term those of the amino acid residues. The anomalous dispersion was
explained by the fact that k_1 and k_2 had opposite signs and, further
$|k_1| > |k_2|$ but $\lambda_1 < \lambda_2$ (Yang, 1961). Equation (1) was soon discarded when
Moffit put forward his equation (equation (2a), below). In addition to its
theoretical foundation, the Moffitt equation uses only three parameters
(a_0, b_0 and λ_0) instead of four (k_1, k_2, λ_1 and λ_2), thus giving a single solution.

The reduced mean residue rotation, $[m']$, in the Moffitt equation was
presented in terms of frequency v (Moffitt, 1956):

$$[m'] = A_0 v^2/(v_0^2 - v^2) + B_0 v^2 v_0 \Delta v_0/(v_0^2 - v^2)^2 \tag{2a}$$

where v_0, Δv_0, A_0 and B_0 are constants. The late William Moffitt had intended to solve equation (2a) with a computer program. At my suggestion, it was transformed into:

$$[m'] = a_0 \lambda_0^2/(\lambda^2 - \lambda_0^2) + b_0 \lambda_0^4/(\lambda^2 - \lambda_0^2)^2 \qquad (3a)$$

with $a_0 = A_0 + B_0 \Delta v_0/v_0$, and $b_0 = B_0 \Delta v_0/v_0$. This simple algebraic rearrangement makes a graphical solution possible by plotting $[m'](\lambda^2 - \lambda_0^2)$ against $1/(\lambda^2 - \lambda_0^2)$ with trial λ_0 values until a straight line is obtained. Alternatively, one can plot $[m']((\lambda^2/\lambda_0^2) - 1)$ against $1/((\lambda^2/\lambda_0^2) - 1)$. Currently, λ_0 is preset at 212 mμ for measurements between 300 and 600 mμ on the basis of earlier work on poly-γ-benzyl-L-glutamate in various helix-promoting solvents (Moffitt & Yang, 1956). Equation (2a) can of course be rearranged into:

$$[m'] = (A_0 + B_0 \Delta v_0/v_0)v^2/(v_0^2 - v^2) + (B_0 \Delta v_0/v_0)v^4/(v_0^2 - v^2)^2. \qquad (2b)$$

Thus, we have in terms of frequency:

$$[m']((v_0^2/v^2) - 1) = a_0 + b_0/((v_0^2/v^2) - 1). \qquad (3b)$$

Recently, Equation (1) has been renewed by substituting $A_1\lambda_1^2$ and $A_2\lambda_2^2$ for k_1 and k_2 and $[m']$ for $[\alpha]$ (Imahori, 1963; Yamaoka, 1964; Shechter & Blout, 1964a, 1964b; Schechter et al., 1964). Some of the problems were discussed (Yang, 1965) and have now been rectified by Carver et al. (1966b). The b_0 from the Moffitt equation seems to still best meet the requirement for estimation of helical content. Carver et al. (1966b) also suggest the use of $(A_{193} - A_{225})$ from their two-term Drude equation as another method for estimating the helical content. It can easily be shown that the term $(A_{193} - A_{225})$ or any pair of $(A_1 - A_2)$ of the many other two-term Drude equations (Yang, 1967) varies approximately with b_0. For instance,

$$-b_0 \cong \Delta'(A_{193} - A_{225}) + \delta\Delta'A_{193} \qquad (4a)$$

or

$$-b_0 \cong \Delta(A_{193} - A_{225}) + \delta'\Delta A_{225} \qquad (4b)$$

where

$$\lambda_{193} = \lambda_0(1 - \Delta/2),$$
$$\lambda_{225} = \lambda_0(1 + \Delta'/2), \; \Delta/2 \text{ and } \Delta'/2 \ll 1$$

and

$$\Delta = \Delta'(1 + \delta) \quad (\text{or } \Delta' = \Delta(1 - \delta')).$$

In recent literature, there have been analyses of the data from several ORD methods. There is nothing wrong making numerous calculations as additional checks (see also the recent review by Harrington et al., 1966). But such agreement is not unexpected, since all these multiple-term Drude equations can be reduced to the Moffitt equation.

(b) Ultraviolet ORD and CD

Figure 1 illustrates the recent ultraviolet rotatory dispersion and CD of the helical form of PGA. Table 1 summarizes the numerical values of both ORD and CD for various conformations. (All ORDs were measured with a

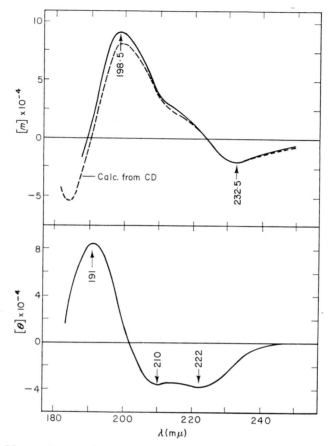

Fig. 1. Mean residue rotation and mean residue ellipticity of the helical poly-L-glutamic acid in water at pH 4·75. Dashed line: calculated $[m]$ from $[\theta]$ using the Kronig–Kramers transform. Concentration: 0·23%.

Cary 60 spectropolarimeter and CDs with a Jasco ORD/UV/CD–5 at 25°C. The data were expressed as mean residue rotation, $[m]$ (or reduced mean residue rotation, $[m']$) and mean residue ellipticity, $[\theta]$, respectively.) The Cotton effect of the helical form is now known to display a 232–233 mμ trough, a 198–199 mμ peak, and a shoulder near 215 mμ with a cross-over near 225 mμ (Blout et al., 1962). Another trough has now been reported near 182–184 mμ (for poly-γ-methyl-L-glutamate in trifluoroethanol) (Applied Physics Corporation and Durrum Instruments Corporation, private communications). The corresponding CD has a double minimum at 222 and 209–210 mμ and a maximum near 191 mμ (Holzwarth & Doty, 1965). Inspection of Fig. 1 shows one of the advantages of CD over ORD; the over-

TABLE 1. The optical rotatory dispersion and circular dichroism of various conformations[a]

	α-Helix[b]		β-Form[c]		Coil[d]	
ORD	λ (mμ)	[m']	λ (mμ)	[m']	λ (mμ)	[m']
Trough	232–233	−15,000	229–230	(−5,000)	238	small
Peak	198–199	+68,000	205	(+24,000)	228	small
Trough	182–184	—	∼ 190	(−17,000)	205	−15,000
Peak					189	+17,000
CD	λ (mμ)	[θ]	λ (mμ)	[θ]	λ (mμ)	[θ]
Minimum	222	−38,000	218	(−20,000)	238	−200
Minimum	209–210	−36,000				
Maximum	191	+85,000	195–197	(+48,000)	218	+4,700
Minimum					199	−35,000

[a] The magnitude of the extrema listed here is still tentative. Dimensions: reduced mean residue rotations, [m'], in deg cm^2 decimole^{-1} and mean residue ellipticity, [θ], in deg cm^2 decimole^{-1} (uncorrected for refractive index).
[b] Poly-L-glutamic acid in water at pH 4·75.
[c] Silk-fibroin in 50% methanol (extrapolated to 100% β-form). The values in the parenthesis are only rough estimates and vary with the solvent composition.
[d] Poly-L-glutamic acid in water at pH 7·39.

lapping Cotton effects may obscure the individual contributions when several optically active absorption bands are close to one another, whereas the corresponding CD bands are oftentimes more easily resolvable. Thus, the helical form suggests two apparent Cotton effects, but its CD spectrum clearly shows three dichroic bands. Even so, these bands overlap; by using curve fitting we may attempt to resolve them into three components and by assuming that they are Gaussian in form we can estimate their rotational strengths. However, such a procedure is somewhat arbitrary and any calculations of the rotational strengths should be viewed with some reservation.

The ORD calculated from the CD data by the Kronig–Kramers transform (Moscowitz, 1960) compares very satisfactorily with the experimentally measured ORD; in particular, it reproduces such features as the trough, peak, shoulder and crossover. The computer analysis also predicts a second trough at 184 mμ, even though this region was still not seen in experiments using PGA in water. Such computation does not introduce the arbitrary assumption of a Gaussian form for each of the dichroic bands. The small difference between the experimental and calculated results are largely attributed to the background rotations which, however, are overshadowed by the Cotton effects of the helical form. This is not too surprising, since the sum of the three rotational strengths, R_i, assuming Gaussian bands, do not vanish (Carver *et al.*, 1966*a*). Theoretical consideration requires that CD bands below 185 mμ must also contribute in such a way that $\sum R_i = 0$. Our conclusion differs in this respect from the recent work of Carver *et al.* (1966*a*). They found that the ORD of the helical form agrees with either one of the two solutions, each consisting of three Gaussian dichroic bands. One such solution agreed well with the experimental CD results and, further, the background rotations in this case were essentially non-existent.

The much-studied PGA is known to precipitate at low pH (below 4). To insure complete coil-to-helix transition the pH of the solution must be adjusted sufficiently low to overcome the electrostatic repulsion; complication arises because the molecules may aggregate prior to precipitation (Schuster, 1965; Tomimatsu *et al.*, 1966). This in turn may affect the magnitude of both ORD and CD (Fig. 2). In the transition region (above pH 4·5), the 232–233 mμ trough occurs and its magnitude increases with increasing helical content. At lower pH's, however, the trough shows a slight red shift, about 1 mμ, together with a further increase in the trough magnitude. This small shift could easily escape detection unless the wavelength scale is expanded for better visual inspection, but the results are quite reproducible. Note that the ORD curves in the transition region always intersect at a common point (near 224 mμ). Once the aggregation becomes appreciable, it no longer passes through the same point and its red shift can be unmistakenly located. The corresponding CD spectra also display a distinct red shift of the 222 mμ minimum—about 1 or 2 mμ. The mechanism of aggregation of helical PGA is still not known, but we tend to believe that they might form some ordered, rather than random, aggregates. The 222 mμ minimum is also seen to change more drastically than the 209–210 mμ minimum (J. Y. Cassim, unpublished). If this proves to be a general phenomenon for ordered aggregation, the relative magnitude of the double minima together with the small red shift might provide a means for studying the quaternary structure of proteins. On the other hand, the use of the 233 mμ trough for estimating helical content leaves much to be desired, since we cannot be absolutely certain whether the coil-to-helix transition is complete prior to the occurrence of aggregation. Fortunately, the b_0 of the Moffitt equation in the visible region is only slightly affected by the presence of aggregation (Schuster, 1965; Tomimatsu *et al.*, 1966).

J. Y. Cassim of this laboratory has now extended the ORD and CD measurements of the PGA aggregates to 186 mμ. He observed a similar small red shift of the peak of the Cotton effects from 198·5 to 199·5 mμ in addition to the shift of the trough from 232·5 to 233·5 mμ (Fig. 2). The corresponding CD extrema also display distinctive, albeit small, red shifts from 222·5 to

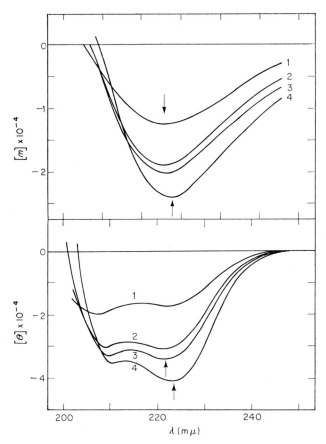

FIG. 2. Mean residue rotation and mean residue ellipticity of poly-L-glutamic acid in water. pH's: 1, 5·12; 2, 4·83; 3, 4·50 and 4, 3·97. Concentrations: 0·10%.

224, 210 to 211, and 191 to 193 mμ. Marked increase in the magnitude of these extrema accompany these shifts; the aggregation–disaggregation process is quite reversible. In the helix–coil transition region all ORD curves also intersect at a wavelength near 191 mμ in addition to that shown near 224 mμ in Fig. 2. The corresponding CD curves intersect near 225 mμ. Once aggregation occurs, the CD curve no longer passes through this "isosbestic" point, although the rapid change of the ellipticity with wavelength makes it less obvious than in the case of ORD curves (see Fig. 2). We have also found, as did Tomimatsu *et al.* (1966), that in dilute salt solutions the ORD and CD of PGA remain essentially constant between pH 4·5 and 4·8, indicating the coil-to-helix transition has reached its plateau.

3. β-Conformation

(a) *Ultraviolet ORD and CD*

The Cotton effects of the β-form have recently received considerable attention. As early as 1957 we knew that the oligomers of γ-benzyl-L-glutamate form intermolecular β-aggregates in solvents of low polarity such as chloroform (Yang & Doty, 1957). The recent unveiling of the three-dimensional structure of lysozyme by X-ray crystallography reinforces the idea that intramolecular as well as intermolecular β-form is a reality, not a speculation. In 1964, E. Iizuka of our laboratory thought that silk fibroin in aqueous solution existed in the cross-β form. Thus, we first investigated the conformation of silk fibroin in water and then in salt solutions. In all cases, the ORD resembled that characteristic of a disordered form such as PGA at neutral pH. On adding dioxane or methanol to the aqueous solution of silk fibroin, however, there was a drastic change in the ORD profile (Fig. 3, Iizuka & Yang, 1966). Instead of a 205 mμ trough for the disordered form (see below), there appears a peak at 205 mμ and a trough at 229–230 mμ. The positions of the troughs and peaks are close to those for an α-helix. At first it was difficult to decide whether this represented a new conformation or whether the overlapping of Cotton effects other than those of the helix caused such spectral shifts. Our work was also handicapped by the lack of CD measurements, which were not taken until the fall of 1965. Unlike the α-helix, the new conformation shows a CD minimum at 218 mμ and a maximum at 197 mμ (Fig. 3). Another difficulty was the time-dependent aggregation of the protein molecules. Although infrared spectra indicated an antiparallel β-form in the mixed solvents (Iizuka & Yang, 1966), these experiments were done in rather concentrated solutions, more than ten times those used in ORD and CD measurements. The question was then whether the β-form also exists in very dilute solutions and, if so, whether it is the cross-β type or intermolecular type or both. Figure 4 shows the reduced mean residue rotation at 229 mμ and reduced viscosity of several silk fibroin solutions as a function of time. The viscosity of a moderately concentrated solution increased rapidly with time, suggesting strong aggregation, but the corresponding specific rotation changed rather gradually. In a very dilute solution, both viscosity and $[m']_{229}$ did not change much with time. Therefore, the β-form does exist even in very dilute solutions where aggregation is not too serious, but the magnitude of the rotation changes with aggregation. Following the "jumping cracker" model of Astbury *et al.* (1959), the polypeptide chains of silk fibroin in mixed solvents are probably folded transversely with glycine-containing bends. They aggregate laterally as well as through additional hydrogen bonds between adjacent bends.

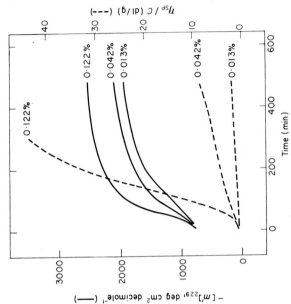

FIG. 4. Time dependence of the β-form of silk fibroin in 1:1 dioxane–water (v/v). Solid line, reduced mean residue rotation at 229 mμ; and broken line, reduced viscosity.

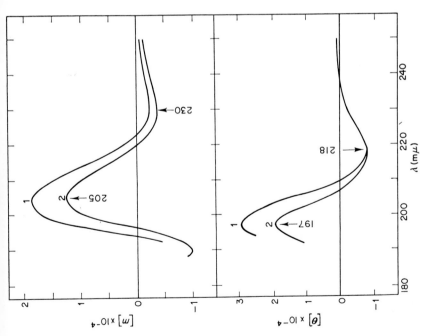

FIG. 3. Mean residue rotation and mean residue ellipticity of the β-form of silk fibroin in methanol–water. Methanol (v/v): 1, 93 %; 2, 50 %. Concentration: 0·15 %.

In the summer of 1965 P. K. Sarkar of our laboratory spent a few months in Professor P. Doty's laboratory, where he studied the Cotton effects of the β-form of poly-L-lysine. This was extremely attractive, since Rosenheck & Doty (1961) had already shown that poly-L-lysine in alkaline pH undergoes an α-to-β transition under mild heating conditions. Furthermore, Holzwarth & Doty (1965) built a circular dichrograph from a spectrophotometer, which can directly test and identify the CD bands of the β-form. Sarkar & Doty's results (1966) are similar to ours on silk fibroin. They were also first to report a negative CD band at 218 mμ for the β-form. In 1965, Davidson et al. (1966) also worked on the α-to-β transition of poly-L-lysine by means of ORD. Later, Townend et al. (1966) again measured the corresponding CD and detected in addition a positive band near 195 mμ which is close to what we found in silk fibroin (197 mμ). Here again, the possible complication due to aggregation must be pointed out. Only very dilute solutions of poly-L-lysine (ca 0·01 %) were used and were heated at pH 12 and at about 50°C for several minutes; moderately concentrated solutions, higher temperatures, or longer period of heating caused aggregation and precipitation.

The β-form of poly-L-lysine is probably of the antiparallel type, as is the case of silk fibroin. Sarkar & Doty (1966) believed it to be the cross-β type; Davidson et al. (1966) thought it to be the intermolecular type. Recent theoretical considerations predict that the Cotton effects of the parallel and antiparallel β-forms should have opposite signs (Pysh, 1966). At present, direct experimental evidence of the parallel type is lacking.

(b) Visible Rotatory Dispersion

Imahori (1960) first found that the visible rotatory dispersion of the β-form also fit the Moffitt equation. Both he and Wada et al. (1961) concluded that the a_0 and b_0 were large positive numbers. This conclusion, however, is no longer true. Silk fibroin in mixed solvents showed a b_0 close to zero, which became more positive when extensive aggregation occurred (Iizuka & Yang, 1966). Usually in the latter case the Moffitt equation can be used only over a narrow range of wavelength, such as 400–600 mμ. On the other hand, both Sarkar & Doty (1966) and Davidson et al. (1966) reported a negative b_0 for the β-form of poly-L-lysine (-150 and -240 respectively). In those non-helical proteins which are believed to contain the β-form, such as γ-globulin and β-lactoglobulin, the b_0 is also close to zero. The Cotton effects as illustrated in Fig. 3 suggest a dextrorotatory contribution in the visible region of the β-form; when the latter is cast into the Moffitt equation, a_0^β would be positive and b_0^β slightly negative. This, however, fails to account for any additional Cotton effects of the β-form that may exist below 190 mμ (data which are at present still unattainable). The possibility of incomplete α-to-β conversion for poly-L-lysine, resulting in a negative b_0, cannot be unequivocally ruled out, even though Davidson *et al.* (1966) found that $[m']_{230}$ reached a plateau after a few minutes of heating. Such a small amount of α-helix, if present, is difficult to detect with present physical methods. It could also be that b_0^β is slightly negative but, in the cases of proteins, the b_0 due to background rotations may be slightly positive, thus leading to a net b_0 close to zero. Thus, the reference value of b_0^β is still very uncertain at present. So far the a_0^β appears to be positive in all cases with one exception. We found that the a_0 of silk fibroin in mixed solvents was more negative than that in aqueous solution. We have no explanation for this "abnormality".

4. Coiled Conformation

(a) *Ultraviolet ORD and CD*

Figure 5 illustrates both the ORD and CD below 250 mμ of PGA in water at pH 7·39. It has a 205 mμ trough, a peak near 190 mμ, and another very small peak and trough between 230 and 240 mμ (top insert). The Cotton effects changed with the addition of salt (Iizuka & Yang, 1965). The corresponding CD displays a strong negative band at 198 mμ and a much smaller positive band at 218 mμ (Holzwarth & Doty, 1965). More recently, Velluz & Legrand's data (1965) show another extremely small negative band near 240 mμ, although they did not mention this (see also Carver *et al.*, 1966*a*). Our results indicate a minimum at 238 mμ for PGA in water (bottom insert). The ratio of the magnitude of the 198, 218 and 238 mμ dichroic bands is roughly 150 : 20 : 1. Also included in Fig. 5 (upper half, dashed line) is the calculated ORD based on the Kronig–Kramers transform. Here again the agreement between experimental and calculated values is good.

Since the CD bands in the present case are more resolvable than the corresponding ORD, we illustrate in Fig. 5 (lower half, dashed line) a hypothetical mixture of 10% helix and 90% coil calculated from the data of PGA in water (assuming a linear model). In relative terms, the 238 mμ minimum of the coiled form shifts toward 230 mμ with a marked increase in its magnitude. Likewise, the 218 mμ maximum is reduced close to zero, whereas the magnitude of the large 198 mμ maximum is reduced by only about 20% with a very small red shift. Thus, the two small dichroic bands may reveal more than the 198 mμ band the formation of any small amount of α-helix, provided of course that no complications arise from the presence of other transitions in this spectral region.

(b) *Visible rotatory dispersion*

The reference compound, PGA in its coiled form, by no means resembles the disordered portion in a protein molecule, which can be very rigid and compact in spite of its lack of any secondary structure. Thus, the rotatory properties of the latter could differ significantly from those shown in Fig. 5,

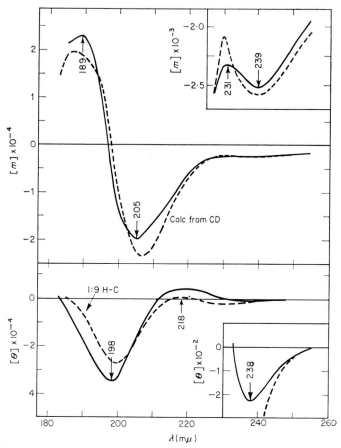

FIG. 5. Mean residue rotation and mean residue ellipticity of the coiled poly-L-glutamic acid in water at pH 7·39. Top dashed line, calculated [m] from [θ] using the Kronig–Kramers transform; bottom dashed line, calculated [θ] of a hypothetic mixture of 1 : 9 helix–coil based on the data in Figs 1 and 5. Concentration: 0·23%.

especially with respect to their magnitude. We have shown previously that the levorotations of PGA in the visible region are reduced gradually with increasing salt concentration (Iizuka & Yang, 1965). We attribute this to the contraction of the polyions in the presence of salts (a contracted coil is less stiff and thereby more free to rotate than its extended counterpart). But the b_0 of the Moffitt equation was found to be relatively insensitive to the solvent composition and close to zero (varying from $+50$ in water to about -50 in 6 M KF or 8 M LiBr), although the corresponding a_0 did change drastically with the salt concentration. An anonymous referee, however, suggested instead that the change in b_0 of about -100 (from water to 6 M KF) represented the formation of about 15% helix. Since infrared spectra and other physical methods are not sensitive enough to detect such a small amount of helical content, if they are present, these alternate interpretations cannot be resolved easily. We are, however, hesitant to take the current ORD analyses too literally and to insist that the estimates of helical content can be better than 5–10%. Likewise, we find it difficult to accept the assumption that the change in solvent environment, such as the use of high salt concentration, would leave unchanged the non-helical b_0 of the disordered form at all. We are now re-investigating the helix–coil transition of several polypeptides by means of both ORD and CD. At this writing we are not ready to provide a definite answer to the above-mentioned alternate interpretations.

5. Some Problems in Estimation of Helical Content

Initially, the direct observation of the 233 mμ trough and 198 mμ peak of the helical conformation appears to be a distinct advantage over the b_0 method (The recent work of Litman & Schellman (1965) on L-3-amino-pyrrolid-2-one and Balasubramanian & Wetlaufer (1966) on diketopiperazines shows distinct trough and peak in the same region as the helices, and thereby clearly suggests that the 233 mμ trough is by no means unique for the helical conformation. The rotatory contributions of such cyclic amides in a protein molecule, if present, seem comparatively small.) The requirement of a small amount of the proteins is an advantage, especially when the sample is scarce. The major obstacle in using the trough for the estimation of helical content is the possible overlapping of Cotton effects due to the non-peptide chromo-phores. The Cotton effects of the aromatic groups and disulfide linkages would not only affect the magnitude of the 233 mμ trough and the 198 mμ peak but could also shift their positions, thus making interpretations difficult, if not impossible. True, these additional Cotton effects will also influence the b_0 in the visible rotatory dispersion. Their drastic changes would occur in the corresponding absorption bands, and so it is not inconceivable that one such Cotton effect happens to have a large dextrorotation near 230 mμ, thus altering significantly the magnitude of the 233 mμ trough of the helical conformation. Similar uncertainties are of course also present in the CD bands, although they have not been widely used in estimation of helical content.

The Moffitt equation assumes that the protein molecule contains only one kind of secondary structure, the α-helix. If the helices and cross-β form or other structures co-exist, the b_0 alone simply cannot provide an answer to their relative amounts. Since the a_0 of the Moffitt equation is also dependent on the amount of secondary structures, we can in principle solve two unknowns by utilizing both parameters. However, the a_0 is very sensitive to the hydrophobic interactions, and the solvent environment; its separation into the helical and residue rotations remains uncertain. (Cassim & Taylor (1965) found that the b_0^{α} varies linearly with refractive index of the solvent used. This complication does not arise when we only study aqueous solutions.) We have already mentioned that the reference values of both a_0^{β} and b_0^{β} are also uncertain, far more so than a_0^{α} and b_0^{α}. Instead, we may ask how much error would have been involved if we had neglected the contribution of the β-form in our treatment. Using the linear model, we can define the experimental b_0 as

$$b_0 = f_{\alpha} b_0^{\alpha} + f_{\beta} b_0^{\beta} + f_c b_0^c \qquad (5)$$

with $(f_{\alpha} + f_{\beta} + f_c) = 1$. It can easily be shown that

$$f_{\alpha} = (b_0^c - b_0)/(b_0^c - b_0^{\alpha}) + f_{\beta}(b_0^{\beta} - b_0^c)/(b_0^c - b_0^{\alpha}) \qquad (6a)$$

or

$$f_{\alpha}(\text{app}) = f_{\alpha} - f_{\beta}(b_0^{\beta} - b_0^c)/(b_0^c - b_0^{\alpha}). \qquad (6b)$$

The first term on the right-hand side of equation (6a) is used currently for estimating the helical content (with b_0^{α} taken as -630 and assuming b_0^c close to zero). If b_0^{β} is zero, the presence of the β-form would not affect the calculated helical content from the experimental b_0. Taking the limits of ± 200 for b_0 (based on current reference values in the literature), we estimate that for every 3 or 4% of β-form present in the protein molecule the $f(\text{app})$ would decrease or increase by 1%, depending on the sign of the b_0. Thus, the current use of the Moffitt equation permits a reasonable estimate of the helical content, even if the molecule contains a moderate amount of the β-form. The helical form would usually dominate the experimental b_0 if the two conformations co-exist. We note that those few proteins believed to contain the β-form usually have non-existent or very low helical content, e.g. γ-globulin and β-lactoglobulin. The uncertainty arises when the helical content is low, for instance, $-b_0$ less than 200. Does this suggest the presence of α-helix or β-form or both? The best procedure seems to be to measure the ORD throughout the entire attainable wavelength range (from 600 to 185 mμ). We have shown in Figs. 1 and 3 and also in Table 1 that the Cotton effects of the helices overshadow those of the β-form. Thus, the observation of a 233 mμ trough would be a strong indication of the presence of the α-helix. The magnitude of the trough also provides a rough estimate of the helical content, although it is less satisfactory than the b_0 method. The CD with a double minimum near 222 and 209–210 mμ provides an additional proof of the existence of the α-helix. Complications arise when Cotton effects of non-peptide chromophores are present. This problem remains to be investigated.

In view of the uncertainties discussed, it is surprising to find that the estimates of helical content in globular proteins so far stand well. It can always be said that any agreement between the ORD method and X-ray results as in the cases of myoglobin and lysozyme is a purely fortuitous coincidence. The fact is that in the middle 1950's ORD suggested (without the benefit of the knowledge of the three-dimensional structure of any protein) that in the majority of globular proteins there was less than 50% helical content. True, "In our view this type of evidence is suggestive, but it falls far short of being conclusive. It leads to a strong presumption that some sort of helical configuration is present, and of a single hand, but as far as we know does not discriminate between the α-helix and other helical configurations of a similar kind which have from time to time been proposed. . . . It may be remarked that there is an encouraging parallelism between the X-ray and optical results. For example, tropomyosin gives a strong 1·5 Å reflection, and is one of the few proteins believed to contain a rather high percentage of α-helix . . .; again, X-ray results suggest that ribonuclease contains an unusually small amount of α-helix or other regularly folded structure, and similarly this protein is put well down the list on the basis of its optical rotation." So stated Crick & Kendrew (1957) in their review on X-ray analysis and protein structure. Since the structures of myoglobin and lysozyme are fully resolved, we are encouraged by the fairly satisfactory estimates of the helical content of the two proteins by ORD. We do not claim that ORD and CD can provide quantitative results as accurate as the X-ray studies in the cases where the latter are applicable. Actually, we are not so interested in the calculations of helical content *per se* by ORD and CD as we are in assessing the relative amounts and changes in the secondary, tertiary, and even quaternary structures of proteins in solution. The ease of operation of ORD and CD also makes them very attractive when studying the kinetics of protein denaturation, for instance. A decade ago we knew little about why protein denaturation is accompanied by an increase in levorotation at the sodium D line. Now we have moved a step forward, albeit small; we can say with some confidence whether such change arises from the disruption of any secondary structure such as the α-helix. ORD for proteins is still being developed and their CD is just beginning. It is simply a concession to reality that we must rely on phenomenological equations in our interpretation of the ORD and CD results. Thus, success must be tempered with caution. But I feel confident that both ORD and CD will play an even more important role than they are playing now in advancing our knowledge of protein conformation, especially since few other physical methods can provide a wealth of information about the conformations of proteins in solution.

ACKNOWLEDGMENT

It is a pleasure to thank Doctors J. Y. Cassim, S. R. Chaudhuri, and E. Iizuka for their stimulating discussions and for providing the experimental data prior to publication. Doctor J. M. Thiery and Professor I. Tinoco, Jr. kindly provided us their computer program. This work was aided by U.S. Public Health Service grants (GM-K3-3441, GM-10880, HE-06285).

REFERENCES

Astbury, W. T., Beighton, E. & Parker, K. D. (1959). *Biochim. biophys. Acta*, **35**, 17.

Balasubramanian, D. & Wetlaufer, D. B. (1966). *J. Am. chem. Soc.* **88**, 3449.

Blout, E. R., Schmier, I. & Simmons, N. S. (1962). *J. Am. chem. Soc.* **84**, 3193.

Carver, J. P., Shechter, E. & Blout, E. R. (1966*a*). *J. Am. chem. Soc.* **88**, 2550.

Carver, J. P., Shechter, E. & Blout, E. R. (1966*b*). *J. Am. chem. Soc.* **88**, 2562.

Cassim, J. Y. & Taylor, E. W. (1965). *Biophys. J.* **5**, 553.

Cohen, C. (1955). *Nature, Lond.* **175**, 129.

Crick, F. H. C. & Kendrew, J. C. (1957). *Adv. Protein Chem.* **12**, 133.

Davidson, B., Tooney, N. & Fasman, G. D. (1966). *Biochem. biophys. Res. Commun.* **23**, 156.

Doty, P. & Yang, J. T. (1956). *J. Am. chem. Soc.* **78**, 478.

Doty, P., Wada, A., Yang, J. T. & Blout, E. R. (1957). *J. Polym. Sci.* **23**, 851.

Fitts, D. D. & Kirkwood, J. G. (1956). *Proc. natn. Acad. Sci., U.S.A.* **42**, 33.

Harrington, W. F., Josephs, D. & Segal, D. M. (1966). *A. Rev. Biochem.* **35**, 595.

Holzwarth, G. M. & Doty, P. (1965). *J. Am. chem. Soc.* **87**, 218.

Iizuka, E. & Yang, J. T. (1965). *Biochemistry, N.Y.* **4**, 1249.

Iizuka, E. & Yang, J. T. (1966). *Proc. natn. Acad. Sci., U.S.A.* **55**, 1175.

Imahori, K. (1960). *Biochim. biophys. Acta*, **37**, 336.

Imahori, K. (1963). *Kobunshi*, **12**, Suppl. 1, 34.

Litman, B. J. & Schellman, J. A. (1965). *J. phys. Chem.*, **69**, 978.

Moffitt, W. (1956). *J. chem. Phys.* **25**, 467.

Moffitt, W. & Yang, J. T. (1956). *Proc. natn. Acad. Sci., U.S.A.* **42**, 596.

Moscowitz, A. (1960). *In* "Optical Rotatory Dispersion", ed. by C. Djerassi, Chap. 12. New York: Wiley.

Pysh, E. (1966). *Proc. natn. Acad. Sci., U.S.A.*, in press.

Rosenheck, K. & Doty, P. (1961). *Proc. natn. Acad. Sci., U.S.A.* **47**, 1775.

Sarkar, P. K. & Doty, P. (1966). *Proc. natn. Acad. Sci., U.S.A.* **55**, 981.

Schuster, T. M. (1965). *Biopolymers*, **3**, 681.

Schechter, E. & Blout, E. R. (1964*a*). *Proc. natn. Acad. Sci., U.S.A.* **51**, 695.

Schechter, E. & Blout, E. R. (1964*b*). *Proc. natn. Acad. Sci., U.S.A.* **51**, 794.

Schechter, E., Carver, J. P. & Blout, E. R. (1964). *Proc. natn. Acad. Sci., U.S.A.* **51**, 1029.

Tomimatsu, Y., Vitello, L. & Gaffield, W. (1966). *Biopolymers*, **4**, 653.

Townend, R., Kumosinski, T. F., Timasheff, S. N., Fasman, G. D. & Davidson, B. (1966). *Biochem. biophys. Res. Commun.* **23**, 163.

Velluz, L. & Legrand, M. (1965). *Angew. Chem.* **4**, 838.

Wada, A., Tsuboi, M. & Konishi, E. (1961). *J. phys. Chem.*, **65**, 1119.

Yamaoka, K. K. (1964). *Biopolymers*, **2**, 219.

Yang, J. T. (1961). *Tetrahedron*, **13**, 143.

Yang, J. T. (1965). *Proc. natn. Acad. Sci., U.S.A.* **53**, 438.

Yang, J. T. (1967). *In* "Poly-α-Amino Acids", ed. by G. D. Fasman. New York: Marcel Dekker.

Yang, J. T. & Doty, P. (1957). *J. Am. chem. Soc.* **79**, 761.

Application of Circular Dichroism and Infrared Spectroscopy to the Conformation of Proteins in Solution

Serge N. Timasheff,[†] H. Susi, Robert Townend,[†] Linda Stevens, Marina J. Gorbunoff[†] and Thomas F. Kumosinski

Eastern Regional Research Laboratory,[‡] Philadelphia, Pennsylvania, U.S.A.

Circular dichroism measurements have been carried out between 185 and 250 mμ on synthetic polypeptides in various conformations: α-helix, antiparallel chain β, disordered, polyproline I, polyproline II. The characteristic bands obtained have been applied to the analysis of protein conformation in aqueous solution. Infrared absorption spectra in the amide I band region have been obtained on polypeptides and proteins in the α-helical, antiparallel chain β- and unordered conformations in H_2O, D_2O, Nujol suspensions and films. Band shifts with changing structure and solvent have been analysed in terms of the Miyazawa–Krimm theory and the results applied to an analysis of protein conformation in solution.

1. Introduction

Spectroscopic techniques have been used over a number of years for examining the conformations of proteins in solution. Recent advances both in theory and instrumentation have made possible a much more critical examination of the solution structure of these complicated biological macromolecules. Thus, while the amount of information obtainable has increased considerably, the limitations of the approach have also become better understood. It would seem, however, that with a number of precautions, a semi-quantitative analysis is possible, at least in some favorable cases.

The theoretical analysis of the amide I and amide II infrared absorption bands of polypeptides by Miyazawa (1960) (also Miyazawa & Blout, 1961), as extended by Krimm (1962), together with the recent complete band assignment of polyglycine (Suzuki *et al.*, 1966), have provided a stronger basis for the correlation of band positions and frequency shifts with probable conformations and conformational changes. In the realm of ultraviolet frequencies, the availability of sensitive recording optical rotatory dispersion (ORD)

---

† Present address: Graduate Department of Biochemistry, Brandeis University, Waltham, Massachusetts 02154.

‡ Eastern Utilization Research and Development Division, Agricultural Research Service, U.S. Department of Agriculture.

173

and circular dichroism (CD) instrumentation with penetration down to 185 mμ has opened to examination the optical rotation bands associated with particular conformations of peptide bonds.

Each of the various spectroscopic techniques is subject to great uncertainty due to band overlaps and shifts; the simultaneous examination of a protein by several such techniques, however, should help to eliminate some of the ambiguities inherent in any single method. On this assumption, we have examined several proteins by optical rotatory dispersion in the visible and ultraviolet regions, ultraviolet circular dichroism and infrared spectroscopy, seeking a quantitatively consistent analysis of all the data. In this approach, three basic structures have been singled out: the α-helix, the β-conformation and the unordered structure. It seems that in at least some proteins a conformational analysis can be carried out as follows. (1) The ORD data between 600 and 300 mμ are corrected for the optical rotation contributions of bands in the 250–310 mμ region, calculated from the corresponding CD spectrum; (2) Moffitt & Yang (1956) a_0 and b_0 parameters are obtained from the corrected data, and analysed in terms of the three structures (Timasheff *et al.*, 1966a), using the corresponding intrinsic a_0 and b_0 parameters as described below; (3) the ORD and CD curves in the region between 185 and 260 mμ are resolved according to the structural contributions calculated in step 2; (4) the ORD curves are calculated from the decomposed CD data and compared with experimental results. The criterion of acceptability of the data analysis consists in the agreement between the calculated and experimental ORD curves, the agreement of the CD and ORD component curves with standard curves obtained with model compounds, and the consistency of the deduced structure with the position of the amide I band in the infrared spectrum. While such an analysis will result perforce in numerical fractions of the various structural components, quite obviously no great significance should be attached to the actual numbers obtained; they can serve, however, as qualitative indicators of the conformational composition of a protein. Such an analysis is therefore of greatest value in assessing the relative amounts of the various structures present in a protein and in rationalizing the changes which occur in protein conformation with changes in environment.

A similar analysis can be carried out using the Schechter & Blout (1964) (Carver *et al.*, 1966b) A_{193} and A_{225} parameters. The two sets of parameters are linearly related; for $\lambda_0 = 212$ mμ,

$$A_{193} = 0 \cdot 51 \, a_0 - 4 \cdot 06 \, b_0$$
$$A_{225} = 0 \cdot 51 \, a_0 + 2 \cdot 97 \, b_0. \tag{1}$$

Therefore, essentially identical results can be expected whether the Schechter–Blout or Moffitt–Yang parameters are used. The b_0 parameter is particularly suitable to the estimation of the helical content, since this parameter is known to be essentially insensitive to non-conformational effects (Tanford *et al.*, 1960; Carver *et al.*, 1966*b*), as is also

$$(A_{193} - A_{225}) = -7 \cdot 03 \, b_0, \text{ at } \lambda_0 = 212 \, m\mu.$$

ORD analyses of antiparallel chain β-structured polypeptides have resulted in zero or very small values of b_0 (Fasman & Blout, 1960; Imahori & Yahara, 1964; Ikeda *et al.*, 1964; Anufrieva *et al.*, 1965). Furthermore, since the b_0 of the unordered conformation is also small, b_0 becomes the parameter of choice for estimating the amount of α-helix. The choice of the a_0 intrinsic parameters is more difficult since this quantity is known to be affected by non-conformational effects, such as solvent and side chain interactions (Tanford *et al.*, 1960; Carver *et al.*, 1966*b*). In the present calculations, a_0 has been varied between 0 and $+360$ for the α-helix, -500 and -690 for the unordered structure and $+400$ and $+700$ for the β-conformation, using in each case the companion b_0 value reported for the particular a_0. The results give a surprisingly consistent qualitative picture. For example, for native β-lactoglobulin A, at pH 2, $a_0 = -140$, $b_0 = -63$ (after correction for the 270–300 mμ Cotton effects); the resulting conformational analysis gives: α-helix, 10–17%; unordered, 45–60%; β, 24–42%. These numbers indicate the type of results that can be expected at present. One can say that, in this protein, there is probably little α-helix, about half unordered and the rest β; furthermore, as will be shown below, the β-conformation is of the antiparallel type. In the following analysis the estimate of the β-conformation has been fixed at the higher value, i.e. 40%, since in the infrared spectrum of this protein the amide I band is dominated by the antiparallel chain β-structure (Timasheff & Susi, 1966).

In what follows, the analysis of β-lactoglobulin will be presented in detail, followed by a summary of results obtained with several other proteins. Since the described applications of circular dichroism and infrared spectroscopy are based on quite recent developments, it seems desirable first to sketch the basis for the analysis of protein conformations in terms of these two techniques.

In our experiments the i.r. spectra were obtained with a Beckman IR7 instrument, the ultraviolet ORD spectra principally with a Cary Model 60 spectropolarimeter, the ORD data in the visible and near ultraviolet region with a Rudolph 200S and a Durrum–Jasco ORD/UV-5 instrument, which was also used to determine the CD spectra.

2. Circular Dichroism

The electronic transitions of the peptide group give rise to a number of spectral bands in the wavelength region below 240 mμ. The strong rotatory power of these bands can be determined either from ORD Cotton effects or from CD absorption bands. While the ORD technique has been widely used with ever increasing success (Carver *et al.*, 1966*a,b*), CD presents the advantage of having relatively narrow positive and negative bands which can be resolved with greater ease than the corresponding infinitely broad ORD bands. The ORD Cotton effects can be calculated band by band from the CD spectrum with the Kronig–Kramers transform (Moffitt & Moscowitz, 1959; Moscowitz, 1960,1962; Beychok & Fasman, 1964). The residue rotation at any given wavelength, λ, $[m']_\lambda$, is related to the ellipticity, $[\theta]_\lambda$, by the relation:

$$[m']_\lambda = \frac{3}{n_\lambda^2+2}\left\{\frac{R_k}{0\cdot696\times10^{-42}}\frac{\lambda_k^0}{\Delta_k^0}\frac{2}{\pi}\left[e^{-x^2}\int_0^x e^{t^2}\,dt - \frac{\Delta_k^\circ}{2(\lambda-\lambda_k^\circ)}\right]\right\} \quad (2)$$

where

$$R_k \approx 0\cdot696\times10^{-42}\sqrt{\pi}[\theta]_k^\circ\frac{\Delta_k^\circ}{\lambda_k^\circ}$$

where $x = (\lambda-\lambda_k^\circ)/\Delta_k^\circ$, λ_0 is the position of the Gaussian kth band, $[\theta]_k^\circ$ is its maximum ellipticity, Δ_k° is the half-width of the band at $[\theta] = [\theta]_k^\circ/e$, R_k is the rotational strength of the band and n_λ is the refractive index of the solution at the given wavelength. The sum of the Cotton effects should result in the experimentally observed ORD spectrum.

Using this approach, the CD spectra of synthetic polypeptides in the α-helical and random conformations have been characterized over the past five years (Holzwarth *et al.*, 1962; Brahms & Spach, 1963; Grosjean & Tari, 1964; Beychok & Fasman, 1964; Holzwarth & Doty, 1965; Velluz & Legrand, 1965; Townend *et al.*, 1966; Sarkar & Doty, 1966) and compared successfully with the corresponding ORD data. More recently, the CD spectrum of the antiparallel pleated sheet β-conformation has been examined in experiments on poly-L-lysine (Townend *et al.*, 1966; Sarkar & Doty, 1966) and silk fibroin (Iizuka & Yang, 1966); the poly-L-lysine spectrum in H_2O at pH 11·7 generates an ORD pattern (Townend *et al.*, 1966) in very good agreement with the experimentally observed one (Davidson *et al.*, 1966). The CD spectra of poly-L-proline in forms I and II and of the collagen triple helix are reported in this paper. The observed and calculated characteristic bands and their intensities are summarized in Table 1, together with the sources of the quoted values. From the several spectra reported so far, it would appear that the CD spectra of polypeptides in the α-helical and unordered (or random) conformations do not vary very seriously with the chemical nature of the side chains and solvents; the 208 mμ α-helix band is the one most sensitive to these variables (Carver *et al.*, 1966*b*). The CD band intensities of the antiparallel chain β-structure, on the other hand, seem to be strongly affected by the polarity of the medium; Iizuka & Yang (1966) have observed that in silk

TABLE 1. Circular dichroism of polypeptides in various conformations

Structure	Band position (mμ)	$[\theta']^a \times 10^{-3}$ (deg cm^2 decimole^{-1})	$R_k \times 10^{-40}$ (erg cm^2 rad)
α-Helix	221–222[b, c, d]	$-30\cdot4^b$; $-30\cdot3^c$	-22^b; $-16\cdot9$; $-18\cdot5^d$
	207[b, c, d]	$-28\cdot5^b$; $-29\cdot2^c$	-29^b; $-13\cdot6^c$; $-12\cdot5^d$
	190–192[b, c, d]	$55\cdot0^b$; $52\cdot5^c$	81^b; $29\cdot7^c$; $38\cdot5^d$
Unordered	238[e]; 235[d]	$-0\cdot2^e$	$-0\cdot05^e$; $-0\cdot15^d$
	217[d, e]	small[b]; $2\cdot4^e$	$0\cdot8^e$; $2\cdot0^d$
	202[b]; 196[e]; 197[d]	$-35\cdot8^b$; $-26\cdot0^e$	$-16\cdot4^e$; $-14\cdot3^d$
Antiparallel-β			
in H$_2$O	217[c, f]	$-14\cdot3^c$; $-16\cdot5^b$	$-10\cdot7^c$
	195[c]	$21\cdot5^c$	$14\cdot1^c$
in SDS or MeOH	217[e, f, g]	$-8\cdot7^e$; $-6\cdot8^f$; $-6\cdot0^g$	$-6\cdot6^e$
	197[e, g]	$29\cdot6^e$; $22\cdot2^g$	$12\cdot1^e$; $24\cdot2^{g, h}$
	190[e]	$15\cdot6^e$	$4\cdot1^e$
theoretical[h]	218; 198; 195	$-$; $+$; $+$	
Parallel-β			
(theoretical)[h]	216; 181	$-$; $+$	-4 to -7; 21–24
Poly-L-proline I	236 (?)[e]	$-4\cdot0^{e, j}$	$-1\cdot7^{e, j}$
in n-propanol[e]	214[e]; 216[i]	$58\cdot0^{e, j}$	$28\cdot4^{e, j}$
	200[e]; 203[i]	$-29\cdot5^{e, j}$	$-18\cdot2^{e, j}$
Poly-L-proline II	221[d, e]; 216[i]	16^d; $12\cdot9^e$	$5\cdot0^d$; $6\cdot5^e$
in H$_2$O	207[d, e]; 202[i]	-40^d; $-34\cdot8^e$	$-33\cdot0^d$; $-32\cdot2^e$
Calfskin collagen	223[e]	$2\cdot1^e$	$0\cdot9^e$
	198[e, i]	$-22\cdot0^e$	$-13\cdot3^e$
	188[i]	$+$	

[a] $[\theta'] = \dfrac{3}{n^2 + 2}[\theta]$.

[b] Holzwarth & Doty (1965).

[c] Townend et al. (1966); the values of R_k reported in this paper were not corrected for refractive index.

[d] Carver et al. (1966a).

[e] This paper.

[f] Sarkar & Doty (1966).

[g] Iizuka & Yang (1966).

[h] Pysh (1966).
Pysh (1967).
Values uncorrected for refractive index.

fibroin the 197 mμ positive peak increased and the 217 mμ negative peak decreased when the polarity of the solvent was changed from 50 to 93% methanol; a similar decrease of the 217 mμ peak was reported by Sarkar & Doty (1966) when poly-L-lysine was caused to assume a β-conformation by dissolving in 0·06 M sodium dodecyl sulfate (SDS) rather than by heating a pH 11–12 aqueous solution to 40–50°C.

The CD spectrum of poly-L-lysine in 0·12 M SDS obtained by us from 185 to 245 mμ is shown in Fig. 1. Again the reported (Sarkar & Doty, 1966) decrease of the 217 mμ band is evident; in addition the absorption in the

195 mμ region has increased, and the 196 mμ band appears to be split into two bands, centered around 190 and 197 mμ. Pysh (1966) has calculated the ultraviolet optical properties of the parallel and antiparallel β-conformations, with the conclusion that the antiparallel form should have ultraviolet (u.v.) absorption and positive CD bands at 195 and 198 mμ. Comparison of the calculated and observed CD band positions seems reasonable in view of both the experimental difficulties encountered at the very low wavelengths and the assumptions inherent in the theory, such as neglect of side chain contributions and solvent effects. Furthermore, the i.r. spectrum of the same sample, shown in Fig. 4, confirms its nature as an antiparallel chain β-form, as will be shown below.   The calculations of Pysh (1966) have also added a new important criterion for distinguishing between parallel and antiparallel pleated sheet β-structures: in the parallel form, the strong positive dichroic band is present at 181 mμ rather than 195–198 mμ.

The ORD spectrum of poly-L-lysine in 0·12 M SDS was calculated from the data of Fig. 1 using the Kronig–Kramers transform (equation 2) and the results are shown in Fig. 1. The three CD bands give rise to two positive and one negative Cotton effects. Their sum is represented by the solid line and is compared with the experimental ORD data of Sarkar & Doty (1966) above 195 mμ, shown by the circles. The agreement is found to be quantitative. Both curves are characterized by a shallow trough at 231 mμ, a peak at 203 mμ and cross-over points at 243, 225 and 194–195 mμ. The calculated curve, in addition, predicts a trough at 187 mμ. It seems significant that the positions of

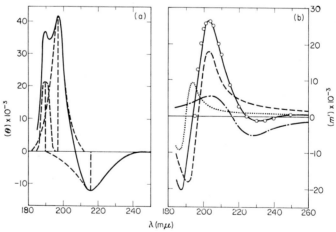

Fig. 1. Circular dichroism of poly-L-lysine at pH 7·8 in 0·12 M SDS. (a) Solid line, experimental curve; broken lines: individual bands. (b) Results of Kronig–Kramers (K–K) transformation showing the three individual Cotton effects and their summation; the circles above 195 mμ are the experimental ORD data of Sarkar & Doty (1966).

both the experimental and the calculated peaks in the presence of SDS have been shifted down by 2–3 mμ from the one observed (Davidson *et al.*, 1966; Sarkar & Doty, 1966) and calculated (Townend *et al.*, 1966) for the same polypeptide in H_2O at pH 11–12, after heating to 50°C.

These observations point to the great caution with which a CD analysis of protein structure must be undertaken. Thus, while the characteristic parameters of the α-helix and random conformation bands do not seem to vary too drastically, both the positions and intensities of antiparallel β-structure bands are a function of the nature of the solvent: in the case of silk fibroin, the intensity of the 197-mμ band increases by 50% between 50 and 93% methanol (Iizuka & Yang, 1966). It can be expected, then, that the antiparallel-β 217-mμ band will be very weak in the highly nonpolar interior of a globular protein, while the 196 mμ band will be strong.

The unordered structure of a protein is more difficult to define. This term embraces a vast variety of conformations present in a structural region devoid of continuous order along the polypeptide chain. Due to steric requirements, however, this structure is limited to a restricted number of possible conformations and can, in approximation, be regarded as a type of conformation with a characteristic CD spectrum; thus, the observed poly-L-lysine (Fig. 2) and calculated polyglutamic acid CD spectra in the unordered form (Carver *et al.*, 1966*a*) are in quite good agreement (Table 1). The CD spectrum of poly-L-lysine at pH 7·8, where it is in the unordered conformation, is shown in Fig 2. It is characterized by a strong negative band at 196 mμ, a weak positive band at 217 mμ, and very weak negative absorption centered at

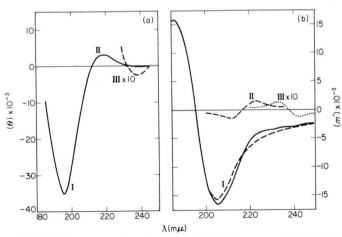

FIG. 2. Circular dichroism of poly-L-lysine at pH 7·8 in water. In (a) the bands are marked I, II, III. (b) ORD curve calculated by the Kronig–Kramers (K–K) transformation, showing the three separate Cotton effects and their summation.

about 238 mμ, and is in good agreement with that reported by Holzwarth and Doty between 205 and 225 mμ. The electron transitions of the first two bands have been discussed before (Holzwarth & Doty, 1965). The weak negative absorption between 230 and 245 mμ is unexpected (Carver *et al.*, 1966*a*) and may be quite likely only the tailing off of the strong negative 196 mμ band (E. S. Pysh, private communication). Kronig–Kramers transformation of the resolved bands results in the ORD spectrum shown on the right-hand side of Fig. 2. This curve is in quite reasonable agreement with those reported for unordered polyglutamic acid (Blout *et al.*, 1962; Yang, 1965; Iizuka & Yang, 1966; Carver *et al.*, 1966*a*). It would appear, then, that the observed ORD and CD curves for polypeptides in the α-helical and unordered conformations might be usable in an analysis of protein spectra. The difference curve between the experimental protein spectrum and the sum of the estimated α-helical and unordered contributions would correspond to the residual conformational and chromophoric side chain spectra. Comparison of the last curve with spectra given by polypeptides in various β or other known conformations in different media could serve to identify the residual structure.

Three other important known conformations are the two types of poly-L-proline helix and the collagen triple helix. The CD spectra of polyproline I and II† between 185 and 250 mμ were determined and are shown in Fig. 3 with the parameters summarized in Table 1. The corresponding data for collagen are shown in Fig. 9 and Table 1. Polyproline I is characterized by a strong positive absorption maximum at 214 mμ and a weaker negative absorption maximum at 198 mμ. Polyproline II gives a pattern with a strong negative absorption peaking at 205 mμ and a weak positive absorption maximal at 230 mμ. It is well known that in any method with overlapping bands, whether it is spectroscopic or moving boundary, when bands are close together, the resulting overlap may distort the apparent contributions of the individual bands and give maxima away from the true centers of the bands. In analysing ORD data for polyproline II, Carver *et al.* (1966*a*) concluded that the corresponding CD spectrum must have a strong negative band at 207 mμ and a weaker positive one at 221 mμ. Their CD measurements on poly-L-proline II between 215 and 260 mμ are indeed essentially identical with ours (Fig. 3) and consistent with their calculated curve. We analysed our data by reflecting the low wavelength side of the spectrum about 207 mμ (shown by the dotted lines in Fig. 3). The difference between this and the experimental data results in a Gaussian positive band at 221 mμ. The positions and rotational strengths of these bands are compared with those calculated by Carver *et al.* (1966*a*) in Table 1 and found to be in reasonable agreement. The CD spectrum of polyproline I was analysed similarly in terms of two strong bands

† This study was carried out in collaboration with Dr. W. F. Harrington.

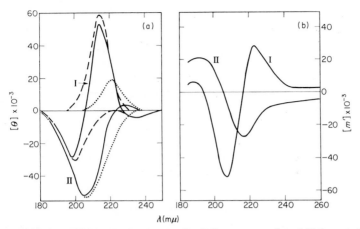

FIG. 3. (a) Circular dichroism of poly-L-proline I (in n-propanol) and II (in water), with the individual bands shown by the dashed and dotted lines. (b) The ORD patterns calculated by Kronig–Kramers transformation (K–K). The calculated residue rotations for form I have not been corrected for refractive index.

and one weak band as listed in Table 1. The positions and magnitudes of the bands were established by reflecting about 200 mμ the low wavelength side of the negative band and about 214 mμ the high wavelength side of the positive absorption. The resolution into bands was considered reasonable when both gave Gaussian shapes (taking the negative absorption above 228 mμ into account) and their sum was exactly the experimentally observed spectrum. Pysh (1967) has predicted theoretically the CD spectra of poly-L-proline. While for both forms of polyproline the positions of the bands are somewhat displaced from the calculated values, their relative energies and relative strengths are in reasonable agreement with theory. The ORD curves, calculated from the CD of both forms, are shown on the right-hand side of Fig. 3. The positions of the peaks, troughs and cross-over points are in excellent agreement with experimental literature values (Blout *et al.*, 1963; Bovey & Hood, 1966; Fasman, 1966; Carver *et al.*, 1966a; W. F. Harrington, & N. V. Rao, unpublished. R. Townend & S. N. Timasheff, unpublished, while the amplitudes of the peaks and troughs are quite consistent with those observed in identical solvents.

Summarizing, it appears that, with a great deal of caution, CD can be used to greater advantage than ORD for the elucidation of polypeptide and protein conformations. The various characteristic structures give rise to sets of positive and negative bands which are distinct in position. In the case of ORD, on the other hand, the trough at 232 mμ, which has been regarded (and is still used frequently) as a criterion for the presence of the α-helix, is also found in the ORD spectrum of the antiparallel chain β-structure (Davidson *et al.*,

1966; Sarkar & Doty, 1966; Iizuka & Yang, 1966). Furthermore, a small trough can also be observed in unordered structures (Yang, 1965; Carver *et al.*, 1966*a*). It is true that the amplitude of this trough varies greatly with conformation; however, the mere fact of its presence cannot be used for diagnostic purposes. The 205 mμ trough, which characterizes a disordered (random) structure, is also found in the ORD spectrum of collagen and poly-proline II; the latter, of course, also has a strong peak at 223 mμ, thus affording a means of distinction between the two conformations. Finally, it should be remembered that two such distinct structures as the collagen triple helix (Blout *et al.*, 1963) and the unordered polypeptide conformation (Blout *et al.*, 1962) give strikingly similar ORD and CD spectra.

3. Infrared Spectroscopy

Infrared spectroscopy in the region of absorption of amide I and amide II bands has been used for many years to investigate the conformation of poly-peptides and fibrous proteins in oriented and unoriented films. The vast amount of accumulated experimental data has made possible an empirical correlation between band positions and conformations.

More recently, a theoretical analysis by Miyazawa (1960) (see also Miyazawa & Blout, 1961) has provided a basis for these correlations. The theory was extended by Krimm in 1962. For ordered polypeptide and protein configurations, vibrational coupling between neighboring peptide groups causes the amide I and amide II bands to split into a number of branches. The frequencies of the strongest branches of amide I bands arising from various configurations is given in Table 2. (The polarization of the bands is omitted, since globular proteins in solution cannot be oriented.) The spectra of native globular proteins, however, are of greatest interest when obtained

TABLE 2. Prominent amide I frequencies for various conformations

Conformation	Solid films[a]	Proteins in H_2O[b]	Proteins in D_2O[b]	Poly-L-lysine D_2O[b]
α-Helix	1650 cm^{-1}	1652	1650	1635
Unordered	1658	1656	1643	1645
Antiparallel-chain β-structure	$\begin{cases} 1632 \text{ (s)} \\ 1685 \text{ (w)} \end{cases}$	1632 (s) 1690 (w)	1632 (s) 1675 (w)	1611 (s) 1680 (w)
Parallel-chain β-structure	(1632)	(1632)	(1632)	
ν_0	1658	1661	1654	1646

[a] From Miyazawa (1960); Miyazawa & Blout (1961); Krimm (1962).
[b] H. Susi, S. N. Timasheff & L. Stevens, unpublished.

in aqueous medium. Such measurements involve serious complications: H_2O has a strong absorption band centered at 1650 cm^{-1} coinciding with the amide I band. In order to circumvent this difficulty, spectra are usually obtained in D_2O which is transparent in this frequency region. Dissolution in D_2O, however, results in deuteration of the peptide group and in corresponding band shifts, as has been observed for synthetic polypeptides (Lenormant et al., 1958; Susuki et al., 1966). A study of polypeptides and three model proteins (myoglobin, α-helix; α_s-casein, unordered; β-lactoglobulin,† β-conformation) in films, Nujol suspension of crystals, D_2O solution and H_2O solution (Timasheff & Susi, 1966; H. Susi, S. N. Timasheff & L. Stevens, unpublished) has made possible amide I band assignments to various conformations in H_2O and D_2O. These are summarized in Table 2. The strongest component of the α-helix band remains invariant in all media; a shift of 15 cm^{-1} toward lower frequencies is observed for the unordered conformation when H_2O is replaced by D_2O (with concomitant deuteration of the peptide groups); a smaller downward shift occurs in the weak component of the amide I band for the antiparallel chain β-structure; the position of the strong component for the antiparallel chain β-band apparently remains unchanged for proteins whether in film, H_2O or D_2O solution. Synthetic polypeptides are not necessarily typical of a given configuration, as shown by the frequencies listed in the last column of Table 2 for poly-L-lysine in D_2O solution. The frequencies observed in H_2O and D_2O solution have been discussed by H. Susi, S. N. Timasheff & L. Stevens, unpublished, in terms of the approach of Miyazawa (1960) and Krimm (1962). The apparent insensitivity of some strong amide I branches to deuteration in the peptide groups is explained by equal but opposite changes of the numerical values of v_0 and the interaction constant D_1'.

Typical amide I bands observed with various conformations in D_2O and H_2O solution are shown in Fig. 4. The i.r. spectrum of poly-L-lysine in $0\cdot12$ M SDS in D_2O is typical for the antiparallel chain β-structure. A strong band is present at 1617 cm^{-1}, a much weaker one at 1680 cm^{-1}. The shift of the strong band to 1617 cm^{-1} (proteins in D_2O: 1632 cm^{-1}; poly-L-lysine in D_2O: 1611 cm^{-1}) in this highly perturbed medium ($\sim 37\%$ w/v non-aqueous) points to the danger of transferring frequency values from one related system to another. In the case of poly-L-lysine, the β-conformation receives additional stabilization energy from hydrophobic side-chain interactions (Davidson et al., 1966). The fact that antiparallel chain β-conformations are not all identical is strikingly evident from the i.r. spectra of aggregating partly denatured proteins; for example, in the methanolic denaturation of β-lactoglobulin, in which the protein is undergoing a native → helical

---

† Infrared spectra of β-lactoglobulin as a film have shown this protein to have much antiparallel chain β-structure; the same is true in H_2O or D_2O.

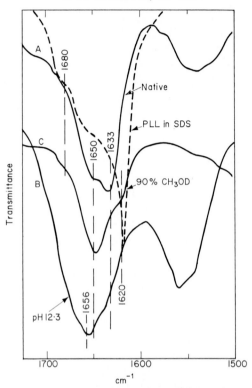

Fig. 4. Infrared spectra of poly-L-lysine and β-lactoglobulin, obtained by differential methods with the help of ordinate scale expansion. Dashed line, poly-L-lysine in 0·12 M SDS in D_2O solution. Solid line, β-lactoglobulin A. Curve A, native β-A in H_2O solution; curve B, alkali denatured β-A in H_2O solution; curve C, CH_3OD denatured in a 90% CH_3OD–10% D_2O mixture.

transition (Tanford *et al.*, 1960; Tanford & De, 1961), a band appears at 1616 cm^{-1} (S. N. Timasheff, H. Susi and L. Stevens, unpublished) at concentrations at which the protein aggregates (H. Inoue & S. N. Timasheff, unpublished), while only a normal 1632 cm^{-1} β-structure band is observed at lower concentrations at which no aggregation occurs; thus, at an intermediate methanol concentration, the i.r. spectrum of this protein contains bands both at 1632 and 1617 cm^{-1}, as well as at 1675 cm^{-1}, indicating the simultaneous presence of two anti-parallel chain β-structures of somewhat different nature.

As an example of protein spectra, the amide I bands of native β-lactoglobulin in H_2O, alkali denatured β-lactoglobulin in H_2O (pH 12·3), and CH_3OD denatured β-lactoglobulin in a CH_3OD–D_2O mixture are shown in Fig. 4. The three patterns have absorption maxima at 1632, 1656 and 1649 cm^{-1} respectively. The weak band at 1616 cm^{-1} in the methanol denatured sample reflects the aggregation mentioned above. The positions of the bands in the three cases are quite consistent with the presence of considerable, or predominant, amounts of antiparallel chain β, unordered, and α-helical structures respectively. While an unequivocal assignment of structures from these spectra is dangerous, the fact that, under identical conditions, the ORD (Timasheff et al., 1966a) and CD (see below) spectra point to the same conclusion renders these interpretations quite plausible. Furthermore, when alkaline denaturation is carried out in D_2O rather than H_2O, the amide I band is shifted to 1643 cm^{-1}, supporting the conclusion that, under these conditions, the protein is predominantly unordered (H. Susi, S. N. Timasheff & L. Stevens, unpublished).

Using the band assignments of Table 2, a number of proteins in D_2O solution and Nujol suspensions have been examined by i.r. spectroscopy in the amide I region. The results for some selected proteins are summarized below and compared with the conclusions drawn from their CD spectra.

4. Conformation of Individual Proteins

(a) β-Lactoglobulin

The i.r. spectra of β-lactoglobulin in three different conformations have been discussed above, while a detailed ORD study has been reported previously (Timasheff et al., 1966a). The CD spectra of β-lactoglobulin A (β-A) in the 185 to 250 mμ (native and various states of denaturation) and 270–310 mμ (native) regions are shown in Figs. 5 and 6. In the peptide group transition region, the spectrum of the native protein is characterized by negative absorption between 245 and 204 mμ, maximal at 216 mμ, with a shoulder at 210 mμ and positive absorption at lower wavelengths with a peak at 193 mμ. While the negative part of the spectrum remains essentially unchanged between pH 1 and 7·5, the positive band shifts slightly toward lower wavelengths between pH 5 and 7·5, where the visible region rotation becomes more negative (Timasheff et al., 1966b); at pH 9·0, the entire spectrum below 215 mμ is displaced to lower wavelengths, while at pH 9·9 the absorption becomes considerably stronger in the negative region, the curve develops a broad maximum between 210 and 215 mμ and the cross-over point shifts down to 199 mμ. These shifts seem to reflect the reversible conformational transition that occurs between pH 6·5 and 10 (Tanford et al., 1959; Tanford & Nozaki, 1959; Tanford & Taggart, 1961; Timasheff et al., 1966b). Above pH 10, β-lactoglobulin undergoes irreversible changes (Pantaloni, 1965). At pH 11, the negative CD band has doubled in intensity from pH 9, and the peak has shifted to 204 mμ, with a marked shoulder at 215 mμ. It is noteworthy that the spectrum of β-A with all disulfide bonds broken by S-sulfonation (Pèchère et al., 1958) is essentially identical with the above pH 11 spectrum of the protein in which the disulfide bridges are presumably still intact. Both the i.r. and ORD spectra of β-A at the same pH indicate the presence of much unordered structure, while the b_0 constant remains unchanged from neutral pH; furthermore, a tyrosine residue (one of four per chain), previously unavailable to chemical modification, becomes reactive with cyanuric fluoride (M. J. Gorbunoff, unpublished). The CD spectrum, after one hour exposure of β-A to pH 13, is strongly negative below 230 mμ; this is consistent with the expected disruption of structure and probable changes in covalent bonds; simultaneously, the i.r. spectrum indicates a predominance of unordered conformation (cf. Fig. 4, pH 12·3) and the a_0 and b_0 constants shift to values close to those observed in 8 M urea (Timasheff *et al.*, 1966a). The disruption of the structure above pH 12 is not instantaneous: in β-B, the CD spectrum changes with time toward one more characteristic of an unordered structure, while the second unavailable tyrosine residue ionizes fully after 1 h at pH 13 (M. J. Gorbunoff, unpublished).

The CD spectrum of β-A in acidic methanol is shown in the inset of Fig. 5. The spectrum is typical of a predominantly α-helical structure. Estimates from

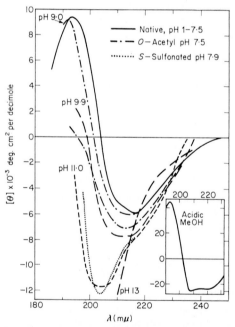

FIG. 5. Circular dichroism of β-lactoglobulin A in the native state and various states of denaturation. Conditions for the individual curves are shown on the figure and discussed in the text.

ORD (Timasheff *et al.*, 1966*a*) and i.r. (S. N. Timasheff, H. Susi and L. Stevens, unpublished) indicate the presence of about 70% α-helix, with the rest being equally divided between antiparallel β and unordered conformations. The observed intensities at 193, 208 and 221 mμ are consistent with such a configurational composition.

The CD spectrum of the native protein was subjected to the three structure analysis described above. Before starting this analysis, however, it was necessary to correct the rotations above 300 mμ for contributions from the Cotton effects between 270 and 310 mμ (Timasheff *et al.*, 1966*b*). This contribution was calculated from the corresponding CD spectrum, which is shown on the top of Fig. 6. The aromatic region CD spectrum of β-A consists

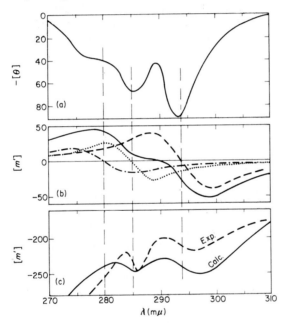

FIG. 6. (a) Circular dichroism of β-lactoglobulin A in the aromatic chromophore region; (b) calculated contribution to ORD; (c) comparison of calculated and experimental ORD curves.

of three principal negative bands at 293, 285 and 280 mμ with ellipticities of −80 to −40 deg cm² decimole⁻¹, i.e. two orders of magnitude smaller than the values associated with the 190–230 mμ bands. There appear to be also some strongly overlapping positive and negative bands below 275 mμ which are evidenced by a generally irreproducible weak, quite noisy, CD spectrum and a noisy ORD pattern between 275 and 260 mμ. The positions of the three principal bands are consistent with a mutually non-random arrangement of tryptophan residues, being at the same wavelengths as CD bands observed in polytryptophan films (R. Townend, S. N. Timasheff & G. D. Fasman, unpublished). The lower wavelength absorption probably reflects order in tyrosine (Beychok & Fasman, 1964) and cystine (Beychok, 1965) residues. Reaction of β-A at pH 7·8 with acetylimidazole results in the blocking of all tyrosine residues (M. J. Gorbunoff, unpublished). The CD spectrum of the derivative, however, is quite similar to that shown in Fig. 6, supporting the conclusion that the observed bands are not caused by tyrosine residues, but rather by tryptophans. The CD spectrum of the derivative below 230 mμ, shown in Fig. 5, shows a change of structure from the native, but still within the region of reversibility.

Kronig–Kramers transformation of the CD spectrum of native β-A between 270 and 310 mμ gave the ORD Cotton effects shown in the middle of Fig. 6; superposition of their sum on the strong background negative rotation stemming from the far ultraviolet bands results in the solid line, shown in the lower part of the figure. This curve is in reasonable agreement with the experimental one, shown by the dotted line. The ORD spectrum appears to consist of either one positive or two negative Cotton effects, while in actuality it is the sum of three; this demonstrates the danger of interpreting aromatic ORD Cotton effects simply by inspection.

It is evident that Cotton effects in the 270–300 mμ region can affect the apparent values of Moffitt–Yang or Shechter–Blout parameters (Fasman *et al.*, 1965; Fasman *et al.*, 1964; Kronman *et al.*, 1965). In the case of β-A, the contribution of the 280, 285 and 293 mμ bands to rotation varies from $-0·9°$ to $-18·0°$ between 578 and 313 mμ. The corresponding uncorrected and corrected rotations are plotted in Fig. 7 in the Moffitt–Yang form. The best straight line drawn through the experimental points at the six highest wavelengths shows a strong deviation at 334 and 313 mμ. Correction of the

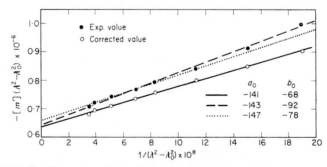

FIG. 7. Moffitt–Yang plot of the ORD of native β-lactoglobulin A between 313 and 578 mμ. ●, Experimental points; ○, same points corrected for contribution from CD bands of Fig. 6. Broken line, best straight line through experimental points; dotted line, best straight line through points at highest six wavelengths; full line, straight line through corrected points.

data point by point for the aromatic bands brings all the points on a straight line. The resulting a_0 and b_0 values for the straight line through the corrected points, the line through the highest wavelength points, and the best straight line through all the uncorrected points are listed on the figure. It is evident that lack of correction affects a_0 much less than b_0; thus, the b_0 values calculated previously for this protein using the last method (Herskovits et al., 1964) are too negative by about 20%. An average of the corrected b_0 values for native β-A gives −60 to −65, leading to the conclusion, discussed above, that this protein contains between 10 and 17% α-helix.

The three-component analysis was carried out as described above with a_0 and b_0 values of −140 and −63. The most likely composition (after comparison with the i.r. spectrum) was chosen as 10% α-helix, 40% antiparallel chain β and 50% unordered structure. (These are the values obtained using the α-helix and unordered conformation intrinsic parameters of poly-L-glutamic acid (Urnes & Doty, 1961) and the β-structure parameters of Ikeda et al. (1964).) Using this composition, the CD and ORD spectra were resolved into components, as shown in Fig. 8. In both ORD and CD, the contributions of the α-helical and unordered conformations were taken as 10 and 50%, respectively, of the corresponding poly-L-lysine spectra (Davidson et al., 1966; Townend et al., 1966; Fig. 2 of this paper). The difference spectra obtained by subtracting 10% α-helix plus 50% unordered from the

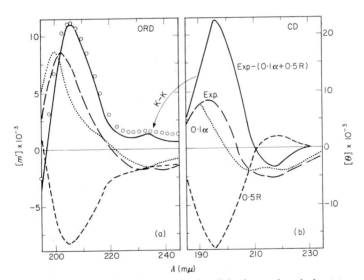

FIG. 8. Resolution of β-lactoglobulin A circular dichroism and optical rotatory dispersion patterns into conformational components, as described in the text. The circles in (a) represent the Kronig–Kramers (K–K) transformation of the solid line in (b) and are to be compared with the solid line in (a).

experimental curves are shown in each case by the solid lines. The CD difference spectrum has a strong positive band, maximal at 196 mμ, and a weak negative band, maximal at 217 mμ, i.e. the same positions as given by the antiparallel β-structure (see Table 1). The rotational strengths of these bands ($9\cdot9 \times 10^{-40}$ and $-1\cdot1 \times 10^{-40}$ erg cm^2 rad) are quite consistent with the location of this structure within the non-polar interior of the globular protein (cf. with Table 1). Kronig–Kramers transformation of the difference CD spectrum results in an ORD pattern almost identical with the experimental difference ORD spectrum. The ORD peak at 206 mμ is typical for an antiparallel β-structure (Blout & Shechter, 1963), while the absence of negative rotation in the 230 mμ region is not surprising in view of the very weak negative rotation found with poly-L-lysine in $0\cdot06$ M SDS (Sarkar & Doty, 1966) to $0\cdot12$ M SDS (Fig. 1) and positive rotation above 245 mμ. The small peak at 233 mμ in the experimental difference spectrum finds an extremely weak counterpart in the calculated curve. This, however, cannot rule out a contribution from aromatic side chain bands in this wavelength region.

The present analysis of the ORD and CD spectra of β-lactoglobulin A in terms of three structures, based on the a_0 and b_0 constants, demonstrates that this approach can be used to identify the presence of β-structure. Variation of the contents of unordered structure by $\pm 15\%$ resulted in difference spectra still consistent with β-structure; the amplitudes, however, of the antiparallel chain β-structure bands were inconsistent with the known intensities of polypeptides in the same conformations, i.e. either both were too low or both were too high. It would seem then that in a favorable case, such as β-lactoglobulin, such a conformational analysis can result in some degree of success; on the basis of these calculations, it seems reasonable to conclude that β-A contains probably a small amount of α-helix, about one-half unordered conformation and the rest antiparallel β-structure.

(b) *Other proteins*

The CD and i.r. spectra of several proteins of different conformation have been examined. The results are summarized in Table 3 and Figs. 9 and 10. These will be discussed in turn.

The CD spectrum of calfskin collagen† in pH 3·5, 0·3 M citrate buffer is shown in Fig. 9(a), and the parameters are summarized in Table 1. It is characterized by a strong negative band at 198 mμ and weak positive absorption at 223 mμ. The ORD spectrum calculated from the CD data has a minimum at 207 mμ and a crossover point at 198 mμ, in good agreement with the values reported by Blout *et al.* (1963). It is quite interesting to note that the collagen triple helix gives CD and ORD spectra very similar to those of the unordered conformation.

† A gift of Dr L. D. Kahn.

TABLE 3. Strongest amide I absorption of various N-deuterated proteins in D$_2$O solution[a]

Protein	Conditions	Frequency (cm^{-1})
Myoglobin	pD 7·0	1650
Lysozyme	6·4	1651 ($\sim$ 1630 shoulder)
β-Lactoglobulin	1–8	1632
	12·3	1643
	90% MeOH	1649
α_s-Casein B	pD 9·4	1643
Phosvitin	3–7·5	1650
Bovine serum albumin	2–6	1649
Bovine carbonic anhydrase	7·4	(1636)
	1·9	(1647)
Insulin	2 (fresh)	1654
Propionyl-CoA carboxylase	7·5	(1654)

[a] Values in parentheses represent preliminary data. Overlapping of different absorption bands can result in apparent absorption maxima which do not represent any single distinct configuration.

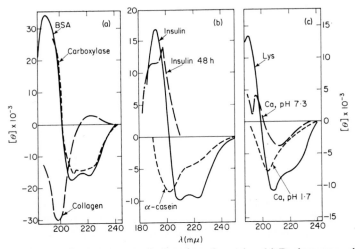

FIG. 9. Circular dichroism spectra of a number of proteins. (a) Bovine serum albumin, pH 5·8, water; collagen, pH 3·5, 0·3 M citrate; propionyl-CoA carboxylase, pH 7·0, 0·1 M tris. (b) α_s-Casein B, pH 7·5, 0·03 M NaF; insulin, pH 2, HCl–water, fresh and after 48 h at room temperature. (c) Lysozyme, pH 5·7, water; bovine carbonic anhydrase in water at pH 7·3 and 1·7.

Phosvitin† is a highly unusual protein in that 78% of its amino acids can
carry a charge; of these 55% are phosphoserines, 17% are cationic, and 6%
are carboxylic; only 10% of the amino acids are hydrophobic (Allerton &
Perlmann, 1965). The dependence of its viscosity and optical rotation on pH
(Jirgensons, 1958a,b) is typical for an unstructured polyelectrolyte. Perlmann
& Allerton (1966) have examined its far ultraviolet ORD behavior. They
found that as the pH's decreased from 7, a deep trough at 205 mμ decreases
in amplitude and a second minimum appears at 232 mμ. The CD spectra at
pH 3·4 and 6·6 are reported in Fig. 10. Both are marked by strong negative

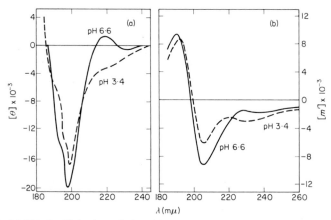

FIG. 10. (a) Circular dichroism of phosvitin at pH 3·4, water–acetic acid and pH 6·6, 0·1
ionic strength phosphate buffer. (b) ORD curves calculated by Kronig–Kramers (K–K)
transformation; solid line, pH 6·6; broken line, pH 3·4, unordered and α-helical.

absorption, maximal at 199 mμ, with reproducible shoulders at 195 mμ (and
190 at 3·4). Above 210 mμ, the pH 6·6 spectrum exhibits a positive band at
214 mμ and a negative band at 233 mμ, just as polypeptides in the unordered
conformation (see Fig. 2). Kronig–Kramers transformation gives an ORD
pattern very similar to the experimentally observed one, including a very
shallow trough at 235 mμ. Since at pH 3·4, the 232 mμ trough could reflect
the presence of either β- or α-helical conformation, the corresponding CD
pattern was examined as a combination of (a) unordered and α-helical, (b)
unordered and antiparallel chain β, using the polylysine curves as standards.
Kronig–Kramers transformation resulted in the ORD patterns shown by the
broken and solid lines of the right-hand side of Fig. 10. It is evident that the
shape of the experimental ORD curve (steep decrease in levorotation between

† This study was carried out in collaboration with Dr G. E. Perlmann and will be
reported in detail elsewhere.

205 and 220 mμ, trough at 232 mμ) is reproduced only if the presence of about 10–15% α-helix is admitted, while β-structure formation does not account for the ORD pattern. Surprisingly, the amide I band in i.r. remained at 1650 cm^{-1} over the pD range studied. This position is inconsistent with the assignment of Table 2 for an unordered structure in D_2O. A possible explanation is that the strong repulsions between the charged side-chains of this protein impose additional constraints on the peptide linkages and cause a displacement in the positions of the corresponding i.r. bands. An alternate interpretation would consist in the assumption that phosvitin has the structure of a collagen-like triple helix; this would be consistent with the CD and ORD spectra, but, in view of the very low proline content (1·5%), it appears to be quite unlikely.

α_s-Casein is another protein which is considered to be unordered (Hipp *et al.*, 1952). The position of its (genetic variant B) amide I band at 1643 cm^{-1} in D_2O and 1656 cm^{-1} in H_2O at pH 9–10, $\Gamma/2 = 0·1$, is consistent with this conclusion. The CD spectrum of the same protein at pH 7 in 0·03 M NaF is shown in Fig. 9(b). The negative band at 201 mμ with a strong shoulder at 220 mμ suggests again an unordered structure, mixed with α-helical or β. This protein, however, is subject to a complex pattern of aggregation (Swaisgood & Timasheff, 1967) and a detailed study of the effect of aggregation on its CD spectrum is in progress.

Insulin, in the native state, has an amide I band in the i.r. at about 1654 cm^{-1} in D_2O, which would be consistent with the predominance of a somewhat constrained α-helical structure. Its CD spectrum at pH 2, shown in Fig. 9(b), has the shape typical for an α-helix with peaks at 192, 209 and 223 mμ; this spectrum remains essentially unchanged up to pH 8·7. The amplitude of the CD bands corresponds to about 25% α-helix, a value consistent with the reported b_0 parameter (Urnes & Doty, 1961; Weil *et al.*, 1965). Furthermore, the amplitude of the 223 mμ band is in excellent agreement with the value found by Beychok (1965). In the case of insulin, however, Lindley & Rowlett (1955) (Lindley, 1955) have shown that, due to constraints imposed by S—S bonds, it is quite possible that insulin contains about 20% left-handed helix. The ORD and CD data would, of course, give only the excess right-handed over left-handed helix. Thus, the CD spectrum is not inconsistent with a helical content of 65% as deduced from the hypochromism of UV absorption near 190 mμ (Rosenheck & Doty, 1961).

After standing for two days at pH 2 and room temperature, the CD spectrum changed to one with positive maxima at 191 and 198 mμ. At acid pH, insulin forms fibrils (Waugh, 1954) which have a cross-β structure (Ambrose & Elliott, 1951). It would appear, then, that the observed transformation of insulin in solution from α-helical to β- conformation is a first step leading to the eventual fibril formation.

Bovine serum albumin (BSA) is considered to have about 50% α-helix (Urnes & Doty, 1961). Its amide I band is centered at 1649 cm^{-1} and the CD spectrum, shown in Fig. 9(a), has bands at 221, 208 and 190 mμ, all characteristic of α-helical conformation, their amplitudes being consistent with 45–50% of that structure. Other predominantly α-helical proteins have been reported to give also typical bimodal CD spectra above 200 mμ and a corresponding band at 191 mμ, e.g. myoglobin (Holzwarth & Doty, 1965) and myosin (Mommaerts, 1966).

The CD spectrum of propionyl-CoA carboxylase † shows a rather complex spectrum below 225 mμ (Fig. 9(a)), with some features characteristic of an α-helix contribution. The position of the amide I band at 1654 cm^{-1} is the same as found with insulin.

Bovine carbonic anhydrase was examined both in the native (pH 7·3) and acid denatured states (pH 1·7). At pH 7·3, the CD spectrum has broad negative absorption, centered at 216 mμ, while below 200 mμ the positive absorption is bimodal with maxima at 196 and about 190 mμ, as shown in Fig. 9(c). The amide I i.r. band is maximal at 1636 cm^{-1} with a shoulder at 1650 cm^{-1}. After acid denaturation this band is shifted to 1647 cm^{-1}, while the CD spectrum consists of a broad negative absorption region between 240 and 190 mμ, quite similar to alkaline denatured β-lactoglobulin. Comparison of these shifts with the ORD data of Rickli *et al.* (1964) and Coleman (1965) on the human enzyme suggests a transition from a native structure which contains considerable amounts of β and unordered components to an acid denatured one which is mostly unordered, with a small amount of α-helix. Such conformational compositions would account for the bimodal positive absorption in CD below 200 mμ in the native enzyme and the lack of positive absorption between 210 and 230 mμ at pH 1·7, as well as being consistent with the positions of the i.r. bands. In the case of carbonic anhydrase, however, particular care has to be exercised in an even semi-quantitative conformational analysis of CD bands because of the strong optical rotational bands related to order in chromophoric side chains (Myers & Edsall, 1965).

The CD spectrum of lysozyme, shown in Fig. 9(c), has negative absorption, maximal at 208 mμ, with a broad shoulder up to 230 mμ, in good agreement with the data reported by Sarkar & Doty (1966) above 200 mμ. Below 199 mμ, the absorption becomes positive and attains a peak at about 190 mμ. The amide I band in i.r. has a maximum at 1650 cm^{-1}, with a shoulder close to 1630 cm^{-1}, in good agreement with Hamaguchi (1964). The results are fully consistent with the known structure of lysozyme (Blake *et al.*, 1965), which consists of about one-third α-helix, 10–15% antiparallel chain β, and the rest of conformations which are grouped together under the general category of unordered.

† A gift from Dr J. Rabinowitz and D. Prescott.

This brief survey of a number of proteins of various structures can serve as an indication of the type of qualitative conformational analysis that may be carried out from a comparison of CD, ORD and i.r. spectra. The next, i.e. semi-quantitative step, must be undertaken only with a great deal of caution and should become more feasible with the availability of more data on standard, well-characterized model compounds.

REFERENCES

Allerton, S. E. & Perlmann, G. E. (1965). *J. biol. Chem.* **240**, 3892.

Ambrose, E. J. & Elliott, A. (1951). *Proc. R. Soc.* **A208**, 75.

Anufrieva, E. V., Bolotina, I. A., Volchek, B. Z., Illarionova, N. G., Kalikhevich, V. I., Korotkina, O. Z., Mitin, Yu. V., Ptitsyn, O. B., Purkina, A. V. & Estin, V. E. (1965). *Biofizika*, **10**, 918.

Beychok, S. (1965). *Proc. natn. Acad. Sci., U.S.A.* **53**, 999.

Beychok, S. & Fasman, G. D. (1964). *Biochemistry*, **3**, 1675.

Blake, C. C. F., Koenig, D. F., Mair, G. A., North, A. C. T., Phillips, D. C. & Sarma, V. R. (1965). *Nature, Lond.* **206**, 757.

Blout, E. R. & Shechter, E. (1963). *Biopolymers*, **1**, 565.

Blout, E. R., Schmier, I. & Simmons, N. S. (1962). *J. Am. chem. Soc.* **84**, 3193.

Blout, E. R., Carver, J. P. & Gross, J. (1963). *J. Am. chem. Soc.* **85**, 644.

Bovey, F. A. & Hood, F. P. (1966). *J. Am. chem. Soc.* **88**, 2326.

Brahms, J. & Spach, G. (1963). *Nature, Lond.* **200**, 72.

Carver, J. P., Shechter, E. & Blout, E. R. (1966*a*). *J. Am. chem. Soc.* **88**, 2550.

Carver, J. P., Shechter, E. & Blout, E. R. (1966*b*). *J. Am. chem. Soc.* **88**, 2562.

Coleman, J. E. (1965). *Biochemistry*, **4**, 2644.

Davidson, B., Tooney, N. & Fasman, G. D. (1966). *Biochem. biophys. Res. Commun.* **23**, 155.

Fasman, G. D. (1966). *Biopolymers*, **4**, 509.

Fasman, G. D. & Blout, E. R. (1960). *J. Am. chem. Soc.* **82**, 2262.

Fasman, G. D., Bodenheimer, E. & Lindblow, C. (1964). *Biochemistry*, **3**, 1665.

Fasman, G. D., Landsberg, M. & Buchwald, M. (1965). *Can. J. Chem.* **43**, 1588.

Grosjean, M. & Tari, M. (1964). *C.r. hebd. Séanc. Acad. Sci., Paris*, **258**, 2034.

Hamaguchi, K. (1964). *J. Biochem. Japan*, **56**, 441.

Herskovits, T. T., Townend, R. & Timasheff, S. N. (1964). *J. Am. chem. Soc.* **86**, 4445.

Hipp, N. J., Groves, M. L., Custer, J. H. and McMeekin, T. L. (1952). *J. Dairy Sci.* **35**, 272.

Holzwarth, G. & Doty, P. (1965). *J. Am. chem. Soc.* **87**, 218.

Holzwarth, G., Gratzer, W. B. & Doty, P. (1962). *J. Am. chem. Soc.* **84**, 3194.

Iizuka, E. & Yang, J. T. (1966). *Proc. natn. Acad. Sci., U.S.A.* **55**, 1175.

Ikeda, S., Maeda, H. & Isemura, T. (1964). *J. molec. Biol.* **10**, 223.

Imahori, K. & Yahara, I. (1964). *Biopolymers, Symp.* **1**, 421.

Jirgensons, B. (1958*a*). *Arch. Biochem. Biophys.* **74**, 57.

Jirgensons, B. (1958*b*) *Arch. Biochem. Biophys.* **74**, 70.

Krimm, S. (1962). *J. molec. Biol.* **4**, 528.

Kronman, M. J., Blum, R. & Holmes, L. G. (1965). *Biochem. biophys. Res. Comm.* **19**, 227.

Lenormant, H., Baudras, A. & Blout, E. R. (1958). *J. Am. chem. Soc.* **80**, 6191.

Lindley, H. (1955). *Biochim. biophys. Acta,* **18,** 194.
Lindley, H. & Rowlett, J. S. (1955). *Biochim. biophys. Acta,* **18,** 183.
Miyazawa, T. (1960). *J. chem. Phys.* **32,** 1647.
Miyazawa, T. & Blout, E. R. (1961). *J. Am. chem. Soc.* **83,** 712.
Moffitt, W. & Moscowitz, A. (1959). *J. chem. Phys.* **30,** 648.
Moffitt, W. & Yang, J. T. (1956). *Proc. natn. Acad. Sci. U.S.A.* **42,** 596.
Mommaerts, W. F. H. M. (1966). *J. molec. Biol.* **15,** 377.
Moscowitz, A. (1960). *In* "Optical Rotatory Dispersion", ed. by C. Djerassi, p. 150. New York: McGraw-Hill.
Moscowitz, A. (1962). *Adv. Chem. Phys.* **4,** 67.
Myers, D. V. & Edsall, J. T. (1965). *Proc. natn. Acad. Sci. U.S.A.* **75,** 4099.
Pantaloni, D. (1965). Doctoral Dissertation, University of Paris.
Pechere, J., Dixon, G. H., Maybury, R. H. & Neurath, H. (1958). *J. biol. Chem.* **233,** 1364.
Perlmann, G. E. & Allerton, S. A. (1966). *Nature, Lond.* **211,** 1089.
Pysh, E. S. (1966). *Proc. natn. Acad. Sci. U.S.A.* **56,** 825.
Pysh, E. S. (1967). *J. molec. Biol.* In press.
Rickli, E. E., Ghazanfar, S. A. A., Gibbons, B. H. & Edsall, J. T. (1964). *J. biol. Chem.* **239,** 1065.
Rosenheck, K. & Doty, P. (1961). *Proc. natn. Acad. Sci. U.S.A.* **47,** 1775.
Sarkar, P. K. & Doty, P. (1966). *Proc. natn. Acad. Sci. U.S.A.* **55,** 981.
Schechter, E. & Blout, E. R. (1964). *Proc. natn. Acad. Sci. U.S.A.* **51,** 695.
Suzuki, S., Iwashita, Y., Shimanouchi, T. & Tsuboi, M. (1966). *Biopolymers,* **4,** 337.
Swaisgood, H. E. & Timasheff, S. N. (1967). *Arch. Biochem. Biophys.* In press.
Tanford, C. & De, P. K. (1961). *J. biol. Chem.* **236,** 1711.
Tanford, C. & Nozaki, Y. (1959). *J. biol. Chem.* **234,** 2874.
Tanford, C. & Taggart, V. G. (1961). *J. Amer. chem. Soc.* **83,** 1634.
Tanford, C., Bunville, L. G. & Nozaki, Y. (1959). *J. Amer. chem. Soc.* **81,** 4032.
Tanford, C., De, P. K. & Taggart, V. (1960). *J. Amer. chem. Soc.* **82,** 6028.
Timasheff, S. N. & Susi, H. (1966). *J. biol. Chem.* **241,** 249.
Timasheff, S. N., Townend, R. & Mescanti, L. (1966*a*). *J. biol. Chem.* **241,** 1863.
Timasheff, S. N., Mescanti, L., Basch, J. J. & Townend, R. (1966*b*). *J. biol. Chem.* **241,** 2496.
Townend, R., Kumosinski, T. F., Timasheff, S. N., Fasman, G. D. & Davidson, B. (1966). *Biochem. biophys. Res. Commun.* **23,** 163.
Urnes, P. & Doty, P. (1961). *Adv. Protein Chem.* **16,** 401.
Velluz, L. & Legrand, M. (1965). *Angew. Chem. int. Ed.* **4,** 838.
Waugh, D. F. (1954). *Adv. Protein Chem.* **9,** 326.
Weil, L., Seibles, T. S. & Herskovits, T. T. (1965). *Arch. Biochem. Biophys.* **111,** 308.
Yang, J. T. (1965). *Proc. natn. Acad. Sci. U.S.A.* **53,** 438.

Optical Activity and Conformation of *Escherichia coli* Ribosomes and Their Constituents

P. K. SARKAR AND JEN TSI YANG

Cardiovascular Research Institute
University of California San Francisco Medical Center
San Francisco, California, U.S.A.

The optical rotatory dispersion (ORD) and circular dichroism (CD) of *Escherichia coli* ribosomes, their subunits, and the constituent RNA and proteins were measured between 350 and 200 mμ. Analyses of the difference ORD and CD spectra between ribosomal subunits and their corresponding RNA moieties suggest that the conformation of the ribosomal protein, at least in the 50 s particle, is partially α-helical (20–25%). Direct analyses of the soluble portion of the whole ribosomal protein by ORD and CD give a similar result. These observations suggest that *E. coli* ribosomal proteins undergo no significant conformational change as they are incorporated in the ribosomes. The CD of ribosomes reveals a new absorption band near 300 mμ; its presence has been found in DNA as well as RNA.

1. Introduction

The organization of RNA and proteins in the ribosomes is one of the important problems in molecular biology. Tissieres *et al.* (1959) demonstrated that ribosomes from *Escherichia coli* are constructed of two basic subunits, the 30 s and the 50 s particles, which in presence of appropriate concentration of Mg^{2+} ions (e.g. above 10^{-4} M) unite to form the biologically active 70 s particle; larger aggregates are formed in the presence of higher concentration of magnesium ions (e.g. 10^{-2} M Mg^{2+}). Both the basic subunits were composed of 63% RNA and 37% proteins.

Electron microscopy (Hall & Slayter, 1959; Huxley & Zubay, 1960) has shown that the 30 s subunit is flat and fits like a lid on the dome-shaped 50 s subunit, to form the biologically active 70 s particle. X-Ray diffraction studies (Zubay & Wilkins, 1960; Klug *et al.*, 1961) indicated that the RNA was largely double helical, and Langridge (1963) found the pattern to fit with that of five double helices of RNA arranged 40–50 Å apart.

It has recently been demonstrated unequivocally (Iwabuchi *et al.*, 1965) that the RNA component of the 50 s particle is a single 23 s RNA molecule and that of the 30 s subunit is a single 16 s molecule. In addition, studies of Waller (1964) and of Leboy *et al.* (1964) have shown that the proteins associated with these two RNA molecules show more than 30 different bands in gel electrophoresis. Recent works from three different laboratories (Hosokawa *et al.*, 1966; Staehlin & Meselson, 1966; Lerman *et al.*, 1966) have indicated that at least some of the binding sites of RNA and the proteins are specific.

We initiated (Sarkar *et al.*, in press) a study of the conformation of ribosomes by optical investigation with the following fundamental questions. (1) What can we learn about the nature of the secondary structure of RNA and proteins from their optical properties? (2) Does the structure of RNA and the proteins in the free state undergo any adaptive alteration when the ribonucleoprotein particles are formed? The answers to these questions were thought to be important in attempting an *in vitro* reconstitution of ribosomes from the constituent RNA and proteins.

The optical rotatory dispersion (ORD) and circular dichroism (CD) of isolated ribosomal subunits (30 s or 50 s), when compared with the rotatory properties of their corresponding RNA components, indicate that the contribution from the protein is much like that containing 20–25 % α-helix. The conformation of the soluble portion of the whole ribosomal protein appears to be very similar, thus indicating the absence of any structural change during the ribosome formation. During studies of CD of ribosomes a new transition near 300 mμ was discovered, which stimulated a reinvestigation of the CD of nucleic acids and this new transition has been found in both DNA and RNA.

2. Materials and Methods

(a) *Preparation and fractionation of ribosomes*

Ribosomes were prepared from a strain of *E. coli* $RNase_{10}^-$ (Gesteland, 1966), obtained from Prof. J. D. Watson's laboratory through the courtesy of Dr M. Capecchi. The method was a slight modification of that of Tissieres *et al.* (1959). Cells were grown at 37°C in a tryptone-broth medium, harvested at the exponential phase, washed with buffer A (0·005 M Tris, 0·004 M Mg^{2+} and 0·1 M KCl), and stored at −20°C. Crude extracts, prepared by alumina grinding and suspending in buffer A, were spun at 10,000 g in a Sorvall table centrifuge. The supernatant was centrifuged at 20,000 rev/min in a Spinco model L ultracentrifuge for 20 min. The supernatant, when spun at 40,000 rev/min for 2½ h, yielded the first pellet of ribosomes. The latter two centrifugation steps were repeated and the final pellet was suspended in a minimum volume of buffer A and dialysed overnight against the same buffer. The ribosomes obtained were stored at −20°C. The yield of ribosomes from 40 g of cells (wet wt) was about 500 mg. Most preparations obtained in this way showed three peaks in the analytical ultracentrifuge (70 s, 50 s and 30 s) in buffer A, and two peaks (50 s and 30 s) after overnight dialysis against buffer B (0·005 M Tris, 0·0005 M Mg^{2+} and 0·1 M KCl). For the separation of 50 s and 30 s particles, a 5–20% linear sucrose density-gradient was used. A typical gradient (27 ml) was loaded with about 20 mg of a mixture of 50 s and 30 s ribosomes and was spun at 22,000 rev/min for 12 h. Fractions collected from the leading edge of the 50 s peak and the trailing edge of the 30 s peak were dialysed exhaustively against buffer B to remove sucrose, and analysed by sedimentation in the ultracentrifuge. Only those fractions which showed a single sharp boundary were used for ORD and CD studies. The quality of the ribosome preparations were assayed routinely by analysing their protein contents. In agreement with the observation of Lerman et al. (1966) the original ribosome pellet obtained always contained some proteins other than the structural proteins of ribosome; the protein content was about $48 \pm 3\%$. Dissociation, however, into 30 s and 50 s subunits, followed by separation in sucrose density-gradients helped removal of some of the additional proteins. The protein content of the 50 s subunits so isolated was $38 \pm 3\%$, but the 30 s subunits still retained some extra proteins bound to the structural ones (protein content $45 \pm 3\%$).

RNA was prepared from ribosomes by treatment with phenol in presence of sodium dodecyl sulfate. In view of the instability of RNA in mildly alkaline environment (Midgley, 1965) an acetate buffer of pH 4·7 was used. The 16 s and the 23 s RNA's were separated on a sucrose density-gradient (5–20%) by spinning for 14 h at 25,000 rev/min. When ORD and CD were to be measured the samples were redialysed against buffer B and their purity checked by ultracentrifugation.

Ribosomal protein was extracted by treatment with acetic acid as described by Waller & Harris (1961). Subsequent treatments were made as reported previously (Sarkar et al., 1967).

Calf thymus DNA and salmon sperm DNA were commercial samples from Worthington Biochemical Corporation, Freehold, New Jersey. Phage DNA was prepared from T2 (kindly supplied by Prof. Michael Chamberlein) by phenol extraction.

(b) Methods

ORD measurements were made with a Cary model 60 instrument at 25°C. A Jasco model ORD/UV/CD-5 was employed for CD measurements. The latter was not equipped with a water-circulation system and the temperature of the experiments varied from 27 to 30°C. Path lengths of the cells were from 1 to 100 mm.

All ORD data are expressed in terms of specific rotation $[\alpha]$. Data from CD are reported in the form of specific ellipticity $[\Psi]$, where $[\Psi] = 330\Delta E/(cl)$, c is the concentration in g/ml, and l is the length in cm. It is related to the more common unit $[\theta]$ (mean residue ellipticity) by the following relationship $[\theta] = [\Psi](M_0/100)$, where M_0 is the mean residue weight.

Sedimentation studies were made with a Model E ultracentrifuge equipped with ultraviolet optics. An Optica spectrophotometer was used to determine the melting curves. Stoppered 1-cm matched cells were used for this purpose. The temperature inside the cells was determined by calibration with a Yellow Spring telethermometer. They were accurate to $\pm 1°C$.

Ribosome concentrations were estimated on the basis of $A_{1\,cm}^{1\%}$ at 260 mμ = 166 (Cannon *et al.*, 1963). DNA and RNA concentrations were determined on the basis of $A_{1\,cm}^{1\%}$ at 260 mμ = 200 and 230 respectively. Protein was estimated by the method of Lowry *et al.* (1952).

3. Results

The ORD and CD of salmon sperm DNA and the mixture of ribosomal RNA (16 s and 23 s) are shown in Fig. 1. The magnitude and location of the troughs and peaks for these two samples, together with those of calf thymus DNA and yeast soluble RNA are presented in Table 1. A new transition with a negative dichroism was found near 297 mμ for RNA and near 310 mμ for DNA. The intensity of this band was very small (about 1/30 of the main positive band at 265 mμ) in RNA and even smaller (about 1/250 of the main positive band at 272 mμ) in DNA. Experiments with T2 DNA of high purity were done to rule out the possibility that the new band in DNA was an artifact due to RNA contamination. With the maximum concentration of the phage DNA that was available (0·027%) the observed dichroism in a 2·5 cm cell was not large enough to confirm its existence, but there were indications of the presence of this band. (For calf thymus and salmon sperm DNA concentrations of over 0·1% had to be used in a 2·5 cm cell to detect the new band.) Apart from this new transition, the results presented here agree well with previously published values of CD of nucleic acids down to 230 mμ (Brahms & Mommaerts, 1964; Brahms, 1965). We have extended the measurements below 230 mμ and have found that both DNA and RNA display another positive band near 222 mμ followed by a negative one near 210 mμ (see Fig. 1 and Table 1). There are indications of the presence of other bands further in the ultraviolet. The current resolution of the absorption bands by CD measurements reveals that the bands at lower wavelengths (below 250 mμ) are closely spaced transitions, the Cotton effects of which, in ORD, are likely to interact. Thus, the use of the first peak in ORD (280–290 mμ) of DNA and RNA in following helix–coil transitions of nucleic acids (Samejima & Yang, 1965) and polynucleotides (Sarkar & Yang, 1965a,b) seems justified.

In agreement with our previous observation on ORD of ribosomes from *E. coli* (Sarkar *et al.*, 1967), and with that of McPhie & Gratzer (1966) on yeast ribosomes, there was no notable difference in the CD of mixtures of

TABLE 1. Parameters of CD and ORD of DNA and RNA

Circular dichroism

Samples	Minimum I		Maximum I		Minimum II		Maximum II		Minimum III	
	λ (mμ)	[Ψ]	λ (mμ)	[Ψ]	λ (mμ)	[Ψ]	λ (mμ)	[Ψ]	λ (mμ)	[Ψ]
Calf thymus DNA	311	− 6	272	+ 2550	245	− 2480	220	+ 1020	~210	~− 500
Salmon sperm DNA	311	− 12	272	+ 2480	247	− 2550	221	+ 1020	~210	~− 500
Yeast soluble RNA	296	− 220	265	+ 5220	233sh[a]	− 550	225	− 390	210	− 4050
(16 s + 23 s) RNA (E. coli)	298	− 231	265	+ 6390	237	− 930	224	+ 400	209	− 4630

Optical rotatory dispersion

Samples	Peak I		Trough I		Peak II		Trough II		Crossovers
	λ (mμ)	[α]	λ (mμ)	[α]	λ (mμ)	[α]	λ (mμ)	[α]	λ (mμ)
Calf thymus DNA[b]	290	+ 1910	257	− 1920	228	+ 3730	216	+ 2830	274, 248
Salmon sperm DNA[b]	290	+ 1930	256	− 2000	228	+ 3920	215	+ 2940	274, 247
Yeast soluble RNA	280	+ 3140	251	− 2770	227	− 160	217	− 1360	264, 212
(16 s + 23 s) RNA (E. coli)	281	+ 3950	252	− 3160	228	+ 380	217	− 1260	264, 232, 223

[a] sh, Shoulder.
[b] Data taken from Samejima & Yang (1965).

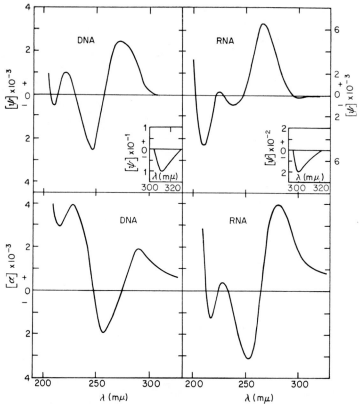

FIG. 1. CD (upper half) and ORD (lower half) of salmon sperm DNA and *E. coli* ribosomal RNA (16 s and 23 s). All solvents are 0·005 M Tris, 0·0005 M Mg^{2+}, and 0·1 M KCl.

70 s, 50 s and 30 s particles and mixtures of 50 s and 30 s particles (Table 2). These results suggest that there is no conformational change when active 70 s ribosomes are formed from the 30 s and the 50 s subunits.

In the CD spectra, the magnitude of the respective bands and the shape of the curves of the individual subunits (30 s or 50 s) were very similar to those of the mixture of ribosomes (Table 2). Slight differences were observed only below 220 mµ, where the mixture of ribosomes tended to show a higher dichroism than the isolated subunits. The superfluous proteins in the mixture of ribosomes may be partly responsible for the discrepancy.

Similar differences were noticed in the ORD pattern of the mixture of ribosomal subunits and those of the individual components. At 233 mµ the specific rotation of the mixtures of subunits was about −2000 whereas that of the 30 s or the 50 s alone was close to −1000 (see Table 2). Furthermore,

TABLE 2. Parameters of CD and ORD of *E. coli* ribosomes and their components

Circular dichroism

Samples	Minimum I λ (mμ)	[Ψ]	Maximum I λ (mμ)	[Ψ]	Minimum II λ (mμ)	[Ψ]	Maximum II λ (mμ)	[Ψ]	Minimum III λ (mμ)	[Ψ]
70 s + 50 s + 30 s ribosomes	296	−150	265	+4240	~225sh[a]	−2090	—	—	209	−6040
50 s + 30 s ribosomes	297	−250	264	+4650	~225sh[a]	−2540	—	—	209	−6770
50 s ribosomes	298	−170	265	+4950	~225sh[a]	−1990	—	—	208	−5490
30 s ribosomes	298	−190	265	+4180	~225sh[a]	−2890	—	—	209	−6240
23 s RNA	298	−250	265	+6820	236	−880	223	+500	209	−5050
16 s RNA	298	−360	265	+6690	238	−620	223	+530	210	−4460
Ribosomal protein	222	−4850	—	—	205	−5820	—	—	—	—

Optical rotatory dispersion

Samples	Peak I λ (mμ)	[α]	Trough I λ (mμ)	[α]	Peak II λ (mμ)	[α]	Trough II λ (mμ)	[α]	[α]₂₃₃	Cross-overs λ (mμ)
70 s + 50 s + 30 s ribosomes[b]	280	+2170	252	−3320	—	—	—	—	−1810	265, 216
50 s + 30 s ribosomes[b]	280	+2810	252	−3300	—	—	—	—	−2040	266, 216
50 s ribosomes	280	+2640	252	−2500	222	+1380	217	+120	−1160	265, 223
30 s ribosomes	280	+2250	252	−2280	222	+400	217	+230	−900	265, 226
23 s RNA	281	+4670	252	−2980	227	+1150	217	−520	+610	264, 236, 221
16 s RNA	281	+4160	252	−3300	227	+680	217	−1130	0	265, 233, 222, 213
Ribosomal protein[b]	—	—	232	−4550	—	—	—	—	—	—

[a] sh, Shoulder.
[b] Data taken from Sarkar *et al.* (1967).

whereas the shoulder at 233 mμ was very prominent in mixtures of ribosomes, it was very weak in the isolated particles. Since the rotation at 233 mμ is related to the secondary structure of proteins, it is reasonable to attribute this additional contribution to the extra protein that is present in the original ribosomes and their mixtures.

The CD and ORD of the isolated 30 s and 50 s subunits and their corresponding 16 s and 23 s RNA samples are shown in Fig. 2. Perhaps the most significant part of the spectrum is that between 240 and 200 mμ; in this wavelength region the isolated ribosomes exhibited a CD profile which indicated the presence of proteins with some ordered conformation. Since the proteins show no dichroism above 250 mμ, this portion of the spectra of the ribosomes approximated that of 63% of their corresponding RNA's. Apart from the differences in the intensities of the bands (see Fig. 2 and Table 2), the incorporation of proteins did not result in any change in the band shape between

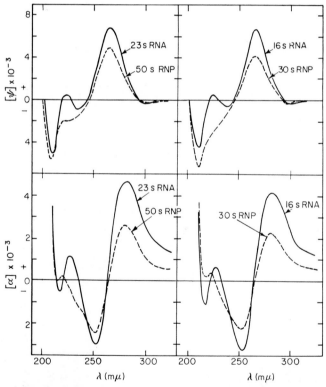

FIG. 2. CD (upper half) and ORD (lower half) of 30 s and 50 s *E. coli* ribosomal subunits with their corresponding RNA moieties. All solvents are 0·005 M Tris, 0·0005 M Mg²⁺ and 0·1 M KCl.

240 and 330 mμ. Below 240 mμ, the differences between ribosomes and RNA became critical. Thus, while the 23 s RNA displayed a positive dichroism ([Ψ] = 500) at about 223 mμ, the corresponding 50 s ribosome subunit exhibited a shoulder with strong negative dichroism ([Ψ] = -2000) at the same wavelength. Since the α-helical polypeptides showed a strong negative band in this region, this was certainly a reflection of the secondary structure of the ribosomal proteins.

The results of the ORD studies of the separated 50 s ribosomal subunit and its corresponding RNA were analogous to those obtained from CD. No negative Cotton effect was observed corresponding to the small negative CD band near 300 mμ. It was presumably masked by the adjacent strong positive band. The peaks and troughs of the Cotton effects occurred in the same wavelength in both ribosomes and RNA until about 250 mμ (see Table 2 and Fig. 2). However, as in CD, the ORD pattern of ribosomes and RNA displayed some important differences below 250 mμ. A shallow shoulder near 230–235 mμ characteristic of right-handed α-helical proteins, was notable in the ribosome curves. The second peak of RNA occurred at 226 mμ, whereas that of ribosomes occurred near 222 mμ, again influenced by the contribution from the proteins. Beyond this, both ribosomes and RNA tended to show another strong positive peak.

Several measurements with 30 s subunit produced inconsistent results both in ORD and in CD, particularly below 250 mμ in ORD and below 220 mμ in CD. The ORD spectra shown in Fig. 2 is an average of four sets of data obtained from samples of different lots with a maximum deviation of $\pm 25\%$ between different samples in the critical wavelength region (below 250 mμ). Similar results were obtained for CD. The spectra shown is an average for three measurements.

The specific rotation of the ribosomal protein was derived from difference spectra by subtracting 63% of the rotatory contributions of the RNA from that of the corresponding ribosome subunit as follows:

$$[\alpha]_{protein} = \frac{[\alpha]_{ribosome} - 0.63\,[\alpha]_{RNA}}{0.37}$$

The specific ellipticity for the protein was computed from the CD spectra in an analogous manner.

The ORD pattern of the 50 s subunit obtained from the difference spectra showed a trough near 233 mμ with a magnitude of about -5000 (Fig. 3). The origin of the minor irregularities in the curve between 260 and 290 mμ is not clear. The proteins are unlikely to show any Cotton effect in this wavelength region unless there is contribution from aromatic amino acid interactions. The results of ORD of the portion of the soluble ribosomal protein from *E. coli* ribosomes (also shown in Fig. 3) did not indicate any such interactions. The rest of the calculated difference ORD spectra mimicked closely that of the experimental curve. If one uses the scale of helix contents of proteins, then using the values of $[\alpha]_{233} = -15,000$ for 100% helix and $[\alpha]_{233} = -2000$ for a randomly-coiled molecule, which were derived from studies with synthetic polypeptides, the result obtained for the protein from the 50 s ribosomal subunit is consistent with about 20–25% helix content. The CD studies provided analogous results. The rotatory contribution of the protein, as obtained from the difference CD spectra of 50 s ribosomal subunit and 23 s RNA (Fig. 3) showed troughs near 225 mμ and near 210 mμ. It should be pointed out that owing to diminished transmittance through the samples, the signal-to-noise ratio was very low below 215 mμ and the data below 215 mμ should be viewed with reservation. Nevertheless, reproducible values could be obtained until 215–220 mμ and repeated measurements with different samples confirmed the presence of a negative band near 220–225 mμ

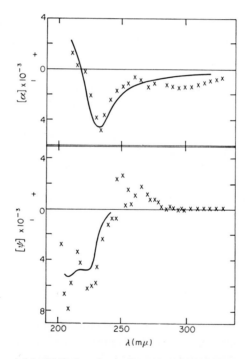

FIG. 3. Experimental (solid line) and calculated (crosses) ORD and CD spectra for the *E. coli* ribosomal protein. The data for the calculated curves are computed from the difference spectra between 50 s ribosome and the 23 s RNA (see Results). The experimental curves are those of the soluble portion of the *E. coli* ribosomal protein extracted from the mixture of ribosomes. The solvent is 0·05 M sodium acetate buffer, pH 4·5. Upper: ORD; lower: CD.

with a magnitude $[\Psi] = -6000$. Recalling (Holzwarth & Doty, 1965) that a randomly coiled protein is expected to show a small positive dichroism between 230 and 210 mμ and that the α-helix displays two strong negative bands at 222 and 208 mμ, and assuming the simple additivity principle, the difference CD spectra also indicates a helix content 20–25% for the 50 s ribosomal protein.

Difference spectra analysis of the protein from the 30 s ribosomes (not shown here) produced a curve very similar to the 50 s protein in CD, but the difference ORD spectrum showed a trough with an $[\Psi]_{233}$ of only -2500. Since the phenomena of ORD and CD are supposed to be complementary from theory, the reason for this apparent discrepancy is not clear. Possible sources of error are (1) the additional protein which was present as contamination in the 30 s ribosomes resulted in larger variation of data between individual samples than in the case of the 50 s ribosomes; (2) the presence of this extra protein was not taken into consideration for calculation of difference spectra. However, as mentioned earlier, reproducible values could be obtained down to about 225 mμ in CD and at this wavelength the difference CD for the protein from the 30 s subunit showed a trough with a magnitude of about -8000 again indicating about 25% α-helix content.

Schlessinger (1960) has reported that the secondary structure of ribosomal RNA is the same in the ribosome as in the free state. His conclusions were based on the fact that both ribosomal RNA and the ribosomes showed the same hyperchromicity on treatment with 8 M urea or on alkaline hydrolysis. The ribosomes used by Schlessinger contained RNase and attempts were not made to compare the secondary structure of RNA in the free state and inside ribosomes by heating experiments. Since the present studies were made with ribosomes with an RNase content of less than 1% of the wild type E. coli (Gesteland, 1966), we tried to make a comparison of the secondary structure of RNA in the ribosomes to that in the free state by studying the melting profiles. Heating to 85°C led to about 45% increase in absorbancy at 260 mμ in both the ribosomal subunits whereas this increase was only about 25% in both 16 s and the 23 s. On cooling back to 25°C, the hyperchromic effect of RNA's was almost completely reversible, whereas in the case of ribosomes there was only about 10% drop in absorbancy. That the hyperchromicity of the ribosomes was not reversed to the same extent as in the RNA's suggests that the RNA inside the ribosomes had been degraded and lost complementarity, presumably by the presence of traces of RNase and other cleavage enzymes (Spahr & Hollingworth, 1961) associated with the ribosomal proteins. It appears therefore that even with ribosomes prepared from this strain, experiments on melting of secondary structure would not permit a comparison of the conformation of RNA in the free state to that when it is a part of the ribosome.

4. Discussion

Recent theoretical calculations of Tinoco (1964) indicate that for any helical polymeric system, the main component of the absorption band, polarized perpendicular to the axis (π–π^* band), with an in-plane moment, is split in its excited state into many closely spaced transitions and the resulting CD curve should produce a peak and a trough with its crossover near the absorption maxima. No component of the absorption band which is polarized parallel to the helical axis with an out-of-plane moment (n–π^* band) was taken into account in these calculations. Several investigators have reported the possibility of existence of an absorption band in nucleic acids near 300 mμ. From a study of polarized absorption spectra of films Rich & Kasha (1960) concluded that such an absorption band, which they assigned to be an n–π^* transition, was present in DNA, RNA and synthetic polynucleotides poly (A+U), poly C, etc. Fresco (1961) and Falk (1964) observed a shoulder in the same wavelength region during their study of the ultraviolet absorption spectrum of nucleic acids. But the existence of such an n–π^* band has remained controversial since Gellert (1961) demonstrated that a closely related double-helical synthetic polynucleotide, copolymer of AT, does not show such an absorption band. Wada (1964) has also questioned its existence in DNA from flow dichroism studies. The CD studies of ribosomes, RNA and DNA reported here merely confirm the existence of the band near 300 mμ. Although its intrinsically low intensity would indicate it to be an n–π^* transition, further investigation of the properties of this band with different polynucleotides and nucleic acids are needed to confirm the assignment.

The solubilization of the total ribosomal protein in mild non-denaturing solvents has been a long-standing problem and has delayed the study of the properties of the ribosomal protein. We tried, therefore, to evaluate the contribution of the protein from the difference spectra of ribosomes and their corresponding RNA moieties and to compare it with the result of the protein that could be obtained in the soluble form.

A critical comparison of the results of the ORD and CD of the 50 s ribosomal subunit with its constituent 23 s RNA indicates that the ribosomal protein from the 50 s particles has a secondary structure (20–25% α-helix) like most globular proteins. Similar results were obtained for the protein from the 30 s ribosomes from the difference CD spectra, but disagreement with ORD and variation between individual measurements left some reservations on the final results which need further experimentation on obtaining 30 s samples free from contaminating proteins. The portion of the whole ribosomal protein that could be solubilized was analysed directly by the above two techniques and the results also indicated the presence of 20–25%

α-helix. This together with the reports (Waller, 1964; Leboy *et al.*, 1964) that the ribosomal proteins isolated from both the 50 s and the 30 s particles are extremely heterogeneous opens up another question as to whether all the ribosomal proteins have similar secondary structure or only a few of them are ordered and the rest are disordered. A recent report (McPhie & Gratzer, 1966) on the ORD of yeast ribosomes and their constituents has two important conclusions. (1) Difference ORD between ribosomes and RNA have indicated that the proteins of yeast ribosomes have contributions like a partial (30%) right-handed α-helix when these proteins are a part of the ribosomal structure. (2) In the isolated state the amount of the protein that could be obtained as a soluble form behaved as a random coil in aqueous solvents. While the results presented here for *E. coli* ribosomes agree with their first observation, they differ with respect to the second. The solubilized yeast ribosomal proteins display no detectable secondary structure in the free state in several solvents (0·05 M sodium acetate, pH 4·5 or 1 M Tris), but the same from *E. coli* ribosomes representing 30–40% of the total protein exhibit a pattern which is consistent with a significant amount of α-helix. This behavior was noticed in several solvents ((a) 0·005 M Tris, 0·1 M KCl and 0·004 M Mg^{2+}, (b) water and (c) 0·05 M sodium acetate pH 4·5) and the conformation was found to be independent of solvent influence (Sarkar *et al.*, in press). Since the amino acid composition of the yeast ribosomal proteins are not significantly different from that of *E. coli* ribosomes such a difference is remarkable and provided the extraction treatment does not denature the proteins irreversibly and the soluble portion of the protein is taken as a representative sample of the total protein, it leads one to conclude that while the yeast ribosomal proteins undergo some conformational change during their incorporation into ribosome (McPhie & Gratzer, 1966), the conformation of the *E. coli* ribosomal proteins does not undergo any such adaptive alterations (present study). In the case of *E. coli* such a situation compares favorably with the idea that the bonds between ribosomal RNA and the ribosomal proteins are likely to be weak bonds (electrostatic or hydrophobic) and at least part of them are specific. The lines of evidence which support this are (1) when ribosomes are exposed to high cesium chloride, part of the ribosomal protein dissociates from the so-called core particles (Hosakawa *et al.*, 1966; Staehlin & Meselson, 1966; Lerman *et al.*, 1966) which, upon removal of the salt, can recombine with RNA to form biologically active ribosomes. (2) Exposure to 1 M Tris dissociates the bonds between ribosomal RNA and ribosomal proteins (Spitnik-Elson, 1962). (3) Current evidence indicates (see the review of Osawa, 1965) that the biogenesis of the ribosomal subunits involves the gradual association of the ribosomal protein to the RNA moieties and during this synthetic process, ribonucleoprotein particles of distinct physical and chemical character as judged by their sedimentation properties and protein contents could be observed under different metabolic conditions.

With the establishment of the presence of a significant amount of secondary structure, the question of definite configurational requirement for ribosome function can be answered with more certainty. The fraction of the protein that bears this secondary structure is still to be identified. It is becoming increasingly clear (Kaji et al., 1966) that different ribosomal proteins are likely to have specific functional roles (binding with aminoacyl-sRNA, binding with mRNA, and other activities related to the synthesis of a peptide chain) and the presence of secondary structure is likely to be helpful in recognizing them and in correlating their structure with their function.

Finally, the results presented here indicate the potential of the techniques for further research. The synthesis of a polypeptide chain involves the presence of a number of ribosomes held together with the mRNA (polysome complex). Helical models of such mRNA–ribosome complexes have been proposed from hydrodynamic studies (Pfuderer et al., 1965). It is not known whether inter-action of ribosomes with sRNA involve any conformational alteration in either counterpart. ORD and CD, being sensitive to conformational changes, might provide an advantageous method to explore and confirm such molecular interactions.

ACKNOWLEDGMENT

It is a pleasure to acknowledge the technical assistance of Miss Barbara Wells. Miss Mary Beth Saffo helped in computing some of the data. This work was supported by USPHS grants HE–06285, GM–10880 and GM–K3–3441.

REFERENCES

Brahms, J. (1965). *J. molec. Biol.* **11**, 785.
Brahms, J. & Mommaerts, W. F. H. M. (1964). *J. molec. Biol.* **10**, 73.
Cannon, M., Krug, R. & Gilbert, W. (1963). *J. molec. Biol.* **7**, 363.
Falk, M. (1964). *J. Am. chem. Soc.* **86**, 1226.
Fresco, J. R. (1961). *Tetrahedron*, **13**, 185.
Gellert, M. (1961). *J. Am. chem. Soc.* **83**, 4661.
Gesteland, R. F. (1966). *J. molec. Biol.* **16**, 67.
Hall, C. E. & Slayter, H. S. (1959). *J. molec. Biol.* **1**, 329.
Holzwarth, G. & Doty, P. (1965). *J. Am. chem. Soc.* **87**, 218.
Hosokawa, K., Fujimura, R. K. & Nomura, M. (1966). *Proc. natn. Acad. Sci. U.S.A.* **55**, 198.
Huxley, H. E. & Zubay, G. (1960). *J. molec. Biol.* **2**, 10.
Iwabuchi, M., Kono, M., Oumi, T. & Osawa, S. (1965). *Biochim. biophys. Acta*, **108**, 211.
Kaji, H., Suzuka, I. & Kaji, A. (1966). *J. molec. Biol.* **18**, 219.
Klug, A., Holmes, K. C. & Finch, J. T. (1961). *J. molec. Biol.* **3**, 87.
Langridge, R. (1963). *Science, N.Y.* **140**, 1000.
Leboy, P. S., Cox, E. C. & Flaks, J. G. (1964). *Proc. natn. Acad. Sci. U.S.A.* **52**, 1367.

Lerman, M. I., Spinin, A. S., Gavrilova, L. P. & Golov, V. F. (1966). *J. molec. Biol.* **15**, 268.

Lowry, O. H., Rosebrough, N. J., Farr, L. A. & Randall, R. J. (1952). *J. biol. Chem.* **193**, 265.

McPhie, P. & Gratzer, W. B. (1966). *Biochemistry*, **5**, 1310.

Midgley, J. E. M. (1965). *Biochim. biophys. Acta*, **108**, 348.

Osawa, S. (1965). *Progr. Nucleic Acid Res.* **4**, 161.

Pfuderer, P., Cammarano, P., Holladay, D. & Novelli, G. (1965). *Biochim. biophys. Acta*, **109**, 595.

Rich, A. & Kasha, M. (1960). *J. Am. chem. Soc.* **82**, 6196.

Samejima, T. & Yang, J. T. (1965). *J. biol. Chem.* **240**, 2094.

Sarkar, P. K. & Yang, J. T. (1965*a*). *J. biol. Chem.* **240**, 2088.

Sarkar, P. K. & Yang, J. T. (1965*b*). *Biochemistry*, **4**, 1238.

Sarkar, P. K., Yang, J. T. & Doty, P. (1967). *Biopolymers*, in press.

Schlessinger, D. (1960). *J. molec. Biol.* **16**, 67.

Spahr, P. F. & Hollingworth, B. R. (1961). *J. biol. Chem.* **236**, 823.

Spitnik-Elson, P. (1962). *Biochim. biophys. Acta*, **55**, 741.

Staehlin, T. & Meselson, M. (1966). *J. molec. Biol.* **16**, 245.

Tinoco, I., Jr. (1964). *J. Am. chem. Soc.* **86**, 297.

Tissieres, A., Watson, J. D., Schlessinger, D. & Hollingworth, B. R. (1959). *J. molec. Biol.* **1**, 221.

Wada, A. (1964). "Biopolymers Symposia", No. 1, p. 476.

Waller, J. P. (1964). *J. molec. Biol.* **10**, 319.

Waller, J. P. & Harris, J. I. (1961). *Proc. natn. Acad. Sci. U.S.A.* **47**, 18.

Zubay, G. & Wilkins, M. H. F. (1960). *J. molec. Biol.* **2**, 105.

PROTEINS AND POLYPEPTIDES

C. Chemical Studies

Intramolecular Cross-Linking of the Sulphydryl Groups of Reduced Ribonuclease by Mercuric Ions

Izchak Z. Steinberg and Ruth Sperling

Department of Chemical Physics, Weizmann Institute of Science
Rehovoth, Israel

Potentiometric, amperometric and spectrophotometric titrations as well as polaro-graphic studies have shown that fully-reduced bovine pancreatic ribonuclease reacts with mercuric ions in a 1 : 4 molar ratio. The S—Hg—S bonds thus formed do not react further with excess mercuric ions. Intermolecular cross-linking of the sulphydryl groups in the reduced protein upon reaction with mercuric ions was considerably diminished when the reactant concentrations were low. Small amounts of p-mercuribenzoate in the reaction medium were found to influence the properties of the products obtained, presumably by facilitating interchange between bridged sulphydryl groups. Tetramercury derivatives of ribonuclease prepared in the presence of p-mercuribenzoate have about two abnormal tyrosine residues per molecule and cross-react with antiserum to ribonuclease. It was therefore concluded that the macromolecular conformation of the tetramercury-ribonuclease thus prepared resembles, partially, the conformation of native ribonuclease.

1. Introduction

Internal disulphide cross-linkages have been shown to be essential for maintaining the three-dimensional molecular configuration of many native proteins and to be, therefore, of prime importance for their biological activity. Thus, the rupture of the disulphide bonds in pancreatic ribonuclease (Sela *et al.*, 1957; Anfinsen & Haber, 1961), lysozyme (Imai *et al.*, 1963; Epstein & Goldberger, 1963), trypsin (Liener, 1957; Epstein & Anfinsen, 1962*a,b*), Taka-amylase A (Isemura *et al.*, 1963), and other enzymes (e.g. by chemical reduction or oxidation) brings about complete loss of their catalytic activity. Cleavage of disulphide bonds in immunoglobulins abolishes their activity both as antigens and as antibodies (Haber, 1964; Whitney & Tanford, 1965; Lummus & Cebra, 1965; Freedman & Sela, 1966). Furthermore, the extensive physical-chemical studies which were performed on ribonuclease and lysozyme have shown that the molecules obtained after cleavage of the disulphide linkages possess, in solution, a configuration which is different from that of the native molecules (Harrington & Schellman, 1956; Harrington & Sela, 1959; Goldberger & Epstein, 1963). Similar results were obtained with other proteins. The intramolecular disulphide bridges may influence the stability of a given configuration of the polypeptide chain in two opposing ways

(Kauzmann, 1959a). On the one hand, the steric constraints imposed on the molecule by the internal cross-linkages may prevent the molecule from folding into a configuration which would otherwise have been stable. On the other hand, if some ordered configuration happens to be sterically compatible with the spatial arrangement of the cross-linkages in the molecule, then the internal bridges will tend to stabilize this configuration by making the random coil form of the chain less favourable. This is due to the fact that the cross-linkages reduce the total number of configurations available to the random coil form, thus reducing its entropy (Schellman, 1955; Kauzmann, 1959b). The disulphide bridges can thus exclude some folded forms and favour others, depending on the positions of the cross-linking points along the chain and on the primary structure of the protein.

Following the pioneering work of Sela et al. (1957) on ribonuclease, evidence has been accumulating over the past few years to indicate that by reoxidation of the protein molecules in which the disulphide bonds have been reduced, biological activity and native macromolecular configuration may be recovered. Bovine pancreatic ribonuclease (Sela et al., 1957; White, 1960,1961; Anfinsen & Haber, 1961), egg-white lysozyme (Isemura et al., 1961; White, 1962; Epstein & Goldberger, 1963; Imai et al., 1963), Taka-amylase A (Isemura et al., 1961,1963), pepsinogen (Frattali et al., 1963), alkaline phosphatase (Levinthal et al., 1962), trypsin (Epstein & Anfinsen, 1962a,b), insulin (Du et al., 1965), and γ-globulins (Haber, 1964; Whitney & Tanford, 1965; Lummus & Cebra, 1965; Freedman & Sela, 1966) are examples. In all the cases in which disulphide bond reformation was studied, the proteins investigated contained more than two cysteine residues per molecule; there were thus in principle numerous ways in which the sulphur atoms could be paired (Sela & Lifson, 1959; Kauzmann, 1959b). The fact that pairing is actually far from being random points to the existence of quite specific intramolecular interactions which favour the native configuration. Side chain interactions, backbone interactions and interactions with the solvent are probably involved in determining the proper S—S pairing (Scheraga & Rupley, 1962). It has even been suggested by some authors that owing to these intramolecular non-covalent bonds the reduced protein chain has marked preference for a configuration, or configurations, which resemble the native one, and that the function of the intrachain disulphide bonds may be to confer additional stability on this configuration (Anfinsen, 1964; Cecil, 1963).

In order to shed more light on the role of the internal cross-linkages in maintaining the three-dimensional configuration of native proteins, it seemed desirable to investigate how stringent are the requirements on the dimensions and nature of these linkages. In the following we report the results of attempts to lengthen the internal S—S bridges of bovine pancreatic ribonuclease by reaction of the fully reduced protein with a bifunctional reagent that binds to sulphydryl groups. Mercuric ion was selected as the bifunctional reagent. Various considerations favoured this choice: (a) Hg^{2+} shows a highly preferential affinity for sulphydryl groups which is much stronger than for any other group present in proteins (Edelhoch *et al.*, 1953; Gurd & Wilcox, 1956; Boyer, 1959). Specific binding to the sulphur atoms will thus result. (b) The bonding between sulphur and mercuric ions though very strong is also reversible (Edelhoch *et al.*, 1953). Interchanges between the various sulphur–mercury bonds can thus be brought about, which will ensure that the final protein derivatives will be the most stable ones thermodynamically. Such "annealing" processes were observed in the reoxidation of reduced ribonuclease, and resulted in the regeneration of the native configuration of the enzyme after prior formation of incorrectly paired structures (Anfinsen *et al.*, 1961; Haber & Anfinsen, 1962). (c) Hg is of relatively small dimensions, having a covalent radius of 1.29 Å and a crystal radius of 1.10 Å (Pauling, 1960). Furthermore, the two covalent bonds that the mercury atom forms are linear. Its introduction into the protein molecule should therefore distort the molecular configuration minimally. On the other hand, numerous compounds of the type $(Hg—R—Hg)^{2+}$, where R is an organic group, are known and can be used to bridge the sulphydryl groups. By using these reagents the extent of distortion of the macromolecular structure may be varied and studied. (d) The reaction between mercuric ions and sulphydryl groups is fast and proceeds under mild conditions (see, for example, Cecil, 1955), which presents certain technical advantages over slowly reacting reagents. (e) Crystals of the heavy metal derivatives of the protein, if successfully prepared, may provide suitable material for X-ray studies of the protein conformation by the method of isomorphous replacement.

In the following, some studies on the reaction between mercuric ions and sulphydryl compounds, including reduced ribonuclease, are described (Section 2). The application of these results to the preparation of ribonuclease derivatives in which the –S—S– bonds have been replaced by –S—Hg—S– bridges is then reported (Section 3). Finally, a few experiments are described which demonstrate some similarities in the properties of a mercurated ribonuclease derivative and of native ribonuclease (Section 4).

2. Some Studies on the Interaction Between Reduced Ribonuclease and Mercuric Ions

Compounds containing sulphydryl groups are known to have a very high affinity for mercuric ions (Cecil, 1963; Edelhoch *et al.*, 1953). The following reactions will be of special interest to us:

$$2RSH + Hg^{2+} \rightleftarrows RS—Hg—SR + 2H^+ \tag{1}$$

$$RS—Hg—SR + Hg^{2+} \rightleftarrows 2(RS—Hg^+) \tag{2}$$

where R is the organic radical of the sulphydryl compound. It may be noted that Hg^{2+} and $RS—Hg^+$ will usually be in the form of complexes with halide ions, uncharged amino groups, etc., present in solution. Some authors prefer to write the $RS—Hg^+$ compounds in the form $(RS)_2Hg_2$ (Kolthoff et al., 1954). The affinity of mercuric ions for sulphydryl groups, reaction (1), is extremely high; the equilibrium constant for the interaction of Hg^{2+} and RS^-, $K = [(RS)_2Hg]/[RS^-]^2[Hg^{2+}]$, is of the order of 10^{40}–10^{43} for low molecular weight compounds (Stricks & Kolthoff, 1953). The equilibrium constant for reaction (2), $K = [RS—Hg^+]^2/[(RS)_2Hg][Hg^{2+}]$, is of the order of 10^7 in the case of mercury binding to human and bovine mercaptalbumin (Edelhoch et al., 1953; Kay & Edsall, 1956). It may, however, have much lower values for other systems (Edsall et al., 1954). In proteins marked modifications of the reactivity of –SH groups may of course occur. The following experiments show that fully reduced bovine pancreatic ribonuclease does bind strongly four mercuric ions per molecule of protein.

(a) Potentiometric titrations

Figure 1 illustrates the potentiometric titration of reduced ribonuclease with mercuric chloride, using a gold amalgam-saturated calomel electrode pair. As can be seen, there is a very sharp end-point in the titration curve when exactly four mercuric ions have been added per protein molecule, with a concomitant jump in potential of about 200 millivolts. Identical potentio-

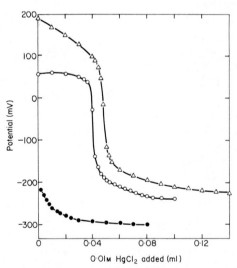

FIG. 1. Potentiometric titration of reduced bovine pancreatic ribonuclease with mercuric chloride. Amount of protein titrated: 0·1 μmoles (○). For comparison, the titration with mercuric chloride of 0·96 μmoles of L-cysteine (△) and 0·077 μmoles of native ribonuclease (●). All titrations were carried out with a gold amalgam-saturated calomel electrode pair at 23°C in 1·0 ml of aqueous 0·1 M acetic acid (pH 3·0).

metric titration curves were obtained when the gold amalgam electrode was replaced by a dropping mercury electrode. In the same figure, the titration of native ribonuclease with mercuric chloride is also presented, and no uptake of mercuric ions by the native molecules is observed. Obviously, during the titration of the reduced protein with mercuric chloride the mercuric ions bind to the sulphydryl groups present in this material.

It is pertinent to note that before the end-point corresponding to addition of $4\,Hg^{2+}$ per protein molecule is reached, the titration curve is quite smooth. The various sulphydryl groups of the reduced protein apparently do not differ enough in reactivity to exhibit separate end-points in the titration curve. It may also be noted that no second end-point is observed when the molar ratio of Hg^{2+} to protein reaches a value $8:1$. Unfortunately, this cannot be taken as proof that reaction (2) does not take place with reduced ribonuclease since also cysteine, with which this reaction does take place (Kolthoff *et al.*, 1954), does not show under the same conditions a pronounced end-point corresponding to reaction (2) (Fig. 1; see also Cecil, 1955).

(b) *Polarography*

Kolthoff *et al.* (1954) demonstrated that at a rotating platinum electrode Hg^{2+} yielded a polarographic cathodic wave which started at about $+0\cdot1$ V (relative to a saturated calomel electrode), the diffusion current being proportional to the mercuric ion concentration. They also showed that in solutions containing a mercuric salt and glutathion (pH 5·6) no appreciable current was observed between $+0\cdot2$ and $-0\cdot2$ V if the mole ratio of mercury to peptide was $1:2$ or smaller. The cathodic wave starting at $-0\cdot2$ V was due to the reduction of mercury in the $(RS)_2Hg$ compound. Upon addition of mercuric salt to $(RS)_2Hg$ this wave became drawn out, starting at a more positive potential, and its height increased. This was due to the formation of $RS—Hg^+$. When the molar ratio of mercury to peptide was in excess of $1:1$, the free mercury wave was observed.

In Fig. 2, polarograms of solutions containing reduced ribonuclease and mercuric chloride in various proportions are reproduced. When the number of mercuric ions per protein molecule is less than $4:1$ the only mercury compound that can be detected in the polarograms is of the type $RS—Hg—SR$. When the molar ratio of mercuric chloride to protein is greater than $4:1$, the wave characteristic of mercuric ions starts to appear. It should be noted that the formation of compounds of the type $RS—Hg^+$ on addition of mercuric chloride in excess of the $4:1$ molar ratio is not observed. This is an indication that reaction (2) does not tend to take place in the case of reduced ribonuclease. Possibly the structure $RS—Hg—SR$ is stabilized by side chain and backbone interactions of the protein molecule.

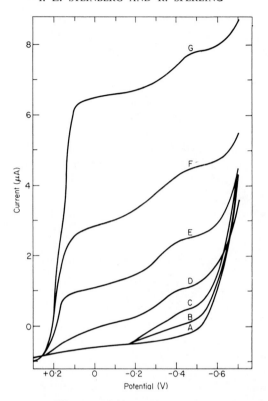

FIG. 2. Polarograms at 23°C of solutions containing reduced ribonuclease and various amounts of mercuric chloride. Amount of protein, 0·102 μmoles; amounts of mercuric chloride: 0·12 μmoles (curve A); 0·24 μmoles (curve B); 0·40 μmoles (curve C); 0·48 μmoles (curve D); 0·64 μmoles (curve E); 0·80 μmoles (curve F); and 1·12 μmoles (curve G). Materials were dissolved in 25 ml. of aqueous 0·1 M acetic acid (pH 3·0). A rotating platinum electrode was used and electrode potentials were measured against a saturated calomel electrode.

(c) Amperometric titrations

The diffusion current at a rotating platinum electrode was recorded on addition of increasing amounts of mercuric chloride to a solution of reduced ribonuclease at constant applied voltage relative to a saturated calomel electrode. Figure 3 illustrates the results for 0·0, −0·2 and −0·4 V. In the first case (graph A) the voltage is too low for compounds of type RS—Hg—SR to react at the platinum electrode. Indeed, no diffusion current is detected when the molar ratio of Hg^{2+} to protein is less than 4 : 1. When this molar ratio exceeds 4 : 1 a diffusion current is indicated which varies linearly with the amount of mercuric chloride added to the solution. Since compounds of the type RS—Hg$^+$ should not be reduced at this voltage (Kolthoff et al.,

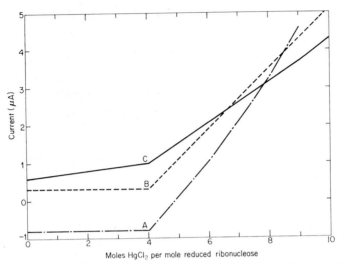

FIG. 3. Amperometric titrations at 23°C of reduced ribonuclease with mercuric chloride at various applied voltages. Curve A, 0·0 V; protein concentration: 3·95 μM. Curve B, −0·2 V; protein concentration: 4·50 μM. Curve C, −0·4 V; protein concentration: 1·98 μM. Titrations were carried out in 25 ml of aqueous 0·1 M acetic acid (pH 3·0). A rotating platinum electrode was used and potentials were measured against a saturated calomel electrode. In the absence of protein, the diffusion current varied linearly with mercuric chloride concentration; the slope was 0·93 μA/μM at an electrode potential of −0·2 V.

1954), it is evident that four mercuric ions react with one reduced ribonuclease molecule and that excess mercuric ion is not converted into a compound of type RS—Hg$^+$. In the amperometric titration at −0·2 V (graph B) only one end-point is observed, at a molar ratio of mercury to protein of 4 : 1. Again, since no second end-point is observed on further addition of mercuric chloride, it may be concluded that a compound of type RS—Hg$^+$ is not formed with reduced ribonuclease. At −0·4 V (graph C), both Hg^{2+} and RS—Hg—SR compounds show electrode reactions. Obviously, in the case of reduced ribonuclease these two types of compounds possess markedly different diffusion coefficients and a clear-cut break is observed in the graph when [Hg^{2+}] : [ribonuclease] = 4 : 1. Also at this voltage no second end-point is observed.

(d) *Spectrophotometric studies*

Marked changes occur in the light absorption spectra of sulphydryl groups when they bind mercuric ions. Some studies on the spectra of low molecular weight model compounds, cysteine and its mercurated derivatives, are presented below, since they have proven to be useful in the study of the interaction between mercuric ions and reduced ribonuclease. These studies may also help in explaining the absorption spectra of mercurated proteins.

Figure 4 presents the absorption spectra of cysteine, cystine and mixtures of Hg^{2+} and cysteine in a 1 : 2 molar ratio and in a 1 : 1 molar ratio. At pH 3·0, cysteine hardly absorbs light above 260 mμ. Cystine shows a pronounced absorption band extending into longer wave lengths with a maximum at 245 mμ and a minimum at 231 mμ. A mixture of mercuric chloride and cysteine in a molar ratio of 1 : 2, presumably yielding an

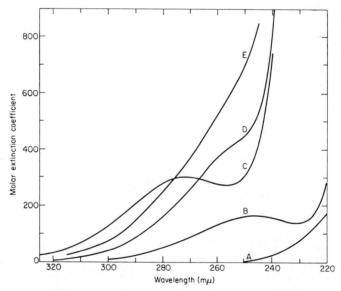

FIG. 4. Absorption spectra at 23°C of cysteine and some of its derivatives. Curve A, cysteine, pH 3·0 (aqueous 0·1 M acetic acid). Curve B, cystine, pH 3·0 (aqueous 0·1 M acetic acid). Curve C, cysteine + HgCl₂ in a 1 : 1 molar ratio, pH 3·0 (aqueous 0·1 M acetic acid). Curve D, cysteine + HgCl₂ in a 2 : 1 molar ratio, pH 3·0 (aqueous 0·1 M acetic acid). Curve E, cysteine + HgCl₂ in a 2 : 1 molar ratio, pH 7·0 (0·1 M sodium phosphate buffer). The molar extinction coefficient was calculated per mole of cysteine, or per mole of half-cystine.

RS—Hg—SR type of compound, absorbs even at longer wavelengths, exhibiting an absorption shoulder with an inflection point at about 250 mμ. When the molar ratio of cysteine to mercury is 1 : 1, presumably forming an RS—Hg$^+$ type of compound, an absorption band is resolved at the long wavelength edge of the spectrum, with a maximum at 277 mμ. Cysteamine and its derivatives show spectra which resemble those of the corresponding cysteine derivatives; the extinction coefficients and positions of band maxima have, however, different numerical values.

The light absorption properties of cysteine, cysteamine and their mercury derivatives described may serve as a convenient tool for the quantitative determination of sulphydryl groups and for following the interaction between sulphydryl groups and mercuric ions. Figure 5(a) shows the spectrophotometric titration of cysteine with mercuric chloride at 250 mμ, at two pH values: 3·0 and 4·6. Two breaks in the titration curves, corresponding to the end-points of reactions (1) and (2), are obtained. Figure 5(b) describes the spectrophotometric titration of reduced ribonuclease with mercuric chloride at the same wavelength. Pronounced end-points are obtained when about

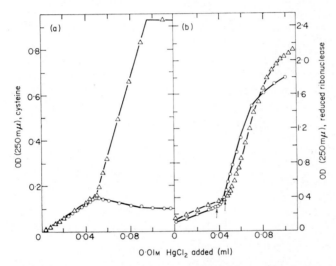

Fig. 5. Spectrophotometric titration at 23°C of sulphydryl groups with mercuric chloride. (a) 1·0 μmoles of cysteine in 3·0 ml solution. ○, pH 3·0 (0·1 M-acetic acid); △, pH 4·6 (0·1 M-acetate buffer). (b) Reduced ribonuclease in 3·0 ml. solution. ○, 0·095 μmoles protein, pH 3·0 (0·1 M acetic acid); △, 0·113 μmoles protein, pH 4·6 (0·1 M acetate buffer). Arrows indicate equivalence points where [HgCl₂] : [protein] = 4 : 1. Light path 1·0 cm.

four mercury ions have been added per protein molecule. The rise in absorption occurring on further addition of mercuric chloride cannot be explained as being due to reaction (2) taking place, since the polarographic studies have shown that this reaction does not occur with reduced ribonuclease. As will be shown below, excess Hg^{2+} causes aggregation of the protein, and this is probably the cause for the rise in optical density after the end-point has been passed.

For some studies to be described below it was important to know whether mercuric ion can compete with p-mercuribenzoate, PMB, in forming covalent bonds with the sulphur atoms of sulphydryl compounds. Since the molar extinction coefficient of the PMB–sulphur compounds, at 250 mμ and pH 4·6, is higher than that of the –S—Hg—S– grouping, which in turn is lower than that of the –S—Hg$^+$ grouping, the above problem was resolved by a spectrophotometric titration of a 1 : 1 molar mixture of PMB and cysteine with mercuric chloride. The results are shown in Fig. 6. Obviously, mercuric ion displaces PMB at the sulphur atoms to form RS—Hg—SR molecules. Excess mercuric ion converts these molecules into RS—Hg$^+$ molecules with a concomitant rise in optical density. From the O.D. values to the left of the end-point, the equilibrium constant

$$K = [(Cys)_2Hg][PMB]^2/[Hg^{2+}][Cys—PMB)^2$$

was calculated to be about 10^3. ([(Cys)$_2$Hg] and [Cys—PMB] denote the concentrations of the cysteine–mercury and the cysteine–PMB compounds, respectively. [PMB] and [Hg^{2+}] denote the concentration of PMB and mercuric salt, respectively, not bonded to cysteine.) A similar titration curve was obtained when reduced ribonuclease was used instead of cysteine, indicating that mercuric ion displaces PMB also at the sulphur atoms of the

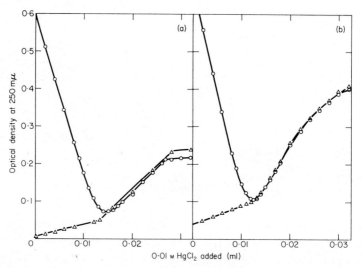

FIG. 6. A spectrophotometric study of the displacement of *p*-mercuribenzoate from its mercaptides by mercuric ions at 23°C. (a) ○, Titration of 0·25 μmoles of the *p*-mercuribenzoate derivative of cysteine with mercuric chloride. △, Titration of 0·25 μmoles of cysteine with the same reagent. (b) ○, Titration of 0·028 μmoles of the *p*-mercuribenzoate derivative of reduced ribonuclease with mercuric chloride. △, Titration of 0·028 μmoles of reduced ribonuclease with the same reagent. In the titrations of the *p*-mercuribenzoate derivatives, the reference cells contained *p*-mercuribenzoate at concentrations equivalent to those of the reagent in the solutions titrated. Titrations were carried out in 14·5 ml aqueous acetate buffer, pH 4·6. Light path 5·0 cm.

reduced protein. It may be noted that Hg^{2+} was reported to displace PMB at the sulphur atoms of glutathione (Benesch & Benesch, 1952); in that case, however, the mercuric compound came out of solution.

3. Preparation of Tetramercury Derivatives of Ribonuclease

From the foregoing it is evident that reduced ribonuclease binds four mercuric ions per protein molecule very strongly and that the mercuric ions most probably bridge pairs of cysteine sulphur atoms. No information, however, was obtained as to the identity of the sulphur atoms which have been paired. The experiments described below were designed to investigate whether the pairing of sulphur atoms via the mercury occurred intermolecularly or intramolecularly, and whether any specific pattern of pairing occurred in those cases where intramolecular binding of mercury took place. It will be demonstrated that by the proper choice of experimental conditions and techniques quite wide control may be exercised over the products obtained.

Intermolecular bridging of the cysteine side chains by the mercuric ions results in aggregation. The extent of macromolecular association was measured by velocity sedimentation experiments at 59,780 rev/min in a Spinco Model E analytical ultracentrifuge. Because of the slow sedimentation of the non-aggregated ribonuclease derivatives, double sector, capillary-type synthetic boundary cells were used (Richards & Schachman, 1959). The relative quantities of the various components present in solution were computed from the measured areas under enlarged tracings of the schlieren patterns obtained.

The sedimentation experiments have shown that the extent of intermolecular aggregation of reduced ribonuclease on combination with mercuric ions depends on the conditions of the reaction. Extensive aggregation was found to take place when a mercuric chloride solution was added to a reduced protein solution or vice versa. In a typical experiment an aqueous solution of 0·01 M $HgCl_2$ was added slowly with stirring to a solution containing 0·75 mg/ml reduced ribonuclease (pH 3·0, 0·1 M acetic acid, 23°C). The final molar ratio of $HgCl_2$ to protein was 4 : 1. Fifteen per cent of the product was monomeric having a sedimentation coefficient $S_{20,w}$ of 1·9 s. The rest sedimented as a heavy aggregate with a sedimentation coefficient of about 30 s. When the order of mixing of the reagents was reversed, about 45% of the product was monomeric. Heating the reaction products in solution for 30 min at 65°C tended to increase the proportion of monomer in the product to some degree.

Markedly improved yields of non-aggregated mercurated ribonuclease were obtained when the reaction between mercuric chloride and reduced protein was conducted under conditions at which each of the reactants was at very low concentration. This was conveniently accomplished by slowly forcing the two reactants in parallel and in stoichiometric proportions into a well-stirred reaction vessel from micrometric syringe burettes operated by synchronous electric motors. At the beginning of the experiment the reaction vessel contained a small volume of buffer solution. Since the reaction between sulphydryl groups and mercuric ions is fast, the concentration of the unreacted reagents in the reaction vessel was very small indeed throughout. A series of experiments thus conducted at pH 3·0 revealed no aggregation at 18–20°C, while increasing amounts of aggregate formed at higher or lower temperatures. Generally, lower yields of non-aggregated material were obtained when the reaction was carried out at higher pH values. It may also be noted that adding mercuric ion to reduced ribonuclease in excess of the 4 : 1 molar ratio caused marked aggregation.

From the foregoing it is evident that conditions may be chosen at which cross-linking of reduced ribonuclease by mercuric ions occurs intra-molecularly. However, it could not be ascertained whether the cysteine residues bridged are the same as those bonded in the native enzyme. The solubility of the non-aggregated product is markedly different from that of native ribonuclease, the mercurated derivative precipitating at pH values above 6·0. Mercurated ribonuclease which was allowed to stay in the reaction mixture for a few weeks at 4°C behaved in a similar fashion. It was thus concluded that on reacting with mercuric ions the cysteine side chains probably pair in an irregular fashion, governed by kinetic factors, and that the sulphur–mercury linkages formed are too strong to permit bond inter-change which would result in one defined configuration of maximal stability (presumably resembling the native structure).

In order to facilitate interchanges between the various sulphur pairs linked by the mercuric ions, experiments were performed in which the mercuric chloride and reduced ribonuclease reacted in the presence of small amounts of p-mercuribenzoate. Although mercuric ions tend to displace PMB from the sulphur atoms, this displacement is not complete; some of the mercury–sulphur bonds are thus opened by PMB and allowed to interchange. In representative experiments, 1·0 ml of 0·1 M acetate buffer, pH 4·6, con-taining 0·04 μmoles PMB was placed in a reaction chamber equipped with a magnetic stirrer. From two micrometer syringe burettes, solutions of $HgCl_2$ and of reduced ribonuclease were slowly driven in parallel into the reaction vessel, the molar ratio of mercuric chloride to protein added being main-tained at 4 : 1. The total amount of protein added was 0·1 μmoles. The temperature was 20°C. The amount of non-aggregated protein obtained ranged from 40 to 80%. No further aggregation took place when the pH was raised to 6·0. At pH 7·0 some material precipitated, but 30 to 50% of the initial quantity of protein remained in solution in a non-aggregated form and was soluble over the wide pH range checked (3·0–14·0). Obviously, the small amount of PMB present in the reaction mixture markedly affected the pattern of the cysteine chain pairing by mercuric ions. The configuration of the mercurated ribonuclease derivative thus obtained is being investigated by various methods. Some preliminary results are reported below.

4. Some Studies Concerning the Conformation of a Tetramercury Derivative of Ribonuclease

There are 105 ways in which the cysteine side chains of reduced ribonuclease can be paired (Kauzmann, 1959b; Sela & Lifson, 1959). As is evident from the foregoing, the presence of PMB in the reaction medium of mercuric chloride and reduced ribonuclease influences the pattern in which the pairing takes place. The present investigation of the mode of the intramolecular cross-linking by mercury ions was based on a comparison of some properties of the tetramercury-ribonuclease obtained with those of native ribonuclease. The properties selected for the investigation were of course such that had been shown to be related to the macromolecular configuration of the ribonuclease molecule. The following studies were performed on the product (or mixture of products) which were obtained on mixing $HgCl_2$ and reduced ribo-nuclease in the presence of PMB as described above. After completion of the reaction, the reaction mixture was dialysed against acetate buffer, pH 4·6, for several hours to remove the PMB. The pH was then adjusted to 7·0, and the fraction of protein which precipitated was removed by centrifugation. The supernatant was found to contain only non-aggregated material. This material will be designated in the following as [RNase.4Hg].

(a) Enzymic activity

The enzymic activity of [RNase.4Hg] toward ribonucleic acid was measured both by the method of Kunitz (1946) and by the method of Anfinsen et al. (1954). No catalytic activity could be detected. Unfortunately, this result cannot be accepted as conclusive evidence that [RNase.4Hg] is intrinsically enzymically inactive, since it is possible that the substrate, which is present in excess and which is known to bind mercuric ions (Katz & Santilli, 1962; Yamane & Davidson, 1962), interferes with the internal bridging in the protein molecules by the mercuric ions. More work will be necessary to clarify this problem.

(b) Spectrophotometric titration of tyrosine residues

Native ribonuclease has three tyrosine residues which titrate normally between pH 9 to pH 11·5, and three "abnormal" tyrosine residues which titrate at room temperature above pH 11·8 (Shugar, 1952; Tanford et al., 1955). All six tyrosine residues titrate normally when the protein is denatured

(Blumenfeld & Levy, 1958; Cha & Scheraga, 1960). Figure 7 illustrates the spectrophotometric titration at 295 mμ of the tyrosine side chains in a preparation of [RNase.4Hg] (23°C). The experimental set-up consisted of a quartz flow cell of 1·0 cm light path placed in a spectrophotometer and a titration assembly containing a glass electrode, a saturated calomel electrode, and a magnetic stirrer. The pH of the solution studied was adjusted in the titration vessel, and then the solution was transferred by an Automatic Transferator (GME, Middleton, Wisconsin) to the flow cell and its optical density recorded. The solution was then returned to the titration vessel by the Transferator, the pH readjusted to a new value and the procedure

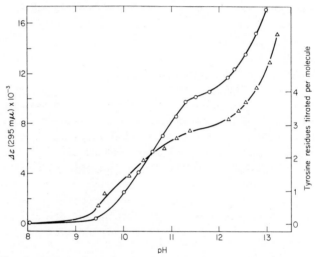

FIG. 7. The change in molar extinction coefficient, $\Delta\varepsilon$ (295 mμ), of [RNase.4Hg] ($\bigcirc$), and of native ribonuclease ($\triangle$), upon increase of pH above neutrality. Titrations were carried out at 23°C in 0·1 M aqueous sodium acetate with NaOH solution. Each tyrosine residue titrated increases $\Delta\varepsilon$ (295 mμ) by 2630 l mole^{-1} cm^{-1} (Tanford et al., 1955).

repeated. The protein concentration was determined by optical density measurements at 280 mμ, pH 7·0, the molar extinction coefficient used being 11·100 l mole^{-1} cm^{-1}. (This value is the sum of the molar extinction coefficient of native ribonuclease and four times the difference in the molar extinction coefficients of monomercury–dicysteine and cystine at pH 7·0 and 280 mμ.)

As is evident from Fig. 7, about four tyrosine residues per protein molecule in the [RNase.4Hg] preparation studied titrate normally in the pH range 9·0–11·5. The remaining tyrosines present in the protein titrate above pH 11·8. At high pH values side reactions accompanied by changes in light absorption may occur; it is therefore more reliable to reckon the number of abnormal tyrosines as those that did not titrate below pH 11·5. It may thus be concluded that the preparation of [RNase.4Hg] described has two abnormal tyrosine residues per molecule.

It is pertinent to note that the number of abnormal tyrosine residues found in [RNase.4Hg] varied within limits from preparation to preparation. In six different preparations studied, the number of abnormal tyrosines ranged from 3·3 to 4·2 per protein molecule. These numbers are apparently averages and the [RNase.4Hg] preparations are probably not homogeneous. Part of the material comprising [RNase.4Hg] may thus have three abnormal tyrosine residues per molecule. Direct experimental information regarding the homogeneity of the various [RNase.4Hg] preparations is, however, as yet lacking.

(c) *Immunological cross-reaction with anti-ribonuclease*

The quantitative precipitin curve of [RNase.4Hg] with rabbit antiserum to bovine pancreatic ribonuclease prepared by immunization with Freund's adjuvant is presented in Fig. 8. Very similar precipitin curves were obtained with the γ-globulin fraction of the antiserum, indicating that no other component in the whole serum interacted with [RNase.4Hg] in the precipitin experiments. Evidently, the precipitin curves of anti-ribonuclease with [RNase.4Hg] and with native ribonuclease are quite different. On the other hand, no reaction was observed between [RNase.4Hg] and a normal rabbit serum, from which it may be concluded that the precipitin curve for [RNase.4Hg] described in Fig. 8 represents a genuine specific antigen–antibody reaction. The possibility that the cross-reaction between [RNase.4Hg] and anti-ribonuclease is due to small amounts of native enzyme in the tetramercury-ribonuclease preparation may be disregarded, since all disulphide bonds in the original ribonuclease were completely reduced and mercurated. Furthermore, [RNase.4Hg] is enzymically inactive. From the slopes of the curves in the antibody excess zone it may be estimated that [RNase.4Hg] brought down about 25% of the amount of antibody that an equal weight of native ribonuclease did.

On destruction of the tertiary structure of native ribonuclease, e.g. by rupture of the disulphide bonds (Brown *et al.*, 1959) or by denaturation by heat or urea (Bennett & Haber, 1963; Morigan & Potts, 1966) cross-reactivity with anti-ribonuclease is completely lost. Some cross-reactivity (up to 10% of the activity of the homologous antigen) was found in the case of reduced ribonuclease which had been reoxidized in 8 M urea, and was attributed to the presence of relatively small size antigenic determinants of the native protein (Mills & Haber, 1963). The appreciable cross-reaction between [RNase.4Hg] and anti-ribonuclease indicates that some of the tertiary structure of the tetramercury-ribonuclease resembles that of the native enzyme.

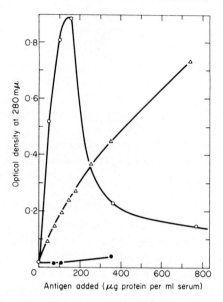

FIG. 8. Quantitative precipitin curves of 0·3 ml rabbit antiserum to bovine pancreatic ribonuclease with [RNase.4Hg] (○), and with native ribonuclease (△). For comparison, the precipitin curve of [RNase.4Hg] with normal rabbit serum (●). The volume of the incubation mixtures was 2·3 ml. The ordinate represents the optical density at 280 mμ (light path 1·0 cm) of the immune precipitate dissolved in 1·1 ml of 0·1 N NaOH.

5. Conclusions

Potentiometric and amperometric titrations, as well as polarographic and spectrophotometric studies have confirmed that mercuric ions do bridge, both stoichiometrically and selectively, between pairs of cysteine–sulphur atoms of reduced ribonuclease. Besides this essential information some additional conclusions can be drawn from the above-mentioned experiments. First, the various sulphydryl groups of reduced ribonuclease are probably not grossly different in reactivity towards mercuric ions, since large differences would have shown up as additional end-points in the potentiometric titrations. Second, as shown by the polarographic studies, the splitting of –S—Hg—S– bridges by excess mercuric ions to yield –SHg^{+} groups does not proceed readily with reduced ribonuclease. This reaction was shown to take place with low molecular weight compounds (Kolthoff et al., 1954) and with mercaptalbumin (Edelhoch et al., 1953). It seems that in the present case the S—Hg—S bridges are stabilized by non-covalent interactions in the rest of the molecule. These interactions should not be identified, however, with those acting in native ribonuclease, since under the conditions of the polaro-graphic experiments the pairing of the cysteine residues may not follow the same pattern as in the native enzyme. Third, it has been demonstrated that both in reduced ribonuclease and in cysteine, mercuric ions form stronger bonds with the sulphydryl groups than does *p*-mercuribenzoate, the equilibrium constant for the displacement reaction on cysteine being approximately 10^3.

Some resemblance between the behaviour of reduced ribonuclease upon oxidation by molecular oxygen (Epstein *et al.*, 1962; Haber & Anfinsen, 1962) and its behaviour upon reaction with mercuric ions may be noted. In both cases, aggregation of the product is diminished by carrying out the reaction at low concentrations. Similarly, reagents which split the internal cross-linkages influence the pattern of pairing of the cysteine residues. In the one case, 2-mercaptoethanol was found to assist the "annealing" of an oxidation product of reduced ribonuclease in which the cysteine residues had been incorrectly paired. In our case, *p*-mercuribenzoate directs the pattern of the internal cross-linking of ribonuclease by mercuric ions.

The preliminary studies performed on [RNase.4Hg] have revealed some similarities between this material and native ribonuclease. The immunological cross-reaction between [RNase.4Hg] and antibody directed against ribonuclease shows that some regions of the molecules of the mercurated protein possess the native conformation of ribonuclease. The presence of abnormal tyrosine residues in [RNase.4Hg] also leads to the same conclusion. At the same time, the significant differences between [RNase.4Hg] and ribonuclease should be borne in mind. [RNase.4Hg] has lower antigenic activity and fewer abnormal tyrosines than the native enzyme. Probably, many but not all of the cysteine side chains in [RNase.4Hg] are paired in the same fashion as in native ribonuclease. The introduction of the mercury atoms into the protein may further distort the macromolecular conformation. Notwithstanding the reservations stated above concerning the validity of the enzymic assay (Section 4(a)), the lack of catalytic activity of [RNase.4Hg] may be explained similarly. Activity may of course be sensitive to more subtle changes in conformation. For example, the lysine residue at position 41, which is essential for catalysis (Hirs *et al.*, 1961), is adjacent to a cysteine residue (Hirs *et al.*, 1960); minor changes in conformation in that vicinity due to the introduction of a mercury atom may, therefore, nullify the enzymic activity.

The available data suggest that not all cysteine side chains in [RNase.4Hg] are paired as in native ribonuclease; however, it still remains an open question whether all the molecules of the reduced protein cross-linked uniquely on reaction with Hg^{2+}, or whether [RNase.4Hg] is heterogeneous. If the latter alternative is the correct one, an appreciable part of [RNase.4Hg] must be made up of molecules the cysteine side chains of which are paired in the same pattern as in the native enzyme. Studies on the homogeneity of [RNase.4Hg] may therefore be of much interest.

ACKNOWLEDGMENTS

The authors would like to express their gratitude to Professor E. Katchalski and Dr A. J. Kalb for valuable suggestions regarding the manuscript. Mr A. Lustig's technical assistance in the sedimentation experiments is gratefully acknowledged. The antiserum to ribonuclease was kindly given to us by Dr I. Schechter. This investigation was partly supported by a research grant from the U.S. Public Health Service (GM-13637-01).

REFERENCES

Anfinsen, C. B. (1964). In "New Perspectives in Biology", ed. by M. Sela, p. 42. Amsterdam: Elsevier.

Anfinsen, C. B. & Haber, E. (1961). J. biol. Chem. 236, 1361.

Anfinsen, C. B., Redfield, R. R., Choate, W. L., Page, J. & Carrol, W. R. (1954). J. biol. Chem. 207, 201.

Anfinsen, C. B., Haber, E., Sela, M. & White, F. H., Jr. (1961). Proc. natn. Acad. Sci., U.S.A. 47, 1309.

Benesch, R. & Benesch, R. E. (1952). Archs Biochem. Biophys. 38, 425.

Bennett, J. C. & Haber, E. (1963). J. biol. Chem. 238, 1362.

Blumenfeld, O. O. & Levy, M. (1958). Archs Biochem. Biophys. 76, 97.

Boyer, P. D. (1959). In "The Enzymes", ed. by P. D. Boyer, H. Lardy & K. Myrbäck, 2nd Ed., Vol. 1, p. 534. New York: Academic Press.

Brown, R. K., Durieux, J., Delaney, R., Leikhim, E. & Clark, B. J. (1959). Ann. N.Y. Acad. Sci. 81, 524.

Cecil, R. (1955). Biochim. biophys. Acta, 18, 154.

Cecil, R. (1963). In "The Proteins", ed. by H. Neurath, 2nd Ed., Vol. 1, p. 379. New York: Academic Press.

Cha, C. Y. & Scheraga, H. A. (1960). J. Am. chem. Soc. 82, 54.

Du, Y. C., Jiang, R. Q. & Tsou, C. L. (1965). Scientia Sin., Peking, 14, 229.

Edelhoch, H., Katchalski, E., Maybury, R. H., Hughes, W. L., Jr. & Edsall, J. T. (1953). J. Am. chem. Soc. 75, 5058.

Edsall, J. T., Maybury, R. H., Simpson, R. B. & Straessle, R. (1954). J. Am. chem. Soc. 76, 3131.

Epstein, C. J. & Anfinsen, C. B. (1962a). J. biol. Chem. 237, 2175.

Epstein, C. J. & Anfinsen, C. B. (1962b). J. biol. Chem. 237, 3464.

Epstein, C. J. & Goldberger, R. F. (1963). J. biol. Chem. 238, 1380.

Epstein, C. J., Goldberger, R. F., Young, D. M. & Anfinsen, C. B. (1962). Arch. Biochem. Biophys., Suppl. 1, 223.

Frattali, V., Steiner, R. F., Millar, D. B. S. & Edelhoch, H. (1963). Nature, Lond. 199, 1186.

Freedman, M. H. & Sela, M. (1966). J. biol. Chem. 241, 2383.

Goldberger, R. F. & Epstein, C. J. (1963). J. biol. Chem. 238, 2988.

Gurd, F. R. N. & Wilcox, P. E. (1956). Adv. Protein Chem. 11, 311.

Haber, E. (1964). Proc. natn. Acad. Sci., U.S.A. 52, 1099.

Haber, E. & Anfinsen, C. B. (1962). J. biol. Chem. 237, 1839.

Harrington, W. F. & Schellman, J. A. (1956). C.r. Trav. Lab. Carlsberg, 30, 21.

Harrington, W. F. & Sela, M. (1959). Biochim. biophys. Acta, 31, 427.

Hirs, C. H. W., Halmann, M. & Kycia, J. H. (1961). In "Biological Structure and Function", ed. by T. W. Goodwin and O. Lindberg, Vol. 1, p. 41. London: Academic Press.

Hirs, C. H. W., Moore, S. & Stein, W. H. (1960). *J. biol. Chem.* **235**, 633.

Imai, K., Takagi, T. & Isemura, T. (1963). *J. Biochem. (Tokyo)* **53**, 1.

Isemura, T., Takagi, T., Maeda, Y. & Imai, K. (1961). *Biochem. biophys. Res. Commun.* **5**, 373.

Isemura, T., Takagi, T., Maeda, Y. & Yutani, K. (1963). *J. Biochem. (Tokyo)* **53**, 155.

Katz, S. & Santilli, V. (1962). *Biochim. biophys. Acta,* **55**, 621.

Kay, C. M. & Edsall, J. T. (1956). *Arch. Biochem. Biophys.* **65**, 354.

Kauzmann, W. (1959*a*). *Adv. Protein Chem.* **14**, 1.

Kauzmann, W. (1959*b*). *In* "Conference on Sulfur in Proteins", ed. by R. Benesch, R. E. Benesch, P. D. Boyer, I. M. Klotz, W. R. Middlebrook, A. G. Szent-Gyorgyi and D. R. Schwartz, p. 93. New York: Academic Press.

Kolthoff, I. M., Stricks, W. & Morren, L. (1954). *Analyt. Chem.* **26**, 366.

Kunitz, M. (1946). *J. biol. Chem.* **164**, 563.

Levinthal, C., Signer, E. R. & Fetherolf, V. (1962). *Proc. natn. Acad. Sci., U.S.A.* **48**, 1230.

Liener, I. E. (1957). *J. biol. Chem.* **225**, 1061.

Lummus, Z. L. & Cebra, J. J. (1965). *Fedn Proc. Fedn Am. Socs exp. Biol.* **24**, 201.

Mills, J. A. & Haber, E. (1963). *J. Immunol.* **91**, 536.

Morigan, T. C., Potts, J. T., Jr. (1966). *Biochemistry,* **5**, 910.

Pauling, L. (1960). "The Nature of the Chemical Bond", 3rd Ed., pp. 253, 514. Ithaca, N.Y.: Cornell University Press.

Richards, E. G. & Schachman, H. K. (1959). *J. phys. Chem.* **63**, 1578.

Schellman, J. A. (1955). *C.r. Trav. Lab. Carlsberg,* **29**, 230.

Scheraga, H. A. & Rupley, J. A. (1962). *Adv. Enzymol.* **24**, 161.

Sela, M. & Lifson, S. (1959). *Biochim. biophys. Acta,* **36**, 471.

Sela, M., White, F. H., Jr. & Anfinsen, C. B. (1957). *Science, N.Y.* **125**, 691.

Shugar, D. (1952). *Biochem. J.* **52**, 142.

Stricks, W. & Kolthoff, I. M. (1953). *J. Am. chem. Soc.* **75**, 5673.

Tanford, C., Hauenstein, J. D. & Rands, D. G. (1955). *J. Am. chem. Soc.* **77**, 6409.

White, F. H., Jr. (1960). *J. biol. Chem.* **235**, 383.

White, F. H., Jr. (1961). *J. biol. Chem.* **236**, 1353.

White, F. H., Jr. (1962). *Fedn Proc. Fedn Am. Socs exp. Biol.* **21**, 233.

Whitney, P. L. & Tanford, C. (1965). *Proc. natn. Acad. Sci., U.S.A.* **53**, 524.

Yamane, T. & Davidson, N. (1962). *Biochim. biophys. Acta,* **55**, 780.

Interactions of β-Lactoglobulins with Large Organic Ions

ASHOKA RAY AND ROMA CHATTERJEE

Department of Chemistry, Bose Institute, Calcutta, India

Additional evidence is presented for the conformation change known to occur at pH 7·5 in different β-lactoglobulins from measurements of organic-ion binding by cow β-lactoglobulin B, buffalo β and goat β. Three kinds of organic ions have been used, viz. a dye anion (methyl orange), a long-chain anion (dodecyl sulphate) and a long-chain cation (dodecyl pyridinium). Results for binding have been obtained by equilibrium dialysis experiments in the pH range 5·4–8·0. The binding constants for the highest-affinity sites increase by factors varying from three to ten, in going from the isoionic pH to pH 7·5. No fresh binding sites are, however, exposed as a result of this conformation change at pH 7·5.

A comparison of the binding behaviours of different β-lactoglobulins with the same ion reveals that some small, but discrete, differences exist in these proteins with respect to the binding constants K_1, but not the number of sites n_1. This comparative study includes a few measurements made with cow β-A at pH 7·5.

Comparing binding at the highest-affinity sites, dodecyl sulphate seems to bind fifty to eighty times more strongly than the dye anion, and three and two, respectively, cationic sites are involved. Dodecyl pyridinium binds about as strongly as methyl orange at pH 5·4 to a set of three high-affinity anionic sites.

The binding of dodecyl sulphate takes place in three stages: a first statistical binding region involving three high-affinity sites; a second "all-or-none" region, involving about twenty-two weaker binding sites, presumably freshly exposed by some molecular unfolding; and a third very weakly binding region, involving a very large number of ions.

A hitherto unobserved aggregation of cow β-lactoglobulin B into a "tetramer", induced by dodecyl sulphate binding in the "all-or-none" region, has been reported from sedimentation-velocity studies at pH 5·4.

The binding of more than three to four moles of the cationic detergent causes precipitation of the proteins at pH 6·8 or above.

1. Introduction

In recent years, binding studies involving large organic ions, especially long-chain detergent ions, have been shown to provide a useful tool for exploring the structure and stability of proteins in solution (Putnam, 1948; Klotz, 1953; Foster, 1960). The forces involved in such binding are mainly of two types, electrostatic and hydrophobic, although some specific interaction may sometimes also be involved, as with certain dye anions (Klotz *et al.*, 1952). The important role played by hydrophobic interactions in proteins has clearly been established recently from both experimental and theoretical considerations (Kauzmann, 1959; Némethy & Scheraga, 1962). This has provided a new impetus for binding studies with not only large organic ions, but also neutral organic molecules of both polar and nonpolar types (Featherstone et al., 1961; Wishnia & Pinder, 1964,1966; Wetlaufer & Lovrien, 1964; Ray et al., 1966).

Anionic detergents are of particular interest because of the physical changes that they produce on various proteins. For example, dodecyl sulphate, which binds to serum albumins in several distinct stages, produces entirely opposite effects on the conformations of these proteins in the first two binding regions. In the first stage of statistical binding, it stabilizes bovine serum albumin against denaturation by urea, heat or extreme pH values (Duggan & Luck, 1948; Klotz & Heiney, 1957; Lovrien, 1963). The second stage of binding itself, however, produces an unfolding in the protein molecule as indicated by electrophoresis, optical rotation, difference spectrophotometry and other studies (Putnam & Neurath, 1945; Pallansch & Briggs, 1954; Leonard & Foster, 1961; Herskovitz & Laskowski, 1962) and this binding is "all-or-none" or "co-operative" in nature.

An "all-or-none" binding involving a cationic detergent, accompanied by denaturation of the protein, has been reported to take place in ovalbumin, but not serum albumin (Foster & Yang, 1954).

Binding studies with β-lactoglobulins have been relatively few so far, although Klotz & Urquhart (1949) have pointed out that among several proteins, β-lactoglobulin ranked second to serum albumin in its capacity to bind the dye anion methyl orange. Two very early investigators (Lundgren, 1945; Bull, 1946) obtained good correlations between the maximum capacity of β-lactoglobulin to bind anionic detergents and the sum of the positive groups in the protein, from electrophoretic and surface film studies respectively. McMeekin et al. (1949) reported the isolation of a crystalline complex of cow β-lactoglobulin with 2 equivalents of firmly bound dodecyl sulphate and the solubility, mobility, titration curve, denaturation temperature and optical activity of the complex. The binding of n-octylbenzene-p-sulphonate by β-lactoglobulin (Hill & Briggs, 1956) was shown from equilibrium dialysis and electrophoretic studies to occur in three distinct stages. At low detergent concentration, two or three molecules of the detergent are bound very tightly, upon which the protein molecule undergoes an unfolding, exposing some twenty-two more weakly binding sites. As the detergent concentration is increased further, a third, very weak, type of binding results, which is micellar in nature. Binding in the first region was shown to be statistical, whereas in the second region it involved an "all-or-none" binding. Very recently, aliphatic hydrocarbons have been shown to combine reversibly with β-lactoglobulin (Wetlaufer & Lovrien, 1964).

However, all these earlier investigations were made with pooled cow β-lactoglobulin. Recently, polymorphism has been detected in this protein

(Aschaffenburg & Drewry, 1955; Bell, 1962), and three different genetic forms have been shown to exist. These are designated as cow β-A, -B and -C. Also β-lactoglobulins from buffalo (Sen & Sinha, 1961) and goat (Askonas, 1954; Sen & Chaudhuri, 1962) have been isolated and studied. Very recently, alkane binding by cow β-A and -B has been studied by Wishnia & Pinder (1966).

The studies of interactions of individual β-lactoglobulins with organic ions have been undertaken by us with a view to investigating the structural changes that might result in these proteins from such interactions, finding out any possible differences that might exist in the tertiary structures of these closely-related proteins in their native states in solution and providing independent evidences for various pH-induced structural changes in these proteins.

This paper describes some investigations made with four different β-lacto-globulins, cow β-A, cow β-B, buffalo β and goat β. Three kinds of organic ions were used, viz. a dye anion (methyl orange), a long-chain anion dodecyl sulphate) and a long-chain cation (dodecyl pyridinium) in the pH range 5·4–8·0. The methods involved equilibrium dialysis and sedimentation-velocity measurements. We have confined ourselves to studying the conformation change that takes place in three proteins between pH 7 and 8. In cow β-lactoglobulin-A, -B and -C, this conformation change has been described as an unfolding or a refolding of part of the two polypeptide chains leading to the exposure of two buried carboxyl groups, as evident from titration, sedimentation and optical-rotation studies (Tanford *et al.*, 1959; Timasheff *et al.*, 1966). Similar conformation changes were also identified in buffalo β and goat β from titration studies (S. Ghosh, S. Chaudhuri and A. Sen, unpublished results; A. Ghose and A. Sen, unpublished results). We also made some comparative binding studies with the β-lactoglobulins at their isoionic pH and at pH 7·5.

2. Materials and Methods

(a) β-Lactoglobulins

Cow β-lactoglobulin-A was a gift sample kindly supplied to us by Dr R. Aschaffenburg and was used as received. Cow β-B was prepared in this laboratory from the milk from cows known to be homozygous for B, following the method of Aschaffenburg & Drewry (1957). Buffalo β-lactoglobulin and goat β-lactoglobulin were also products of this laboratory prepared by methods described before (Sen & Sinha, 1961; Sen & Chaudhuri, 1962). Each of these three β-lactoglobulins was recrystallized not less than four times and was stored at 2°C after being freeze-dried.

Protein solutions were prepared by dissolving the freeze-dried samples in phosphate buffer, centrifuging to remove any denatured materials, which were present only in insignificant amounts, and diluting to give a final concentration of 0·5%. The protein concentration was determined by measuring the absorbance in a Hilger Uvispek spectrophotometer, the value $A_{1\,cm}^{1\%} = 9·6$ (Timasheff & Townend, 1961) being used for all the proteins. The molecular weight of all the proteins was assumed to be 35,500.

(b) Methyl orange (MO)

This was a commercial sample of reagent grade, supplied by E. Merck & Co., and was used without further purification.

(c) Sodium dodecyl sulphate (SDS)

This was a highly pure sample kindly supplied by Prof. K. J. Mysels, of the Department of Chemistry, University of Southern California, and was used as such.

(d) Dodecyl pyridinium bromide (DPB)

This was a gift sample from Diversey (U.K.) Ltd, and described as being of single-chain length. It was washed repeatedly with ether–acetone mixture (4:5 v/v) and dried before use. The critical micelle concentration of the purified sample was determined by ultraviolet spectrophotometry. The value in water at 25°C was $1·23 \times 10^{-2}$ M, which was slightly higher than the value $(1·21 \times 10^{-2}$ M) obtained previously by using the same method (Mukerjee & Ray, 1966).

(e) Buffer

Phosphate buffers (0·1 M) made from sodium mono- and dibasic phosphates were used for most measurements. In order to study the competition by buffer ions especially, in view of the fact that sodium ions are bound by cow β-lactoglobulins to a considerable extent at higher pH values (Baker & Saroff, 1965), some measurements in 0·04 M ($\mu = 0·1$) phosphate buffer at pH 7·5 were also included.

All pH measurements were carried out in a Cambridge bench model pH meter.

(f) Equilibrium dialysis

In equilibrium dialysis experiments, 5 ml of protein solution in buffer, taken in a Visking Cellophane bag, were equilibrated with 10 ml of a solution of the detergent or the dye in the same buffer taken in a tube. The tube was stoppered with a rubber bung wrapped with aluminium foil and mounted on the disc of a rotator, designed specially for gently agitating the solutions in the tubes. The motor-driven rotator worked at 6 rev/min, and its axis of rotation was 45° to the horizontal, so as to prevent any leakage of solutions from the tubes. The rotator was placed in a room of which the temperature was maintained at $25° \pm 1°$C. Equilibration was usually complete in about 16 h. For most measurements, 20 to 22 h were allowed for actual equilibration, except in experiments with SDS, for which only 17 h were allowed, to prevent hydrolysis of this compound.

(g) Determination

Only the outside solutions were analysed either for the dye or for the detergents. Methyl orange was determined by measuring its absorbance at 465 mμ. Sodium dodecyl sulphate was determined by extracting its methylene blue complex in chloroform, described previously in detail by one of us (Ray et al., 1966). Dodecyl pyridinium bromide was similarly determined by extracting its bromophenol blue complex (Mukerjee & Mukerjee, 1962) in chloroform. DPB (5 ml) and 5 ml of bromophenol blue (64 mg/l) were mixed with 5 ml of hydrochloric acid in a dry flask to lower the pH to 2. The mixture was then vigorously shaken with 5 ml of chloroform, the chloroform layer was withdrawn with the help of a dry syringe and its absorbance was measured at 416 mμ. As the extraction of the dye–detergent complex was rather sensitive to pH, the adjustment of pH at 2 with hydrochloric acid was crucial.

To determine the loss of detergent or dye by adsorption on the glass or the membrane, some control experiments were also run, in which the protein in the bag was replaced by buffer solution. It was found that the loss of SDS this way was negligible, although some small, but definite, amounts of MO and DPB were thus adsorbed. Such losses were determined at different free MO or DPB concentrations and were applied as corrections in computing their binding by the proteins.

(h) Sedimentation velocity

Measurements were carried out in a Spinco model E Analytical Ultracentrifuge with Kel-F, 12 mm, 4° cells at 25°C and at 59,780 rev/min. The sedimentation coefficients were determined from the sedimentation patterns with the help of a tool-makers' microscope.

3. Results

(a) Equilibrium dialysis studies

(i) Methyl orange

The amounts of MO bound by cow β-B and buffalo β-lactoglobulin in 0·1 M phosphate buffers at pH 5·4 and 7·5 are shown in Fig. 1, in which the average number of moles of MO bound per mole of protein, $\bar{v}$, is plotted against the logarithm of free MO concentration. In Fig. 2, the binding

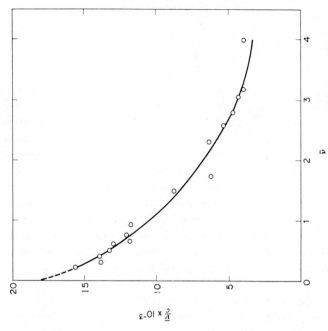

FIG. 2. Graph of $\bar{v}/c$ versus $\bar{v}$ for methyl orange binding by buffalo β-lactoglobulin at pH 7·5.

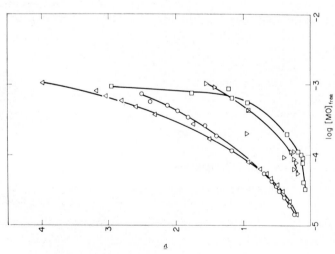

FIG. 1. Graphs showing binding of methyl orange by cow β-lactoglobulin-B and buffalo β-lactoglobulin in 0·1 M phosphate buffers. Cow β-B, $\triangledown$, at pH 5·4; $\bigcirc$, at pH 7·5. Buffalo β, $\square$, at pH 5·4; $\triangle$, at pH 7·5.

isotherm of buffalo β-lactoglobulin at pH 7·5 is plotted in the form suggested by Scatchard (1949), assuming that simple mass-action law applies to the interaction of the protein with the dye anion and that interaction between sites is negligible. The equation for the isotherm may be written:

$$\frac{\bar{v}}{c} = Kn - K\bar{v} \tag{1}$$

where n is the number of equivalents sites per molecule of protein that are available for binding, K is the intrinsic association constant of binding and c is the equilibrium concentration of the free dye. The curvature in the graph in Fig. 2 indicates the presence of more than one class of binding sites. The experimental values of $\bar{v}/c$ *versus* $\bar{v}$ in Fig. 2 can be best described by equation (1), if it is assumed that there are two classes of sites present: when $n_1 = 2$ and $K_1 = 8·7 \times 10^3$; and when $n_2 = 6$ and $K_2 = 5 \times 10^2$. However, n_2 and K_2 values obtained in this way are much less accurate than n_1 and K_1 values. Similar treatments were applied to the other isotherms obtained with MO, and the n_1 and K_1 values are summarized in Table 1 for comparison.

TABLE 1. Binding constants for β-lactoglobulins at 25°C, in 0·1 M phosphate buffers, at a protein concentration of 0·5%

Protein	Organic ion	pH	n_1	$K_1 \times 10^{-4}$
Cow β-B	Methyl orange	5·4	2	0·20
Buffalo β		5·4	2	0·15
Cow β-B		7·5	2	1·0
Buffalo β		7·5	2	0·87
Cow β-B	Dodecyl sulphate	5·4	3	10
Buffalo β		5·4	3	12
Cow β-B		7·5	3[a]	31
Cow β-A		7·5	3[a]	37
Cow β-B	Pyridinium bromide	5·4	3	0·20
Buffalo β		5·4	3	0·15
Goat β		6·0	3	0·23
Cow β-B		6·0	3	0·25
		6·8	3	1·6
		7·5	3	2·7
		7·5	3[a]	2·3
		8·0	3	5·0
Cow β-A		7·5	3	1·5
Buffalo β		7·5	3	1·7
Goat β		7·5	3	1·3

[a] 0·04 M phosphate buffer.

Figure 3 shows the spectra of MO ($4 \cdot 61 \times 10^{-5}$ M) obtained in $0 \cdot 1$ M buffer at pH $7 \cdot 5$ in presence of equal concentrations ($0 \cdot 25\%$) of cow β-B and buffalo and goat β-lactoglobulins and in absence of any protein. The spectral changes brought about by the three proteins were identical.

(ii) *Sodium dodecyl sulphate*

Figure 4 gives the binding isotherm of cow β-B and buffalo β-lactoglobulin with SDS in $0 \cdot 1$ M buffer ($\mu = 0 \cdot 1$) at pH $5 \cdot 4$ and of cow β-B with SDS in $0 \cdot 04$ M buffer ($\mu = 0 \cdot 1$) at pH $7 \cdot 5$. A few points obtained with cow β-A at pH $7 \cdot 5$ ($\mu = 0 \cdot 1$), are also included in this Figure.

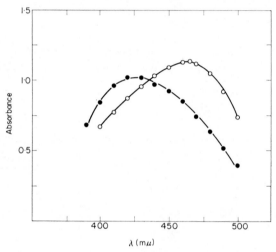

FIG. 3. Spectra of methyl orange ($4 \cdot 61 \times 10^{-5}$ M) at pH $7 \cdot 5$ in $0 \cdot 1$ M phosphate buffer: $\bigcirc$, without protein; $\bullet$, with $0 \cdot 5\%$ of cow β-B, buffalo or goat β-lactoglobulin. The absorbance values were identical within experimental error for all the three proteins.

Scatchard plots of $\bar{v}/c$ versus $\bar{v}$ are given in Fig. 5 for SDS binding by cow β-B and cow β-A at pH $7 \cdot 5$. Two classes of binding sites are clearly seen to be present in the cow β-B–SDS system, one with $n_1 = 3$ and $K_1 = 3 \cdot 6 \times 10^5$, and the other with $n_2 \approx 28$ and $K_2 = 7 \times 10^3$, calculated by using equation (1). It has to be remembered that the Scatchard formulation may describe the first statistical binding region fairly well, but it can only be a crude approximation for the second or "all-or-none" binding region, which involves considerable unfolding (Hill & Briggs, 1956) as well as aggregation in the protein molecule, as will be shown later in this paper. The n_1 and K_1 values for SDS binding by cow β-A at pH $7 \cdot 5$ and cow β-B and buffalo β-lacto-globulin at pH $5 \cdot 4$ are given in Table 1.

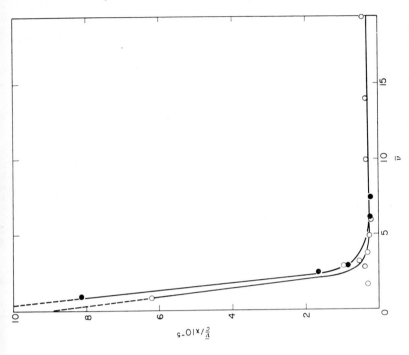

FIG. 5. Graphs of $\bar{v}/c$ versus $\bar{v}$ for sodium dodecyl sulphate binding in 0·04 M phosphate buffer at pH 7·5: ○, cow β-B; ●, cow β-A.

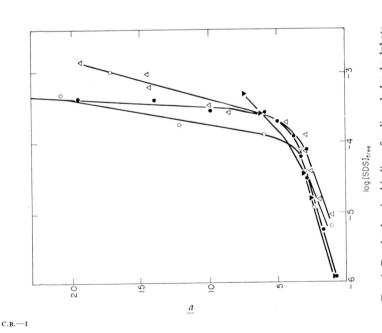

FIG. 4. Graphs showing binding of sodium dodecyl sulphate in 0·1 M phosphate buffer at pH 5·4: ○, cow β-B; △, buffalo β and in 0·04 M phosphate buffer at pH 7·5; ●, cow β-B; ▲, cow β-A.

9

In Fig. 6 we have shown a graph of $\bar{v}$ versus free SDS concentration, c, for both cow β-B and cow β-A. In this kind of graph, it is easy to recognize that three different binding regions exist, involving binding of 3 moles of SDS in the first region, about 22 moles in the second region and a very large number in the third region. No protein precipitation was effected even by the most concentrated solution of SDS used.

(iii) Dodecyl pyridinium bromide

Figure 7 shows the binding isotherms of cow β-B with DPB in 0·1 M buffers at pH values of 5·4, 6·0, 6·8, 7·5 and 8·0. The binding is found to increase as the pH is increased. In Fig. 6 a graph of $\bar{v}$ versus free DPB concentration, c, is included for cow β-B at pH 7·5, which reveals the presence of two binding regions involving 3 to 4 moles and about 20 moles of the detergent. A few

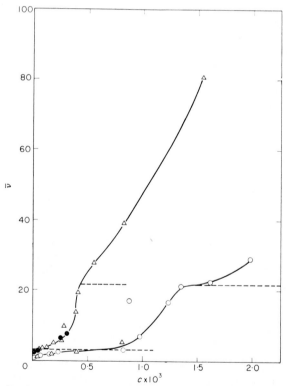

FIG. 6. Graphs of $\bar{v}$ versus free-detergent concentration, 0·04 M phosphate buffer, pH 7·5: ●, cow β-A + SDS; △, cow β-B + SDS; ○, cow β-B (0·5%) + DPB; △, along lower curve, cow β-B (1·0%) + DPB.

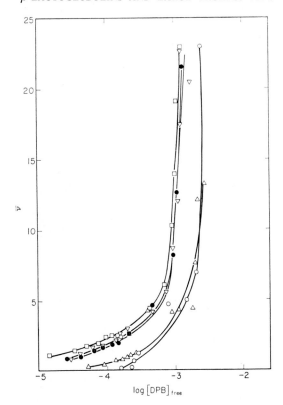

FIG. 7. Graphs showing binding of dodecyl pyridinium bromide by cow β-lactoglobulin-B in 0·1 M phosphate buffers: ○, pH 5·4; △, pH 6·0; ●, pH 6·8; ▽, pH 7·5; □, pH 8·0.

points obtained at a higher protein concentration, 1% (Fig. 6), indicate the absence of any protein-concentration effect on DPB binding under these conditions. Figures 8 and 9 depict the DPB binding isotherms of cow β-B, buffalo and goat β-lactoglobulins at the isoionic pH values of the proteins and at pH 7·5. Figure 9 also includes a few points for binding of DPB by cow β-A. Measurements with this protein could not be extended to higher-binding region, as sufficient material was not available. Also included in Fig. 9 is a curve obtained in 0·04 M buffer ($\mu = 0·1$), obtained with cow β-B and DPB. The n_1 and K_1 values for DPB binding are summarized in Table 1.

In DPB experiments at pH 6·8 or above, precipitations of proteins were effected after about 3–4 moles of detergents were bound. The turbidity of the protein solution in the bag increased gradually as the detergent concentration was increased.

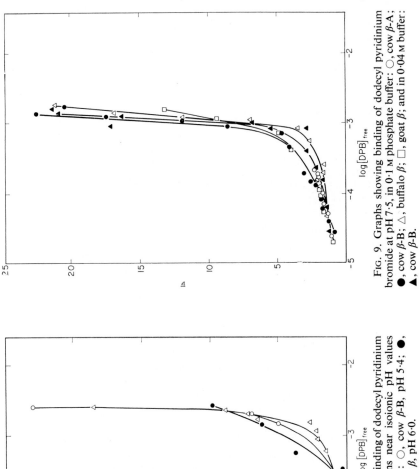

Fig. 9. Graphs showing binding of dodecyl pyridinium bromide at pH 7·5, in 0·1 M phosphate buffer: ○, cow β-A; ●, cow β-B; △, buffalo β; □, goat β; and in 0·04 M buffer: ▲, cow β-B.

Fig. 8. Graphs showing binding of dodecyl pyridinium bromide by β-lactoglobulins near isoionic pH values in 0·1 M phosphate buffers: ○, cow β-B, pH 5·4; ●, buffalo β, pH 5·4; △, goat β, pH 6·0.

(b) Sedimentation-velocity measurements

The sedimentation-velocity patterns of 0.5% cow β-B with three different concentrations of SDS, obtained in 0.1 M buffer at pH 5·4, are shown in Fig. 10. In the low-binding region ($\bar{v} = 3$), a single peak is observed, which has an $S_{20,\,w}$ value of 3.0×10^{-13} sec, which is very close to that for native protein at this concentration. In the intermediate region ($\bar{v} = 5$), in addition to the 3 s peak, a smaller, but a faster moving, peak appears, which has an $S_{20,\,w}$ value of 7.0×10^{-13} sec. As the SDS concentration is increased, the peak height of the heavy component gradually increases, and that of the light component decreases until the latter completely vanishes, as is shown in Fig. 10(c) ($\bar{v} > 20$). The sedimentation coefficient of the heavy component, however, remains unchanged.

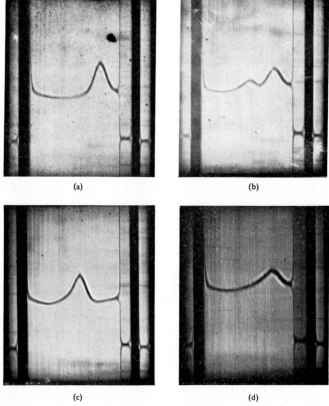

(a)   (b)

(c)   (d)

Fig. 10. Sedimentation patterns of cow β-B (0.5%) in 0.1 M phosphate buffer at pH 5·4, 25°C, 59,780 r.p.m.: sedimentation from right to left. With SDS, (a) $S_{20,\,w}$, 3.0×10^{-13} sec, $\bar{v} = 3$; (b) $S_{20,\,w}$ (slow peak), 3.1×10^{-13} sec, (fast peak), 7.0×10^{-13} sec, $\bar{v} = 5$; (c) $S_{20,\,w}$, 7.0×10^{-13} sec, $\bar{v} > 20$; with CTAB, (d) $S_{20,\,w}$, 2.5×10^{-13} sec, $\bar{v} \approx 20$ (Ca).

Sedimentation-velocity measurements were also extended to mixtures of cow β-B with DPB and another cationic detergent, cetyl trimethyl ammonium bromide (CTAB) at pH 5·4 and 6·8. Binding with these long-chain cations, yielded only a single peak, even when very high concentrations of detergents were used at pH 5·4, but the patterns became more and more broad and diffuse at higher detergent concentrations. One such pattern, obtained with cow β-B and $5·48 \times 10^{-3}$ M CTAB (calculated $\bar{v} \approx 20$, assuming CTAB binds at least at strongly as DPB), is shown in Fig. 10(d). The $S_{20, w}$ value is $2·5 \times 10^{-13}$ sec, which is lower than the value for the native protein. Such a lower value may indicate a molecular expansion or a dissociation of the molecule into subunits.

4. Discussion

As the net negative charge on the protein increases with the increase of pH, the binding of an anion is expected to go down, because of increased electrostatic repulsions. Any increase in the binding of an organic anion which does not involve any specific interaction at a higher pH is, therefore, possible if the hydrophobic contribution to the binding is so increased as to overcome this higher electrostatic-repulsion effect. This is likely in proteins such as the β-lactoglobulins, which are known to undergo a conformation change in the pH region 7 to 8, described as a partial unfolding or a refolding of the polypeptide chains.

With two β-lactoglobulins, cow β-B and buffalo β, we observed much higher binding of MO at pH 7·5 than at their isoionic pH 5·4 (Fig. 1). The binding constants for the first class of sites increase by about factors of five and six respectively. A similar increase has been observed in the association constant, K_1, for the combination of first 3 moles of SDS with cow β-B. These are bound about three times as strongly at pH 7·5 as at pH 5·4 (Table 1).

Binding of cations, however, is expected to be favoured more by electrostatic interactions at a higher pH. An examination of the binding isotherms (Fig. 7) for the combination of DPB with cow β-B at several pH values between 5·4 and 8·0, reveals that there is only a small increase in binding in changing the pH from 5·4 to 6·0, whereas the relative increase is highest between pH 6·0 and 6·8. The increments in the net negative charge on the protein are, however, about equal between the pH intervals 5·4–6·0 and 6·0–6·8. Such a large increase in binding at pH 6·8, which is also reflected in the binding constants of the first class of sites at these pH values (Table 1), is presumably caused mainly by the conformation change that sets in near pH 6·8. As the pH is further increased to 7·5–8·0, the DPB binding increases further. DPB binding by two other β-lactoglobulins, buffalo and goat, determined at pH 5·4 and 6·0 respectively and at 7·5 (Figs. 8 and 9) can also be interpreted in a similar way in terms of conformation changes at pH 7·5. Such changes have already been observed in the titration studies of buffalo (S. Ghosh, S. Chaudhuri and A. Sen, unpublished work) and goat (A. Ghose and A. Sen, unpublished work) β-lactoglobulins.

However, the number of binding sites involved in the initial binding region remains unaffected by the conformation change at pH 7·5 for the combination of DPB with all the three β-lactoglobulins, of MO with cow β-B and buffalo β and of SDS with cow β-B. This probably indicates that the various cationic or anionic sites that are involved in these reactions are identical at the isoionic pH and at pH 7·5. The strengths of binding, however, increase in going from pH 5·4 to pH 7·5, presumably because the hydrophobic contribution to binding is enhanced at pH 7·5 owing to the exposure of fresh hydrophobic surfaces resulting from conformation change.

Recently, it has been shown that cow β-B and cow β-A bind Na^+ more strongly at pH 7·5 than at their isoionic pH values (Baker & Saroff, 1965). As we used large concentrations of Na^+ in the buffers, we also studied the effect of varying the concentration of Na^+ on DPB binding by cow β-B at pH 7·5 (Fig. 9). It was observed that, within the limits of experimental error, DPB binding remained unaffected on reducing the buffer concentration from 0·1 M to 0·04 M. This indicates that Na^+ and DPB are probably not competing for the same binding sites, consistent with the hypothesis (Baker & Saroff, 1965) that a special kind of geometry is involved in Na^+ binding sites in cow β-B and cow β-A. Since the net charge on the protein would still be large and negative at pH 7·5, even after Na^+ binding, the interpretations of anion-binding results as presented above will still hold good.

Comparing the binding behaviours of different β-lactoglobulins with the same ion at the same pH, we find that the differences are rather small. For example, buffalo β seems to bind MO a little less strongly than cow β-B at both pH 5·4 and pH 7·5, although a study of the effects of equal concentrations of cow β-B, buffalo β and goat β on the spectrum of MO at pH 7·5 (Fig. 3) shows that the effects produced by the three proteins are indistinguishable. Small differences also exist in the binding constants of DPB at pH 5·4 and 7·5 in cow β-B and buffalo β (Table 1). However, differences between these two proteins become more pronounced at higher $\bar{v}$ values, with respect to both MO and SDS binding (Figs. 1 and 4). Such results are consistent with the earlier observation, based on electrophoretic studies (Sen & Sinha, 1961), that small, but characteristic, differences do exist between the cow β-B and buffalo β proteins.

Cow β-A is known to be identical with cow β-B, except that it differs chemically from the latter in having one extra carboxyl group in each of the two polypeptide chains in the molecule (Tanford & Nozaki, 1959) and it is capable of undergoing a tetramerization reaction between pH 3·7 and 5·2

(Timasheff & Townend, 1961). However, with respect to the binding of SDS and DPB at pH 7·5, cow β-A appears to differ only little from cow β-B (Figs. 6 and 9). Goat β-lactoglobulin is considerably different from cow β-B and buffalo-β, for example, in having a higher isoionic pH, 6·06, in its titration behaviour and with respect to few other physical properties (A. Ghose and A. Sen, unpublished work), but it seems to be very much like cow β-B at pH 5·4 in its binding of DPB at pH 6·0. At pH 7·5, however, the binding seems to be somewhat weaker than that by cow β-B (Table 1).

It is also instructive to compare the binding behaviours of the same protein at the same pH with different ions. With cow β-B or buffalo β at pH 5·4, MO is bound almost as strongly as DPB, whereas SDS binds about fifty to eighty times more strongly than the other two ions. Also, the dye anion binds to only two sites, whereas SDS binds to three. It is likely that one of the three sites involved in SDS binding in the statistical region is inaccessible to the bulky MO ion; alternatively, the nature of the cationic sites involved may be different for the two anions. Such high affinities for long-chain anions, compared to either long-chain cations or bulky dye anions, were also observed in serum albumin and were interpreted by Klotz (1953) in terms of the hypothesis that the carboxylate ions were blocked by hydrogen bonding with the hydroxyl groups in the protein. A similar explanation may be needed to understand the differential behaviour of β-lactoglobulins towards long-chain anions and cations.

Studies of ultracentrifugal patterns provide some additional information about the physical changes that take place in the β-lactoglobulins as a result of binding of detergent ions. The binding of one detergent anion by β-lactoglobulin has already been shown (Hill & Briggs, 1956) to involve an initial statistical binding to the native protein, which is followed by an "all-or-none" binding to an "unfolded" protein, as evidenced by the appearance of two electrophoretic peaks. Further, in the ultracentrifuge, with SDS and cow β-B, we get two different components corresponding to the above two regions (Fig. 10(a), (b) and (c)). The appearance of two components at $\bar{v} = 5$ and the complete conversion of the light component into the heavy one at a still higher $\bar{v}$ value, > 20, not only confirms that an "all-or-none" binding is taking place, thereby strengthening the electrophoretic evidence, but also proves that an aggregation is involved, for which no other evidence so far appears to have been obtained. The high S value ($7·0 \times 10^{-13}$ sec) of the heavy component suggests that a higher aggregate such as a "tetramer" of the 35,500 unit, combined with about 22 moles of dodecyl sulfate, is formed, rather than a "dimer". This aggregation phenomenon is particularly interesting in view of the fact that SDS is used widely as a protein dissociating agent. Further studies of this aggregation of β-lactoglobulin induced by SDS binding are in progress.

Binding of detergent cations, however, was not found to induce any aggregation in cow *β*-B, as is evident from the single peak (2·5 s) shown in Fig. 10(d).

Note added in proof. Subsequently to the submission of this paper, we have further observed that similar aggregation is induced by SDS in the other three *β*-lactoglobulins also, viz. cow *β*-A, buffalo *β* and goat *β*, as well as in *α*-lactalbumin, ovalbumin and bovine serum albumin, at pH 5·4. This will be published elsewhere.

ACKNOWLEDGMENT

We thank Prof. A. Sen for helpful discussions, and Dr D. M. Bose, Director, Bose Institute, for his interest in the work. One of us (A. R.) also thanks Council of Scientific and Industrial Research for a Pool Grant.

REFERENCES

Aschaffenburg, R. & Drewry, J. (1955). *Nature, Lond.* **176**, 218.
Aschaffenburg, R. & Drewry, J. (1957). *Nature, Lond.* **180**, 376.
Askonas, B. A. (1954). *Biochem. J.* **58**, 332.
Baker, H. P. & Saroff, H. A. (1965). *Biochemistry*, **4**, 1670.
Bell, K. (1962). *Nature, Lond.* **195**, 705.
Bull, H. B. (1946). *J. Am. chem. Soc.* **68**, 747.
Duggan, E. L. & Luck, F. M. (1948). *J. biol. Chem.* **172**, 205.
Featherstone, R. M., Muehlbaecher, C. A., De Bon, F. L. & Forsaith, J. A. (1961). *Anesthesiology*, **22**, 977.
Foster, J. F. (1960). *Plasma Proteins*, **1**, 179.
Foster, J. F. & Yang, J. T. (1954). *J. Am. chem. Soc.* **76**, 1015.
Herskovitz, T. T. & Laskowski, M., Jr. (1962). *J. biol. Chem.* **237**, 2481.
Hill, R. M. & Briggs, D. R. (1956). *J. Am. chem. Soc.* **78**, 1590.
Kauzmann, W. (1959). *Adv. Protein Chem.* **14**, 1.
Klotz, I. M. (1953). *In* "Proteins", ed. by H. Neurath and K. Bailey, Vol. IB, p. 727. New York: Academic Press.
Klotz, I. M. & Heiney, R. E. (1957). *Biochim. biophys. Acta*, **25**, 205.
Klotz, I. M. & Urquhart, J. M. (1949). *J. Am. chem. Soc.* **71**, 1597.
Klotz, I. M., Barkhard, R. K. & Urquhart, J. M. (1952). *J. Am. chem. Soc.* **74**, 202.
Leonard, W. J., Jr. & Foster, J. F. (1961). *J. biol. Chem.* **236**, PC 73.
Lovrien, R. (1963). *J. Am. chem. Soc.* **85**, 3677.
Lundgren, H. P. (1945). *Textile Res. J.* **15**, 335.
McMeekin, T. L., Polis, B. D., Della Monica, E. S. & Custer, J. H. (1949). *J. Am. chem. Soc.* **71**, 3606.
Mukerjee, A. & Mukerjee, P. (1962). *J. appl. Chem.* **12**, 127.
Mukerjee, P. & Ray, A. (1966). *J. phys. Chem.* **70**, 2150.
Némethy, G. & Scheraga, H. A. (1962). *J. chem. Phys.* **36**, 3401.
Pallansch, M. J. & Briggs, D. R. (1954). *J. Am. chem. Soc.* **76**, 1396.
Putnam, F. W. (1948). *Adv. Protein Chem.* **4**, 79.
Putnam, F. W. & Neurath, H. (1945). *J. biol. Chem.* **159**, 195.
Ray, A., Reynolds, J. A., Polet, H. & Steinhardt, J. (1966). *Biochemistry*, **5**, 2606.
Scatchard, G. (1949). *Ann. N.Y. Acad. Sci.* **51**, 660.

Sen, A. & Chaudhuri, S. (1962). *Nature, Lond.* **195**, 286.
Sen, A. & Sinha, N. K. (1961). *Nature, Lond.* **190**, 343.
Sen, A. & Sinha, N. K. (1961). Symposium Electrochemistry, National Institute of Science of India.
Tanford, C. & Nozaki, Y. (1959). *J. biol. Chem.* **234**, 2874.
Tanford, C., Bunville, L. G. & Nozaki, Y. (1959). *J. Am. chem. Soc.* **81**, 4032.
Tanford, C. & Taggert, V. G. (1961). *J. Am. chem. Soc.* **83**, 1634.
Timasheff, S. N. & Townend, R. (1961). *J. Am. chem. Soc.* **83**, 464.
Timasheff, S. N., Mescanti, L., Basch, J. J. & Townend, R. (1966). *J. biol. Chem.* **241**, 2496.
Wetlaufer, D. B. & Lovrien, R. (1964). *J. biol. Chem.* **239**, 596.
Wishnia, A. & Pinder, T. (1964). *Biochemistry*, **3**, 1377.
Wishnia, A. & Pinder, T. (1966). *Biochemistry*, **5**, 1534.

The Relation of Immunological Activity and Primary Structure in Cytochrome *c*

E. MARGOLIASH, M. REICHLIN AND A. NISONOFF

Department of Molecular Biology, Abbott Laboratories, North Chicago, Illinois, and the Department of Medicine, State University of New York at Buffalo and the Buffalo General Hospital, Buffalo, New York, and the Department of Microbiology, University of Illinois School of Medicine, Chicago, Illinois, U.S.A.

The production of antibodies in rabbits to cytochromes *c* from various species is described. These antibodies are shown to react with cytochrome *c* itself and to be associated with the γG-globulin fraction of serum.

Antisera prepared against any one of the cytochromes *c* cross-react to varying extents with the proteins from over 25 other species. In this regard the cytochrome *c*–anticytochrome *c* system behaves similarly to other immunological systems involving sets of related proteins. Thus, many antisera have the greatest specificity to the protein by which they were elicited and in some instances antisera contain an antibody population that reacts exclusively with the homologous cytochrome *c*. Conversely, the non-specific antibody population is in general directed against antigenic determinants that are immunologically similar in all cross-reacting proteins. Cytochromes *c* from different species which have identical primary structures cannot be distinguished immunologically.

The study of the immunological cross-reactions of proteins that have minimal differences in amino acid sequence has made it possible to localize some of the antigenic determinants carried by the cytochrome *c* molecule. These sites involve large hydrophobic residues, such as tryptophan, tyrosine, phenylalanine and isoleucine.

All anticytochrome *c* sera react with rabbit cytochrome *c*, and it is possible to obtain a weak antibody response by injecting γ-globulin conjugated rabbit cytochrome *c* to rabbits. The mechanism by which rabbits produce such auto-antibodies is discussed.

1. Introduction

The first attempts to determine whether cytochrome *c* could act as an antigen date back to the time when various futile attempts were made to utilize preparations of the protein therapeutically, in human conditions in which different types of damage led to tissue anoxia. The first authors to report such studies indicated that the material was not antigenic (Proger & Dekaneas, 1946). Shortly thereafter it was nevertheless shown that preparations of hog, beef and horse cytochrome *c* could in fact yield immunologic responses in rabbits (Roth *et al.*, 1949; Becker & Munoz, 1949). These investigations were all carried out with cytochrome *c* preparations containing about 0·34% iron

(Keilin & Hartree, 1945) and contaminated to an extent of about 25% by a non-cytochrome fraction, probably consisting largely of myoglobin globin (Margoliash, 1954a; Fridovich, 1962). It is very likely that the antibodies produced by such preparations were directed against this non-cytochrome fraction and not against the cytochrome c itself.

Indeed, after the introduction of cation exchange chromatography for the purification of the protein (Paléus & Neilands, 1950; Margoliash, 1954b) leading to preparations containing 0·45% iron, numerous attempts to elicit antibodies failed. Among the best documented of these negative results may be cited the recent studies of Storck et al. (1964), who were unable to observe immunologic responses in rabbits and guinea pigs to horse heart cytochrome c by precipitin, immuno-diffusion, anaphylactic shock or ileum contraction tests. Similarly, Jonsson & Paléus (1966) reported that rabbits injected with chicken or with beef heart cytochrome c produced no demonstrable antibodies, except in a single case in which a trace of antichicken cytochrome c antibody was detected by a particularly sensitive mixed absorption test.

The only clearly positive result, obtained before the investigation reported in the present paper, was that of Okada et al. (1964), who observed that rabbits injected with the iso-1-cytochrome c of baker's yeast (Slonimski et al., 1965; Sherman et al., 1965) yielded non-precipitating antibodies, as evidenced by skin reactions, specific hemolysis and passive cutaneous anaphylaxis tests. The antigen–antibody complexes were also detected by gel filtration on Sephadex G–75, and the highest antibody titre was given by rabbits injected with the disulphide dimer of the yeast cytochrome c. Though the authors state that there was no cross-reaction with beef heart cytochrome c, a careful examination of the corresponding gel-filtration chromatogram reveals a shoulder at the leading edge of the cytochrome c peak, which might well indicate the presence of a small amount of antigen–antibody complex.

A preliminary account of part of the results reported below has been presented (Reichlin et al., 1966).

2. Production of Antibodies to Cytochrome c

(a) Methods of immunization

All cytochromes c were prepared by the aluminium sulphate extraction procedure (Margoliash & Walasek, 1967), purified by cation-exchange chromatography (Margoliash, 1954b,1962) and/or by Sephadex gel filtration (Flatmark, 1964), crystallized from near-saturated solutions of ammonium sulphate and recrystallized. Such products contain 0·45% of iron and are entirely free from non-cytochrome impurities and from the de-amidated and polymeric artifacts commonly found in amorphous preparations. They are probably essentially similar to crystalline cytochromes c obtained by other methods.

Two methods of immunization of rabbits were used, employing the native protein and the protein conjugated to acetylated bovine γ-globulin, respectively (Reichlin et al., 1966). It may be noted that no attempt was made to separate any excess of free cytochrome c from the conjugated material. With several cytochromes c, when the native protein was the immunizing agent, the response was relatively weak and occurred only after repeated injections continued for several months. For example, with horse heart cytochrome c, out of the first series of six rabbits, three animals responded, two weakly and one satisfactorily. Quite different results were obtained with human cytochrome c (see below).

When the γ-globulin conjugated cytochrome c was injected, most of the animals responded promptly. For example, with tuna cytochrome c, of the first series of four rabbits, all responded within two months, and the maximum binding capacities obtained were 60, 113, 113 and 280 μg of cytochrome c per ml of serum. These values are corrected for a non-specific binding of about 12 μg of cytochrome c per ml of serum observed with a pool of serum from non-immunized rabbits or with sera of 10 individual non-immunized rabbits.

Binding was measured by a modification of the technique of Farr (1958). The cytochrome c was very lightly iodinated with ^{125}I to an extent of 0·05 to 0·3 atoms per molecule of protein. Various amounts of the labelled cytochrome c were reacted with a standard amount of serum, the antigen–antibody complex was precipitated in 15% sodium sulphate at pH 8·0 and the radioactivity of the precipitate determined and corrected for contamination by residual supernatant. Alternatively, the precipitate was washed four times with 15% sodium sulphate solution, dissolved and counted. Typical results are presented in Fig. 1.

(b) *Precipitating versus non-precipitating antibodies*

Native human and horse heart cytochromes c yielded precipitating antibodies that fixed guinea pig complement, whereas the tuna and turkey cytochromes c yielded non-precipitating antibodies that failed to fix complement, but could be revealed by the modified Farr technique or by passive hemagglutination (Stavitsky, 1954). Human cytochrome c acted differently from the other proteins, in that most animals produced a high titre of antibody in the relatively short time of two months.

When the conjugated proteins were used for immunization the tuna and turkey proteins elicited non-precipitating antibodies that had characteristics similar to those non-precipitating antibodies produced by the native proteins,

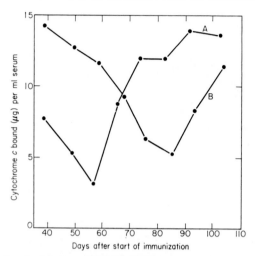

FIG. 1. Graphs showing binding of ^{125}I-labelled human cytochrome c by sera of A, rabbit H7 and B, rabbit H8, immunized with bovine γ-globulin conjugated human cytochrome c. Binding was determined by the modified Farr (1958) technique, with 0·3 ml of serum and 5 μg of ^{125}I-labelled human cytochrome c. Values are corrected for the small degree of non-specific binding by sera of non-immunized rabbits.

whereas the human protein caused the appearance of precipitating antibodies. As noted above, the response to the conjugated antigens was always rapid.

Thus, it appears that cytochromes c differ very markedly in their immunogenic capacities. Human cytochrome c yields precipitating antibodies by either method of immunization and the native horse protein also gives rise to precipitating antibodies. The tuna and turkey cytochromes c elicit only non-precipitating antibodies that are incapable of fixing complement. With the latter two, total binding capacities tend to be higher and the antibody response occurs more promptly and in a much higher percentage of animals when γ-globulin conjugated antigen is used than when the native protein is used for immunization.

3. General Characteristics of Anticytochrome c Antibodies

Because of the numerous reported failures to obtain antibodies to highly purified cytochrome c preparations, it was necessary to ascertain whether the antisera described above did indeed react with the cytochrome c itself and not with possible trace impurities in the preparations.

(a) Non-precipitating sera

From a non-precipitating antituna cytochrome c serum a relatively colourless γ-globulin fraction was prepared. After combination with unlabelled tuna heart cytochrome c, the total globulins and the antigen–antibody complex were precipitated with sodium sulphate, as described above, and the combined cytochrome *c* estimated from the amount of the heme protein remaining in the supernatant, as determined from the absorbance at 410 mμ (Soret band maximum). The results presented in Table 1 show that 5 mg of γG-globulin from rabbit F4 bound 63% and 37% of the cytochrome *c* when

TABLE 1. Binding of tuna heart cytochrome *c* by γG-globulin preparations containing 5 mg of globulin: results are for percentage of total cytochrome *c* recovered in precipitates

Source of globulin Precipitation technique	Rabbit F5 Sheep antiserum	Rabbit F4		Non-immune rabbits	
		Sheep antiserum	Na$_2$SO$_4$	Sheep antiserum	Na$_2$SO$_4$
Amount of cytochrome *c* tested					
20 μg (^{125}I)	29	61	—	5	—
30 μg	—	—	63	—	7
60 μg	—	—	37	—	9

tested with 30 and 60 μg of the protein respectively, whereas 5 mg of a non-specific γG-globulin bound less than 10% of the cytochrome *c*.

In a similar type of experiment, ^{125}I-labelled cytochrome *c* was used and the total globulins and antigen–antibody complex were precipitated by a sheep serum that was monospecific for rabbit γG-globulin. The amount of cytochrome *c* bound to the antibody was estimated as described above. As shown in Table 1, 5 mg of γG-globulin preparations from rabbits F4 and F5 challenged with 20 μg of ^{125}I-labelled tuna cytochrome *c* bound 61% and 29% of the antigen, as compared to 5% for a non-specific γG-globulin.

(b) *Radioimmunoelectrophoresis*

Radioimmunoelectrophoresis was used to show that the anticytochrome *c* antibodies were associated exclusively with the γG globulin fraction of serum. A typical example is given in Fig. 2. The right half of the figure is a photograph of the electrophoretogram, and the left half of the figure is the corresponding contact radioautogram. The materials electrophoresed from the four wells and those subsequently diffused in from the troughs are marked on the figure. The results clearly show that the radioactivity is strictly limited to the γG-globulin arc of the immune sera, and no radioactivity is fixed by any of the components of the normal rabbit serum. Other controls are similarly negative.

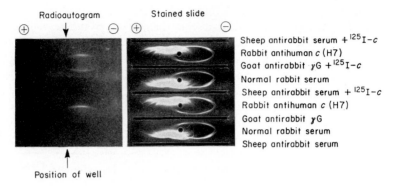

Radioautogram   Stained slide

Sheep antirabbit serum + $^{125}I-c$
Rabbit antihuman c (H7)
Goat antirabbit γG + $^{125}I-c$
Normal rabbit serum
Sheep antirabbit serum + $^{125}I-c$
Rabbit antihuman c (H7)
Goat antirabbit γG
Normal rabbit serum
Sheep antirabbit serum

Position of well

FIG. 2. Radioimmunoelectrophorogram of antihuman cytochrome c serum (serum H7 and normal rabbit serum. The right half of the figure is a photograph of the immuno-electrophorogram and the left half is a contact radioautogram of the immunoelectrophorogram. The sera electrophoresed from the four wells and the sera and ^{125}I-labelled human cytochrome c subsequently diffused from the adjacent troughs are identified on the right of the figure. "Sheep antirabbit serum" refers to a sheep serum directed against whole rabbit serum. "Goat antirabbit γG" refers to a goat serum monospecific for rabbit γG-globulin. "^{125}I-c" refers to ^{125}I-labelled human cytochrome c, which was diffused from the trough after the serum placed in the same trough had been allowed to diffuse out for 24 h.

(c) *Precipitating sera*

(i) *Ouchterlony precipitation*

By the direct Ouchterlony technique (Ouchterlony, 1949) a single precipitin band near the antibody well, was observed in all cases. This band contained heme as evidenced by the non-specific benzidine–hydrogen peroxide staining reaction.

(ii) *Direct immunoelectrophoresis*

Direct immunoelectrophoresis (Scheidegger, 1955) revealed the presence of a single arc in a position corresponding exactly to that expected from the electrophoretic mobility of cytochrome c in agar gel. This arc was benzidine–hydrogen peroxide positive.

(iii) *Quantitative precipitin reaction*

Quantitative precipitin analysis (Heidelberger & Kendall, 1935) showed that the precipitating anticytochrome c antibody–cytochrome c system behaved as expected for a homogeneous immune system (Reichlin *et al.*, 1966). A typical example in which the human protein–antihuman cytochrome c serum system was used is given in Fig. 3. In the antibody excess and equivalence regions the supernatant analysed by the Ouchterlony technique (Ouchterlony, 1949) was found to contain only antibody, and the recovery of

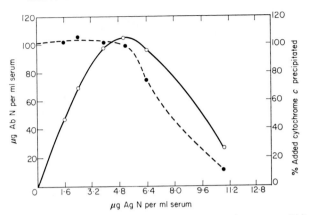

FIG. 3. Quantitative precipitin curve for the human cytochrome c–rabbit antihuman cytochrome c system. The solid line indicates the amount of antibody nitrogen (Ab N) in the precipitates per ml of serum. The broken line represents the percentage of added cytochrome c recovered in the specific precipitates.

added cytochrome c in the precipitates was quantitative, whereas in the antigen excess region the supernatant reacted with added antibody, but not with added antigen.

(iv) *Complement fixation*

All the precipitating sera gave typical complement fixation curves with the homologous antigen (Mayer *et al.*, 1948), the curves showing a single maximum at appropriate antigen–antibody ratios (see Fig. 4). It was found that with any ferricytochrome c, more complement was fixed than with the same protein in the ferrous form, the effect being entirely reversible. Thus, the two oxidation states of the molecule have different antigenic structures, a situation that must be related to the fact that ferro- and ferricytochrome c have different protein conformations, as indicated by numerous lines of evidence (see Margoliash & Schejter, 1966).

4. General Characteristics of Cross-reactions between Anticytochrome c Sera with Cytochromes c from Different Species

It was found that sera directed against any one of the four cytochromes c that to date have been used for the preparation of antibodies, namely, the human, horse, tuna and turkey proteins, cross-react to varying extents with every one of the cytochromes c prepared from some 26 species, covering the entire phylogenetic scale. These include numerous mammals, birds, reptiles, amphibia, fish, several invertebrates and baker's yeast. In some instances, the degree of cross-reaction with the yeast protein was negligible.

E. MARGOLIASH, M. REICHLIN AND A. NISONOFF

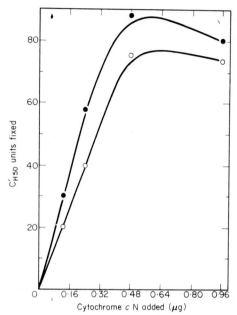

FIG. 4. Graphs showing complement fixation by ●, horse ferricytochrome c and ○, horse ferrocytochrome c with rabbit antihorse cytochrome c serum.

Quantitative comparisons of the reactions of each particular antiserum with various different cytochromes c were performed by two techniques.

In competition experiments, a relatively small amount of ^{125}I-labelled cytochrome c is mixed with the competing unlabelled protein, the mixture reacted with a fixed amount of antiserum, the antigen–antibody complex precipitated in 15% sodium sulphate, and the bound labelled cytochrome c determined from the radioactivity of the precipitate. By carrying out the experiment with a range of concentrations of the competing protein and by comparisons with suitable controls, it is possible to estimate the maximal percentage of the labelled cytochrome c that can be prevented from binding with the antibody by the competing cytochrome c. Since the binding of antigen to antibody is only slowly reversible, under the conditions used, the order of addition of the two antigens to the reaction mixture has a major influence on the results. When both test and competing proteins are presented together to the antibody, as just described, the final measurement may be considered, at a first approximation, to represent an expression of the relative kinetics of binding of the two antigens. Most of the experiments considered in the present paper were carried out in this fashion and a large enough excess of competing protein was utilized, so that little or no additional effect was observed upon further increasing the amount of competitor.

The second technique used in the study of cross-reactions was the comparison of complement fixation as a function of the concentration of the antigens being compared, for a fixed amount of antiserum. Since both the maximal amount of complement fixed and the overall shape of the complement fixation curve vary, numerically these results are presented in two ways. Taking at 100% the number of units of complement fixed at the maximum of the complement fixation reaction with the homologous protein, one can state the maximal percentage of the homologous reaction that can be effected by cross-reacting cytochromes c. This is listed as "percentage of homologous reaction" in the Tables. A second expression of the relative efficiency of the antigens in the complement fixation reaction is the amount of cytochrome c required to attain half maximum reaction under the conditions of the test. This is listed in the Tables as "Ag 1/2 maximum" in μg.

(a) *Antibodies specific to the cytochrome* c *by which they were elicited*

In testing various antisera for their cross-reactions with cytochromes c from different species, it became apparent that some antisera showed the greatest specificity to the particular protein by which they had been elicited. Examples of such antisera are given in Table 2 in terms of competition

TABLE 2. Competition between homologous and heterologous cytochromes c for binding to antibody: results are for percentage label displaced

Antiserum (0·3 ml, 1/16 dilution)	Antituna SF2 + 5	Antihorse 7B3	Antiturkey TH1 + TH3
Homologous ^{125}I-labelled test cytochrome c	8 μg	4 μg	2 μg
Amount of competing cytochrome c	200 μg	200 μg	50 μg
Species			
Tuna	98	45	58
Turkey	50	48	95
Chicken	48	50	93
Horse	55	100	65
Human	40	70	55
Rabbit	50	60	70
Hippopotamus	58	60	80
Hog	52	70	60
Frog	65	50	60
Elephant	50	70	65
Screw worm fly	75	70	60
Yeast (iso-1)	10	5	15

measurements. Thus, with the antituna cytochrome c serum SF2+5, 200 μg of tuna cytochrome c prevented the binding of 98% of 8 μg of the tuna protein; the next best competing protein is the screw worm fly cytochrome c, which prevented 75% of the binding, and the worst is baker's yeast iso-1-cytochrome c, the maximal effect of which was to prevent only 10% of the binding. Similar results are listed for antihorse cytochrome c serum 7B3 and antiturkey cytochrome c TH1+TH3.

Further examples of such relatively specific antisera are given in Table 3, in which the results are reported in terms of the complement fixation reaction

TABLE 3. Cross-reactions in complement fixation tests

Antiserum	Antihuman 74B1		Antihorse 7B3 + 4	
	Percentage of homologous reaction at maximum	Antigen at 1/2 maximum (μg)	Percentage of homologous reaction at maximum	Antigen at 1/2 maximum (μg)
Cytochrome c				
Human	100	0·8	16	2·0
Chimpanzee	100	0·8	16	2·0
M. mulatta	—	—	25	2·0
Kangaroo	33	1·7	38	0·6:
Guanaco	20	1·8	39	1·1
Cow	12	1·3	60	0·8
Sheep	12	1·3	60	0·8
Pig	12	1·3	60	0·8
Okapi	—	—	60	0·8
Hippopotamus	20	1·2	26	1·4
Impala	—	—	60	0·8
Horse	10	1·6	100	0·4
Rabbit	13	1·9	35	2·3
Dog	20	4·0	25	1·3
Tuna	4	1·5	27	0·8
Chicken	4	2·5	19	1·1
Turkey	4	2·5	19	1·1

with an antihuman cytochrome c serum and an antihorse cytochrome c serum. In both cases the homologous protein is clearly a more effective antigen than all the other cross-reacting proteins, with one exception, which is discussed below.

An important result of these experiments is that cytochromes c which have identical primary structures cannot be distinguished immunologically. Several examples are apparent in Tables 2 and 3. Thus, the human (Matsubara & Smith, 1963) and chimpanzee (S. B. Needleman, R. Gardisky and E.

Margoliash, unpublished) proteins have the same amino acid sequences, and react identically with antihuman cytochrome c and antihorse cytochrome c sera (Table 3). The pig (Stewart & Margoliash, 1965), cow (Nakashima et al., 1966) and sheep (Chan et al., 1964) cytochromes c form a similar set of proteins with the same primary structures and show identical complement fixation reactions with the two antisera listed in Table 3, Chicken (Chan & Margoliash, 1966) and turkey (S. K. Chan, I. Tulloss and E. Margoliash, unpublished results) cytochromes c also have identical primary structures and show the same immunological behaviour in complement-fixation reactions with antihuman cytochrome c and antihorse cytochrome c sera (Table 3), as well as in competition experiments with antituna, antihorse and antiturkey cytochrome c sera (Table 2).

In terms of the maximal specificity of certain antisera for the homologous proteins, the above results imply that when a cytochrome c different from that used for inducing the antibody has the same primary structure as the homologous protein, the antiserum will be unable to distinguish between them. Thus, the antiturkey cytochrome c listed in Table 2 reacts maximally and identically with both turkey and chicken cytochromes c, and the antihuman cytochrome c serum reported in Table 3 has the same greatest specificity for both human and chimpanzee cytochromes c.

It should be noted that though proteins that are chemically identical, have invariably turned out to be identical immunologically, the reverse is not true, since some sera do not distinguish between cytochromes c that have different amino acid sequences.

A corollary of the observation that some antisera have the highest specificity for the homologous protein, is that in such antisera there exist populations of antibodies, which within the limitations of the measurements, react exclusively with the cytochromes c by which they were elicited, or with chemically identical proteins from other species. The extent of this exclusive reaction varies with each antiserum, from none at all to a prominent proportion of the total reaction. An example of the later case is given in Table 4. With 0·3 ml of a 1/16 dilution of antituna cytochrome c serum SF4, 100 μg of tuna cytochrome c prevented 90% of the binding of 8 μg of ^{125}I-labelled tuna cytochrome c. The next most effective natural cytochrome c was the screw worm fly protein, which prevented 40% of the binding, whereas 22 other cytochromes c tested prevented only from 0 to 30% of the binding. The 8 μg of the test tuna cytochrome c used was sufficient to cover nearly all of the antibody sites, and the 100 μg of the competing protein was sufficient to displace an amount of test protein very near the maximal amount that could be displaced at very high concentrations of competing protein. Thus, about half the antibody sites in this antituna cytochrome c serum must be capable of reacting only with determinant sites on tuna cytochrome c.

TABLE 4. Competition between various cytochromes c for
binding to rabbit antituna cytochrome c serum SF4

Competing cytochrome c	Percentage label displaced
Tuna	90
Acetylated tuna	55
Screw worm fly	40
22 other cytochromes c	below 30

Antiserum, 0·3 ml of a 1/16 dilution;
test protein, 8 μg of ^{125}I-labelled tuna
cytochrome c; competing cytochromes c,
100 μg.

(b) *Non-specific populations of antibodies directed towards common groups*

A second conclusion that arose from the cross-reaction studies is that, in
general, the non-specific population of antibodies is directed against groups
which antigenically, but not necessarily chemically, are common to all
cytochromes c, including the homologous protein. Two types of observations
serve to document this situation.

(i) *Non-additivity of competition*

As shown in Table 5, with several pairs of cytochromes c competing for
binding to an antihorse cytochrome c serum with ^{125}I-labelled horse protein,
each pair of cytochromes c does not displace more of the homologous protein
than the most effective member of the pair. Thus, each member of the pairs

TABLE 5. Non-additivity of competition with
pairs of heterologous cytochromes c

Antiserum, rabbit antihorse cytochrome c serum 6B6 (0·3 ml, 1/40
dilution); test protein, ^{125}I-labelled horse cytochrome c (0·8 μg). 20 μg
of an individual competing protein gave near maximal inhibition.

Competing cytochromes c	Percentage displacement of test protein
Turkey (40 μg)	43
Human (40 μg)	63
Turkey + human (20 μg each)	52
Turkey (40 μg)	43
Kangaroo (40 μg)	66
Turkey + kangaroo (20 μg each)	63
Rabbit (40 μg)	66
Screw worm fly (40 μg)	58
Rabbit + screw worm fly (20 μg each)	67

of antigens must have been reacting with the same antibody sites as the second member of the pairs. In these cases, the non-specific antibody population is indeed directed against groups that are sufficiently similar in the various heterologous antigens, to be capable of reacting with the same antibody sites, at antigen saturation. The experimental conditions in such tests are adjusted so that the amount of test antigen is sufficient to react with nearly all the antibody, and the amount of competing heterologous antigen is sufficient to produce maximal displacement of the test antigen.

(ii) *The antibody to one cross-reacting heterologous cytochrome* c *contains all the reactivity of poorer reacting proteins*

If an anticytochrome c serum is precipitated with a cross-reacting heterologous antigen, and the antibody in the precipitate is re-isolated, this purified antibody contains essentially all the material reacting with other poorer reacting heterologous proteins. An example is given in Table 6. In this case an antihuman cytochrome c serum was precipitated with kangaroo cytochrome c and the antibody in the precipitate recovered by gel filtration through a column of Sephadex G–100 in M acetic acid. Considering the number of units of complement fixed by human cytochrome c at maximal reaction as 100% for both the original and purified antibody preparations, the results in the first two columns of Table 6 show that the purified preparation contains a much larger proportion of antibodies combining with the cross-reacting proteins tested than does the original serum. Moreover, though only a relatively small fraction of the complement-fixing activity of the original serum

TABLE 6. Recovery of antibodies to all heterologous cytochromes c in specific precipitate of a single cross-reacting cytochrome c

Sera, rabbit antihuman cytochrome c and same serum purified by precipitation with kangaroo cytochrome c. The antibodies in the precipitate recovered by gel filtration.

Reacting cytochrome c	Percentage of homologous reaction at maximum of complement fixation curve		Percentage recovery of total activity in purified antibody
	original serum	purified antibody	
Human	100	100	15
Kangaroo	25	64	40
Elephant	20	60	45
Rabbit	15	46	46
Horse	6	27	68
Chicken	4	21	80
Tuna	4	19	80

was recovered in the purified antibody, with respect to its reaction with human cytochrome c, a very much larger proportion of the complement-fixing activity was obtained in the kangaroo cytochrome c purified antibody, not only as to its reaction with the kangaroo protein, but also with respect to all the other cross-reacting proteins (Table 6, third column). The numerical recovery values listed in Table 6 vary from 40 to 80% for the heterologous proteins, whereas values near 100% would be expected for a perfect experiment. In addition to actual experimental errors, such values probably reflect the difficulties of calculating recoveries accurately since one has to assume a doubtful linear relation between the number of units of complement fixed and the concentration of antigen. It should also be noted that the supernatant from the original purification of antibody with the kangaroo cytochrome c, either in complement fixation or Ouchterlony precipitation, reacts only with human cytochrome c and not with any of the other cross reacting proteins of this particular series of cytochromes c.

Thus, as concluded from the competition experiments described above with an antihorse cytochrome c serum, the antibody population in the original antihuman serum that reacts with kangaroo cytochrome c probably includes all of the antibodies that react with other cytochromes c of lesser affinity to the original serum than the kangaroo protein.

Only one exception to the above generalization has so far been encountered. It involves the relations of human, *Macaca mulatta* and kangaroo cytochromes c reacting with antihuman cytochrome c sera, and is fully discussed in the next section.

5. Localization of Antigenic-determinant Sites in Cytochrome c

Perhaps the most attractive possibility raised by the study of cross-reactions is an approach to the localization of antibody-binding sites in cytochrome c. Since all the indirect evidence available to date, including studies of the optical rotatory dispersion of the protein (see review by Margoliash & Schejter, 1966), indicates that the tertiary structures of all cytochromes c are essentially identical, when two cytochromes c differ in their reactivity with one or more antisera, these differences must be related to differences in the amino acid sequence between the two proteins. Moreover, the positions at which the residue differences occur must either affect or be at antibody-binding sites.

The simplest situation is that represented by a single residue difference between two cytochromes c. Though it is also possible to understand the results obtained when more extensive differences occur, these are far more difficult to unravel and the interpretations are more uncertain. This paper will limit itself to presenting two cases in which single residue differences lead, relatively unequivocally, to the localization of two antigen-determinant sites on the protein molecule. The relevant portions of the amino acid sequences are given in Table 7.

TABLE 7. Amino acid sequences of several cytochromes c in areas relevant to discussion of antibody specificities

Cytochrome c	Amino acid sequences						
	46	47	48	57	58	59	
Horse	——Pro-Gly-**Phe-**Thr-**Tyr**-Thr-Asp——			Lys-Gly-**Ile-Thr-Trp-**Lys-Glu——			
Donkey	——Pro-Gly-**Phe-** **Ser-Tyr**-Thr-Asp——			Lys-Gly-Ile-**Thr-Trp-**Lys-Glu——			
Human	——Pro-Gly-**Tyr-** **Ser-Tyr**-Thr-Ala——			Lys-Gly-Ile- **Ile** -**Trp-**Gly-Glu——			
M. mulatta	——Pro-Gly-Tyr- Ser -Tyr-Thr-Ala——			Lys-Gly-**Ile-Thr-Trp-**Gly-Glu——			
Kangaroo	—— ——Pro-Gly-**Phe-**Thr-**Tyr**-Thr-Asp——			Lys-Gly-**Ile- Ile -Trp-**Gly-Glu——			

The numbers above the residues refer to the residue positions in the overall sequences. The horse and donkey cytochromes c have identical primary structures except for the difference at residue 47, whereas the human and *Macaca mulatta* proteins vary only at residue 58. Horse cytochrome c differs from the human protein at 12 positions. Kangaroo cytochrome c differs from the human and horse proteins at 10 and 7 positions respectively. The amino acid sequences are according to Margoliash *et al.* (1961) for horse cytochrome c, O. F. Walasek & E. Margoliash (unpublished) for the donkey protein, Matsubara & Smith (1963) for human cytochrome c, Rothfus & Smith (1965) for the *Macaca mulatta* protein, and Nolan & Margoliash (1966) for kangaroo cytochrome c.

(a) *Immunological relations of horse and donkey cytochromes* c

The cytochromes *c* of the horse and the donkey differ at a single residue only. In position 47, the horse protein carries a threonyl residue, whereas the donkey protein bears a serine. These two cytochromes *c* are otherwise identical.

The results in Fig. 5 demonstrate that an antihorse cytochrome *c* serum cannot distinguish between the horse and donkey proteins, whereas Fig. 6 shows that with two antihuman cytochrome *c* sera the donkey protein fixes more complement than the horse protein. This difference amounting to about 15% is small, but quite distinct and reproducible. At position 47, in which the horse protein carries a threonine, the donkey and human proteins both have a serine (Table 7), and the human protein varies in several other positions from both the horse and donkey cytochromes *c*.

Clearly, position 47 affects at least one antigenic site with antihuman, but not with antihorse, cytochrome *c* serum. The simplest interpretation of these phenomena is that the threonine or serine side chains do not afford antigen–antibody bonds, but rather affect the geometry of a binding site. An antibody that is adapted to the binding site containing the threonine is not influenced if the threonine is replaced by the smaller serine, but an antibody that is adapted to the serine-containing site does not react as effectively if an extra methyl group is interposed between antibody and antigen at the binding area. It is indeed remarkable that one can thus detect the presence of a single extra strategically placed methyl group. An alternative explanation would require that the site in question be non-immunogenic for horse cytochrome *c* while the very similar location in the human protein can lead to the formation of antibodies. Because of lack of material it has not yet been possible to carry out experiments that may help to distinguish between these hypotheses, by

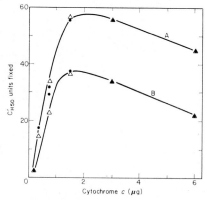

FIG. 5. Graphs showing complement fixation by ●, horse and △, donkey cytochromes *c* with rabbit antihorse cytochrome serum 7B3 + 4: curve A, 1 to 13 dilution of the serum; curve B, 1 to 20 dilution of the serum.

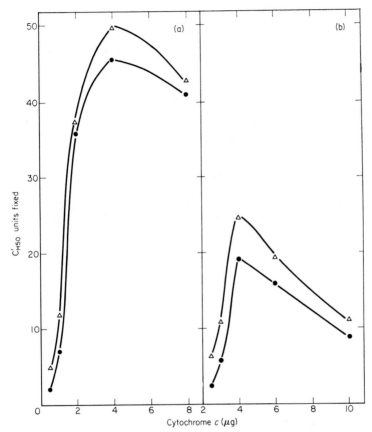

FIG. 6. Graphs showing complement fixation by ●, horse and △, donkey cytochromes *c* with (a) rabbit antihuman cytochrome *c* serum 74B1 and (b) rabbit antihuman cytochrome *c* serum 76B1.

demonstrating that antidonkey cytochrome *c* sera differentiate or do not differentiate between the horse and donkey proteins.

The simplest possibilities as to the actual antibody-binding side chains for this determinant site are those carried by adjacent aromatic residues in positions 46 and 48, phenylalanine and tyrosine. So far there have been no results that implicate any other residues or regions of the molecule in this antigenic site.

(b) *Immunological relations between human,* Macaca mulatta *and kangaroo* cytochromes c

Human cytochrome *c* differs from the *Macaca mulatta* protein only at a single residue. At position 58, the human protein contains an isoleucine and the monkey cytochrome *c* bears a threonine (Table 7), in both cases the adjacent positions being occupied by isoleucine and tryptophan, residues 57 and 59, respectively. For comparison, the kangaroo protein has the same tripeptide sequence as human cytochrome *c* in this region, and the horse protein is the same as the *Macaca mulatta* cytochrome *c*, though both kangaroo and horse cytochromes *c* differ in numerous other positions from each other and from the human and monkey proteins.

Figures 7 and 8 show that there is as much as a 50% difference in the reactions of human and monkey cytochromes *c*, by using antihuman cytochrome *c* sera and both complement fixation and precipitin analysis, the human protein always being more active than *Macaca mulatta* cytochrome *c*. However, as demonstrated in Fig. 9, with an antihorse cytochrome *c* serum the monkey protein fixes more complement than human cytochrome *c*.

These observations can be interpreted to identify the side chain of the isoleucine in position 58 as being part of an antigenic determinant for the antihuman cytochrome *c* serum, and to represent an actual binding site for the antibody. The situation is similar, but not identical to that discussed above for the immunological relations of horse and donkey cytochromes *c*. The

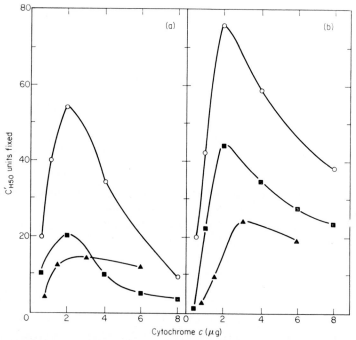

FIG. 7. Graphs showing complement fixation by ○, human; ■, *Macaca mulatta* and ▲, kangaroo cytochromes *c* with (a) antihuman cytochrome *c* serum 76B2 (1 to 40 dilution) and (b) antihuman cytochrome *c* serum 74B2 (1 to 60 dilution).

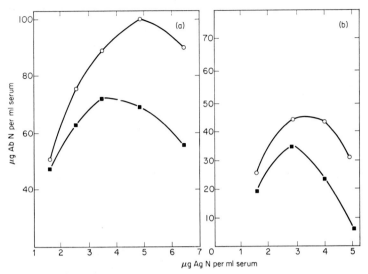

FIG. 8. Quantitative precipitin curve for ○, human and ■, *Macaca mulatta* cytochromes *c* reacting with (a) antihuman cytochrome *c* serum 74 and (b) antihuman cytochrome *c* serum 76. The amount of antibody nitrogen (Ab N) in the specific precipitates per ml of serum is plotted against the amount of cytochrome *c* nitrogen (Ag N) added to the reaction mixture, per ml of serum.

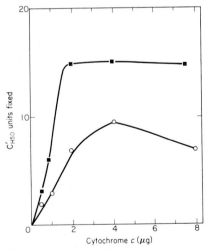

FIG. 9. Graphs showing complement fixation by ○, human and ■, *Macaca mulatta* cytochromes *c* with rabbit antihorse cytochrome *c* serum 7B3 + 4.

difference between the two cases presumably results from the fact that the serine and threonine in position 47 do not appear to afford side chains that bind to the antibody, whereas the isoleucine in position 58 does in fact react with some antihuman cytochrome *c* antibodies.

A direct confirmation of the above results came from experiments in which an antihuman cytochrome *c* serum was adsorbed with a large excess of *Macaca mulatta* cytochrome *c*. The absorbed serum was still able to react

TABLE 8. Antibodies specific to human and kangaroo cytochromes *c*

Antihuman cytochrome *c* serum 76B1 + 2 absorbed with 60 μg of *Macaca mulatta* cytochrome *c* for 0·3 ml of a 1/20 dilution in normal rabbit serum. Test protein, 1 μg ^{125}I-labelled human cytochrome *c*. The percentage of the test protein bound was determined by the modified Farr technique, in the absence and in the presence of 60 μg of various unlabelled cytochromes *c*. Data are corrected for the small non-specific binding by normal rabbit serum. The unabsorbed and absorbed diluted sera (0·3 ml) bound 0·52 μg and 0·14 μg of the test protein respectively. The "percentage inhibition of binding" is given relative to the amount of ^{125}I-labelled cytochrome *c* bound by the absorbed serum.

Competing unlabelled cytochrome *c*	Percentage inhibition of binding	Competing unlabelled cytochrome *c*	Percentage inhibition of binding
M. mulatta	28	Dog	13
Human	96	Chicken	13
Kangaroo	90	Turkey	14
Rabbit	16	Duck	8
Beef	11	Tuna	12
Horse	8	Screw worm fly	1

with human or kangaroo cytochromes *c*, as evidenced by the inhibition experiments reported in Table 8, but did not react to any appreciable extent with any of the other cytochromes *c* tested, though the latter group readily bound to the original serum. It is remarkable that of all the cross-reacting cytochromes *c* tested, the kangaroo and human proteins are the only ones to contain the Ile–Ile–Trp sequence in positions 57–59. Thus, it appears that antihuman cytochrome *c* sera adsorbed with *Macaca mulatta* cytochrome *c* contain antibodies directed against a single determinant. As expected, these antibodies did not yield any precipitates with either the human or monkey proteins, since complexes containing no more than one antibody molecule and two molecules of cytochrome *c* could possibly have formed.

In the present case, as for the first antigenic site described above, it is possible that the two hydrophobic residues, isoleucine and tryptophan, adjacent to the binding isoleucine in position 58, are also involved in this antigenic determinant.

(c) *Some generalizations concerning antigenic determinants in cytochrome* c

It must be emphasized that the interpretations given above for the immunological differences between the two pairs of cytochromes c, in which a single residue is the only change in primary structure between the members of each pair, represent nothing but the simplest possible explanation of the observed results. More complex situations are possible, in that the small primary structure variation may lead to a change in the conformation of the molecule at a site far removed from the variant amino acid, and the differences in immunological behaviour may be the expression of that conformation change. This appears, however, to be unlikely, particularly when the critical substitution involves such similar residues as threonine and serine, and all the evidence accrued to date suggests that cytochromes c, with even much more extensive differences in amino acid sequence, amounting in some cases to as much as 50% of the entire polypeptide chain, have essentially the same conformation (see review by Margoliash & Schejter, 1966). The conclusions reached in the preceding section are thus relatively well based.

The process described above appears to constitute a general procedure for identifying antigenic determinants that may well be applicable to all proteins, provided a sufficient variety of primary structures is available for homologous sets of macromolecules. Since the most favourable situation is that in which a single residue substitution occurs, the recently described series of single residue mutants of iso-1-cytochrome c of baker's yeast (Sherman *et al.*, 1966), may be particularly useful in the case of cytochrome c.

The procedure is limited only by the availability of appropriate variant primary structures. Of all the cytochromes c for which primary structures are known to date, except for the constant 11 amino acid segment between residues 70 and 80, invariant sequences are no longer than two amino acids (Margoliash & Schejter, 1966), so that this limitation is not serious. There is, moreover, some evidence to indicate that the constant sequence between residues 70 and 80 is probably in close approximation to the side of the cytochrome c heme which is "buried" inside the protein (see Margoliash & Schejter, 1966), so that it is unlikely to contain active antigenic determinants.

As already indicated, it is possible to interpret the immunological differences between cytochromes c having differences of more than one residue, in a fashion similar to that used in the cases which involve single substitutions. Such interpretations are, however, more hazardous and must be considered much more uncertain than those relating to the simple cases. Nevertheless, from such considerations it appears that cytochrome c probably contains a limited number of antigenic determinant sites that account for a vast majority of all anti-bodies made. The two sites that have been directly implicated above show remarkable similarities, in that they involve groups of large hydrophobic residues, particularly tryptophan, tyrosine, phenylalanine and isoleucine.

This situation appears at first sight to be in contradiction to the current concepts of the structure of globular proteins, since one might well expect a relatively large proportion of such residues to be "buried" inside the protein and not to be available at the surface for reaction with antibody molecules. However, on the one hand there is no knowledge of the state of the poly-peptide chain when it reaches the antibody synthesizing location *in vivo*, and on the other, the conformation of the antigen in the antigen–antibody complex is also unknown. The question therefore arises as to whether cytochrome *c* in the antigen–antibody complex is in its native state or is partly or com-pletely uncoiled. It is not inconceivable that, following initial reaction with surface groups, which may well include a hydrophobic side chain, the affinity of the antibody for the antigen is sufficient to cause an "unfolding" of the polypeptide chain, so that the final state is one in which the antibody is combined with side chains that are normally "buried" inside the molecule. It is not possible to approach this question by dis-sociating the antigen from the specific complex, since monomeric "denatured" cytochrome *c* spontaneously and very rapidly reverts to its native conforma-tion (Margoliash & Lustgarten, 1962). Cytochrome *c*, however, presents a unique opportunity of solving this problem directly, through an examination of the spectral absorption band at 695 mμ, which is highly sensitive to conformation changes (see Margoliash & Schejter, 1966). Such experiments are being carried out. If it can be shown that cytochrome *c* is in its native state in the antigen–antibody complex, one would be forced to consider that the hydrophobic groups with which the antibodies react are all situated on the surface of the native molecule.

6. Cross-reactions with Rabbit Cytochrome *c*

All the antisera elicited in rabbits cross-react to very substantial extents with rabbit cytochrome *c*. Examples are given in Fig. 10 with the complement-fixation reaction. Essentially identical results are obtained with direct-binding measurements or the competition technique described above. Moreover, rabbits injected with γ-globulin conjugated rabbit cytochrome *c* respond with the production of a low level of anticytochrome *c* antibodies which show the general characteristics of all anticytochrome *c* antibodies, discussed in Section 4 above. Such responses have so far amounted to no more than 5 to 10% of the antibodies produced by heterologous immunization, and it has proved to be impossible to detect any antibodies whatsoever in rabbits injected with native rabbit cytochrome *c*. More data are, however, required for final conclusions regarding the immunogenicity of rabbit cytochrome *c* in rabbits.

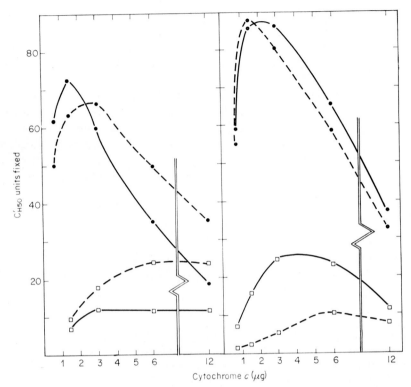

FIG. 10. Graphs showing complement fixation by ●, horse and □, rabbit cytochromes *c* with rabbit antihorse cytochrome *c* sera 6B6 (full line) and 7B3 (broken line) on the left half of the Fig. Complement-fixation curves by ●, human and □, rabbit cytochromes *c* with rabbit antihuman cytochrome *c* sera 76B1 (full line) and 74B1 (broken line) on the right half of the Fig.

This situation is very reminiscent of the breakage of acquired tolerance by antigens related to, but not identical with, the antigen used for induction of the tolerant state. Thus, for example, Weigle (1965) demonstrated that a state of tolerance induced in rabbits to bovine serum albumin can be terminated by injecting bovine serum albumin derivatives or serum albumins from other species. If, in the present case, the animals are at no point tolerant to their own cytochrome *c*, as is apparently the case, for example, with their own lens or cornea tissues, one would expect that immunization with rabbit cytochrome *c* would lead to excellent antibody responses. Thus, if the phenomenon of tolerance were irrelevant to the entire situation with cytochrome *c*, it would be difficult to explain why our preliminary results indicate that no antibodies are obtained with native rabbit cytochrome *c* and that the response to the conjugated rabbit protein is poor. It is not possible to argue that the only reason for the small response to the rabbit protein is its particularly weak immunogenicity *per se*, since one could not explain why only rabbit cytochrome *c* should have this characteristic, out of a series of five cytochromes *c* having structural identities extending from 79 to 94% of the amino acid sequence.

It thus seems possible that with cytochrome *c*, antibodies are produced as a result of a breakage of tolerance by antigens related to the protein occurring in the immunologically responding host, this tolerance being of the natural rather than of the acquired variety. This hypothesis is now being tested. If it does turn out to be a correct interpretation of the phenomena, cytochrome *c* may provide a rather powerful tool for studying the mechanism of natural tolerance.

REFERENCES

Becker, E. H. & Munoz, J. (1949). *J. Immun.* **63,** 173.
Chan, S. K. & Margoliash, E. (1966). *J. biol. Chem.* **241,** 507.
Chan, S. K., Needleman, S. B., Stewart, J. W. & Margoliash, E. (1964). Unpublished results.
Farr, R. S. (1958). *J. infect. Dis.* **103,** 239.
Flatmark, T. (1964). *Acta chem. scand.* **18,** 1517.
Fridovich, I. (1962). *J. biol. Chem.* **237,** 584.
Heidelberger, M. & Kendall, F. E. (1935). *J. exp. Med.* **62,** 697.
Jonsson, J. & Paléus, S. (1966). *Int. Archs Allergy,* **29,** 272.
Keilin, D. & Hartree, E. F. (1945). *Biochem. J.* **39,** 289.
Margoliash, E. (1954*a*). *Biochem. J.* **56,** 529.
Margoliash, E. (1954*b*). *Biochem. J.* **56,** 535.
Margoliash, E. (1962). *Brookhaven Symp. Biol.* **15,** 266.
Margoliash, E. & Lustgarten, J. (1962). *J. biol. Chem.* **237,** 3397.
Margoliash, E. & Schejter, A. (1966). *Adv. Protein Chem.* **21,** 113.
Margoliash, E. & Walasek, O. F. (1967). *In* "Methods in Enzymology", ed. by S. P. Colowick and N. O. Kaplan, Vol. IX. New York: Academic Press. In press.
Margoliash, E., Smith, E. L., Kreil, G. & Tuppy, H. (1961). *Nature, Lond.* **192,** 1125.
Matsubara, B. & Smith, E. L. (1963). *J. biol. Chem.* **238,** 2732.
Mayer, M. M., Osler, A. G. & Heidelberger, M. (1948). *J. Immun.* **59,** 195.
Nakashima, T., Higa, H., Matsubara, H., Benson, A. & Yasunobu, K. T. (1966). *J. biol. Chem.* **241,** 1166.
Nolan, C. & Margoliash, E. (1966). *J. biol. Chem.* **241,** 1049.
Okada, Y., Watanabe, S. & Yamamura, Y. (1964). *J. Biochem., Tokyo,* **55,** 342.
Ouchterlony, O. (1949). *Acta path. microbiol. scand.* **26,** 507.
Paléus, S. & Neilands, J. B. (1950). *Acta chem. scand.* **4,** 1024.
Proger, S. & Dekaneas, D. (1946). *Science, N.Y.* **104,** 389.
Reichlin, M., Fogel, S., Nisonoff, A. & Margoliash, E. (1966). *J. biol. Chem.* **241,** 251.
Roth, L. W., Richards, R. K. & Sheppard, I. M. (1949). *Proc. Soc. exp. biol. Med.* **70,** 116.

Rothfus, J. A. & Smith, E. L. (1965). *J. biol. Chem.* **240**, 4277.
Scheidegger, J. J. (1955). *Int. Archs Allergy,* **7,** 103.
Sherman, F., Taber, H. & Campbell, W. (1965). *J. molec. Biol.* **13,** 21.
Sherman, F., Stewart, J. W., Margoliash, E., Parker, J. & Campbell, W. (1966). *Proc. natn. Acad. Sci. U.S.A.* **55,** 1498.
Slonimski, P. P., Acher, R., Péré, G., Sels, A. & Somlo, M. (1965). *In* "Mécanismes de Régulation des Activités Cellulaires chez les Microorganismes", p. 435. Paris: Centre National de la Recherche Scientifique.
Stewart, J. W. & Margoliash, E. (1965). *Can. J. Biochem.* **43,** 1187.
Stavitsky, A. B. (1954). *J. Immun.* **72,** 360.
Storck, J., Tixier, R. & Uzan, A. (1964). *Nature, Lond.* **201,** 835.
Weigle, W. O. (1965). *Ann. N.Y. Acad. Sci.* **124,** 133.

Substrate–Enzyme Conformational Relationships of Glutamine Synthetase†

ALTON MEISTER

*Department of Biochemistry, Tufts University School of Medicine
Boston, Massachusetts, U.S.A.*

Ovine brain glutamine synthetase exhibits unusual optical specificity. Thus, the enzyme utilizes both isomers of glutamic acid, only the L-isomer of α-methylglutamic acid, only the *threo*-D-isomer of β-methylglutamic acid, and only the threo-L-isomer of γ-methylglutamic acid. In addition, the enzyme acts on β-glutamic acid (β-aminoglutaric acid) to form the D-isomer of the corresponding amide, β-glutamine (β-aminoglutaramic acid). These observations together with information derived from studies on the four β-hydroxyglutamic acids and the four γ-hydroxyglutamic acids, have made it possible to map out the conformation of glutamate at the active site of the enzyme. The findings indicate that glutamic acid is bound to the enzyme in a fully extended conformation in which the α- and γ-carboxyl carbon atoms are as far apart as possible. L-Glutamic acid is oriented on the enzyme in such a manner that the α-hydrogen atom is directed away from the active site of the enzyme, while D-glutamic acid is bound to the enzyme in a way in which the α-hydrogen atom of this substrate is oriented towards the enzyme. The proposed conformations of these substrates are in accord with the observations on specificity and lead to plausible suggestions concerning the relationships between the binding sites of glutamic acid and ATP. Studies on the relative reactivity of hydroxylamine and ammonia with the various amino acid substrates have provided data which seem to bear on the question of the binding site on the enzyme for ammonia. α-Aminoadipic acid reacts at an appreciable rate with hydroxylamine but at a much lower rate with ammonia suggesting that the δ-methylene moiety of this substrate interferes with the binding of ammonia to the enzyme or to the attack of ammonia on the activated γ-carboxyl carbon atom, or both. The enzyme (mol. wt. 525,000) can be dissociated to give eight apparently identical subunits, which can be demonstrated by ultracentrifugation and by electron microscopy. The arrangement of nucleotide binding sites on the subunits is considered in relation to data available at this time

Glutamine synthetase is a widely distributed enzyme which appears to be the only catalyst of physiological significance that functions in the conversion of glutamic acid to glutamine.‡ Glutamine is not only one of the building blocks

† This paper summarizes recent work on glutamine synthetase carried out in this laboratory. A number of the findings discussed here have been published; it is a pleasure to acknowledge the collaboration of Herbert M. Kagan, Ezra Khedouri, Vaira P. Wellner, Lois R. Manning and Mary Z. Papastavros. This research has been supported by the National Heart Institute of the National Institutes of Health, Public Health Service, and the National Science Foundation.

‡ For a review, see Meister (1962).

of protein, but serves also as a source of nitrogen for the synthesis of purines, pyrimidines, and other compounds of metabolic importance. In addition, the synthesis and degradation of glutamine are of crucial importance in the cellular metabolism of ammonia.

The reaction catalysed by glutamine synthetase involves the cleavage of adenosine triphosphate to adenosine diphosphate and inorganic phosphate:

$$\text{Glutamate} + \text{ATP} + \text{NH}_3 \overset{\text{Mg}^{2+}}{\rightleftharpoons} \text{Glutamine} + \text{ADP} + \text{P}_i$$

When ammonia is replaced by hydroxylamine, the corresponding hydroxamic acid is formed; ammonia may also be replaced by other nucleophilic reagents such as methylamine and hydrazine. The reaction also proceeds when Mg^{2+} ions are replaced by Mn^{2+} or Co^{2+} ions. We have tested a number of nucleoside triphosphates in place of ATP; thus far, only deoxy-ATP has been found to be significantly active. This paper is concerned mainly with studies on the specificity of the enzyme for its amino acid substrate L-glutamate, and the implications of these findings. The experiments reviewed here were carried out with highly purified glutamine synthetase isolated from ovine brain (Pamiljans et al., 1962); purified glutamine synthetase from peas exhibits a similar substrate specificity (Kagan & Meister, 1966b).

Levintow & Meister (1953) observed that purified glutamine synthetase from peas was active with both L-glutamate and D-glutamate. The finding that the enzyme catalyses the synthesis of hydroxamic acid from L- and D-glutamate at similar rates while D-glutamine is formed considerably less rapidly than L-glutamine, suggested that the synthesis of glutamine involves an initial activation of glutamate of low optical specificity followed by a more specific reaction of the activated intermediate with ammonia. This suggestion has been supported by further study. Investigations reviewed elsewhere (Meister, 1962) and the findings that the enzyme is active with β-glutamic acid (β-aminoglutaric acid) and utilizes β-aminoglutaryl monophosphate for the synthesis of ATP (Khedouri et al., 1964) support the view that enzyme-bound γ-glutamyl phosphate is an intermediate in the synthesis of glutamine.

Studies on the amino acid specificity of ovine glutamine synthetase received considerable impetus from two observations that were made in our laboratory at about the same time. (1) It was discovered that, in contrast to its relatively unspecific activity toward the optical isomers of glutamate, the enzyme is active toward the L-isomer of α-methylglutamic acid but not the corresponding D-isomer (Kagan et al., 1965). (2) It was found that β-glutamic acid is a substrate for glutamine synthetase and that the product of this reaction is D-β-glutamine rather than L-β-glutamine (Khedouri & Meister, 1965). In an effort to explain this curious optical specificity we constructed space-filling models of the substrates. In building these models we made two assumptions. One of these was that the carboxyl carbon atoms of the substrates are as far apart as possible and therefore that the glutarate carbon chain is fully extended when linked to the active site of the enzyme; this is in accord with the observation that aspartic acid is neither a substrate nor an inhibitor of the enzyme. Secondly, we postulated that the enzyme has specific binding sites for the amino and carboxyl groups of L-glutamic acid, and that the respective functional groups of the other substrates combine with the same enzyme sites. Accordingly, we constructed models of L-glutamic acid and D-glutamic acid in the fully extended conformation (Fig. 1).† Although the carboxyl carbon atoms of both molecules are in the same respective positions with relation to each other, it is evident that this is not true for the amino nitrogen atom. However, as shown in Fig. 2, if the molecule of D-glutamic acid shown in Fig. 1 is rotated 69° to the right about an axis formed by a straight line intersecting the centers of carbon atoms 1, 3 and 5, the amino nitrogen atom of the model of D-glutamic acid is brought to the same position in space (relative to the axis of rotation of both L- and D-glutamic acids) as that of L-glutamic acid. Examination of Fig. 2 indicates that while the α-hydrogen atom of L-glutamic acid is directed upwards, the α-hydrogen atom of D-glutamic acid is on the opposite side of the molecule. If the molecules as

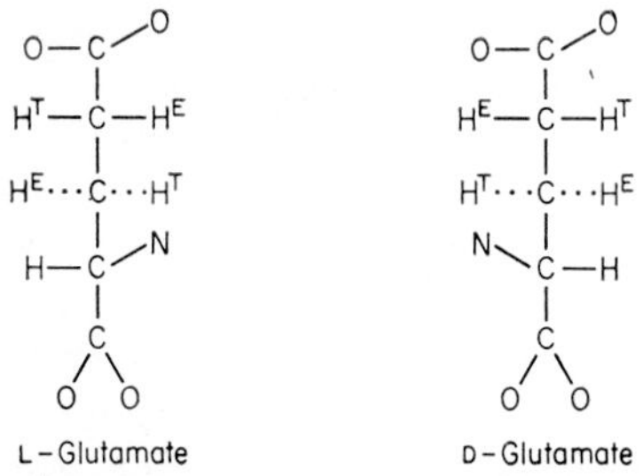

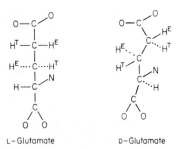

FIG. 1. For explanation see text. Dotted lines in this and other figures indicate that the substituent lies below the plane of the paper.

FIG. 2. For explanation see text.

† Figures 1, 2, 3 and 6 are schematic representations prepared from photographs of the space-filling models.

shown in Fig. 2 are assumed to be on the surface of the enzyme, it would appear that replacement of the α-hydrogen atom of D-glutamic acid by a methyl group might interfere with its attachment to the enzyme, while similar substitution of the α-hydrogen atom of L-glutamic acid would not. Such an explanation would be in accord with the strict stereospecificity of the enzyme toward α-methyl-L-glutamic acid.

We have also constructed similar models of D-β-glutamine and L-β-glutamine. As shown in Fig. 3, there is a close similarity between the conformation of D-β-glutamine and that of L-glutamine (or L-glutamic acid; see Fig. 2). Thus, the β-amino nitrogen atom of D-β-glutamine lies in almost the

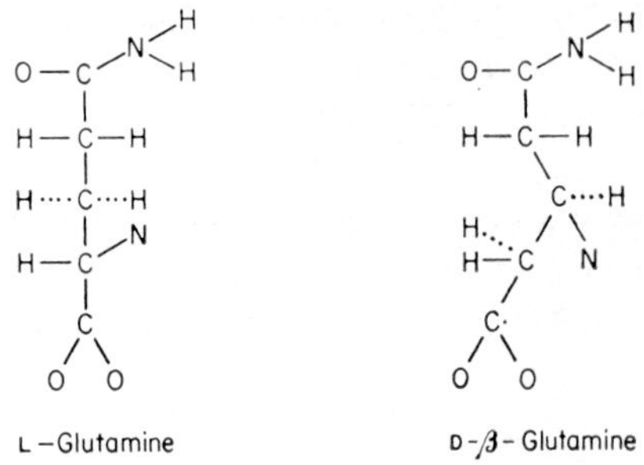

FIG. 3. For explanation see text.

same position as the α-amino nitrogen of L-glutamine. Furthermore, the relative positions in space of the amino nitrogen atom and carboxyl carbon atoms of D-β-glutamine closely approximate those of L-glutamine. A model of L-β-glutamine was also examined and it was found that the carboxyl and amino groups of this model cannot be brought into the same relationship with each other as those of L-glutamine. Thus, only one of the optical isomers of β-glutamine has a conformation closely equivalent to that shown in the model of L-glutamine (Fig. 3). These considerations therefore lead to an explanation of the experimental finding that the preferred conformation of β-glutamic acid on the enzyme is that which leads to D-β-glutamine synthesis.

Although the substrate conformations indicated above are consistent with the findings made with the isomers of α-methylglutamic acid and with the stereospecific synthesis of D-β-glutamine by the enzyme, we sought further confirmation of this hypothesis. Examination of the models represented in Fig. 2 indicates that both of the β-hydrogen atoms of L-glutamic acid as well as the erythro-β-hydrogen atom of D-glutamic acid are oriented in approximately the same direction as the α-hydrogen atom of D-glutamic acid. On the other hand, the threo-β-hydrogen of D-glutamic acid occupies a position that is almost equivalent to that of the α-hydrogen atom of L-glutamic acid. We therefore predicted that substitution by a methyl group of either of the

β-hydrogen atoms of L-glutamic or the erythro-β-hydrogen atom of D-glutamic acid would lead to loss (or marked reduction) in enzymatic susceptibility (Kagan & Meister, 1966a). At the same time, we were led to the prediction that substitution of the threo-β-hydrogen atom of D-glutamic acid by a methyl group would not lead to loss of enzymatic susceptibility. β-Methyl-glutamic acid had previously been shown to be a substrate for glutamine synthetase (Levintow et al., 1955); however, the β-methylglutamic acid available for these studies was a mixture of isomers, and experiments designed to determine the identity of the active isomer (or isomers) were not carried out. To answer this question, we incubated glutamine synthetase with chemically synthesized β-methylglutamic acid (mixture of four isomers), Mg^{2+}, ATP and hydroxylamine. The reaction proceeded rapidly at first, but reached a plateau when close to 25 % of the substrate had been converted to the corresponding hydroxamate. Addition of more enzyme did not increase the extent of utilization of substrate and it could therefore be concluded that only one of the four isomers of β-methylglutamic acid was a substrate. The enzymatically susceptible isomer of β-methylglutamic acid was isolated in a large-scale experiment as follows. After the reaction had reached completion, the reaction mixture was placed at 100° for 20 min in order to cause cyclization of the enzymatically synthesized β-methyl-γ-glutamylhydroxamic acid to β-methylpyrrolidone carboxylic acid. The mixture was then deproteinized and placed on a column of Dowex 50(H^+) and the column was washed with water until the effluent was no longer acid. The effluent was evaporated to yield a product which was heated at 100° in 2 N hydrochloric acid. The product, pure β-methylglutamic acid, was obtained in 80 % yield; it was found to be a substrate for rat kidney D-glutamic acid cyclotransferase and its optical rotatory dispersion curves in water and in 3 N hydrochloric acid were also indicative of a D-amino acid. In order to confirm the belief that this isomer of β-methylglutamic acid was indeed a D-isomer, and further to determine which of the two possible D-isomers it was, we carried out the chemical transformations indicated in Fig. 4. The product was found to be D-*allo*isoleucine thus indicating unequivocally that the isomer of β-methyl-glutamic acid utilized by glutamine synthetase was *threo*-β-methyl-D-glutamic acid. This finding is in accord with the prediction made from study of the models. It is of associated interest that experiments on the four β-hydroxyglutamic acids gave results that were similar to those obtained with the corresponding methyl substituted derivatives. Thus, *threo*-β-hydroxy-D-glutamic acid is a much better substrate than are the other three isomers of β-hydroxyglutamic acid. That *erythro*-β-hydroxy-D-glutamic acid and the two β-hydroxy-L-glutamic acids exhibit some activity may be explained by the fact that the hydroxyl group occupies less space than the methyl group; it is also possible that attachment of the hydroxy-substituted glutamic acids to the enzyme is facilitated by hydrogen bonding.

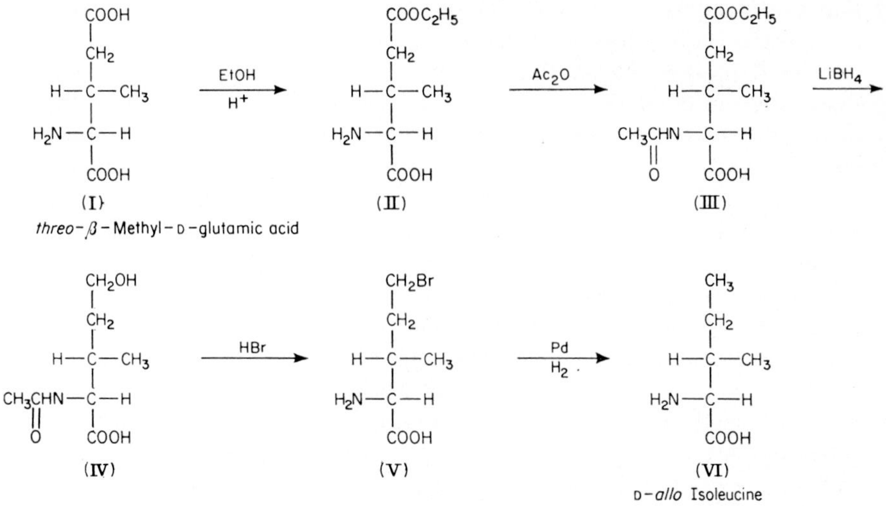

$$
\begin{array}{ccccc}
\text{COOH} && \text{COOC}_2\text{H}_5 && \text{COOC}_2\text{H}_5 \\
| && | && | \\
\text{CH}_2 && \text{CH}_2 && \text{CH}_2 \\
| & \xrightarrow[\text{H}^+]{\text{EtOH}} & | & \xrightarrow{\text{Ac}_2\text{O}} & | & \xrightarrow{\text{LiBH}_4} \\
\text{H—C—CH}_3 && \text{H—C—CH}_3 && \text{H—C—CH}_3 \\
| && | && | \\
\text{H}_2\text{N—C—H} && \text{H}_2\text{N—C—H} && \text{CH}_3\text{CHN—C—H} \\
| && | && \quad\| \quad | \\
\text{COOH} && \text{COOH} && \text{O} \quad \text{COOH} \\
(I) && (II) && (III)
\end{array}
$$

threo-β-Methyl-D-glutamic acid

$$
\begin{array}{ccccc}
\text{CH}_2\text{OH} && \text{CH}_2\text{Br} && \text{CH}_3 \\
| && | && | \\
\text{CH}_2 && \text{CH}_2 && \text{CH}_2 \\
| & \xrightarrow{\text{HBr}} & | & \xrightarrow[\text{H}_2]{\text{Pd}} & | \\
\text{H—C—CH}_3 && \text{H—C—CH}_3 && \text{H—C—CH}_3 \\
| && | && | \\
\text{CH}_3\text{CHN—C—H} && \text{H}_2\text{N—C—H} && \text{H}_2\text{N—C—H} \\
\| \quad | && | && | \\
\text{O} \quad \text{COOH} && \text{COOH} && \text{COOH} \\
(IV) && (V) && (VI)
\end{array}
$$

D-allo Isoleucine

FIG. 4. Conversion of enzymatically-susceptible isomer of β-methylglutamic acid to D-alloisoleucine.

Examination of the conformations indicated in Fig. 2 indicates that the erythro-γ-hydrogen atoms of both L- and D-glutamic acid occupy about the same position in space and lie just between the γ-carboxyl and amino groups of these molecules. Study of the models suggested that introduction of an erythro-γ-methyl group might provide considerable steric hindrance to formation of an activated γ-carboxyl derivative such as γ-glutamyl phosphate and also to interaction of the amino group with the enzyme or metal nucleotide complex. The threo-γ-hydrogen atom of D-glutamic acid is very close to the α-hydrogen atom of D-glutamic acid. It would therefore be expected that threo-γ-methyl-D-glutamic acid, like α-methyl-D-glutamic acid, would not be a substrate. On the other hand, the threo-γ-hydrogen atom of L-glutamic acid is not far from the α-hydrogen atom of this molecule and very close to the position of the threo-β-hydrogen atom of D-glutamic acid; replacement of the α-hydrogen atom of L-glutamic acid or of the threo-β-hydrogen atom of D-glutamic acid by a methyl group does not lead to loss of enzymatic susceptibility. These considerations suggested that threo-γ-methyl-L-glutamic acid would be a substrate for glutamine synthetase. To test this, the susceptibility of several preparations of γ-methylglutamic acid was examined (Kagan and Meister, 1966b). It was found that chemically synthesized γ-methylglutamic acid containing about an equal mixture of the four individual isomers was utilized about 25% by glutamine synthetase. We also obtained by crystallization a racemic diastereoisomer which was inactive. A mixture of the two L-isomers obtained by catalytic reduction and hydrolysis of

γ-methylene-L-glutamine was about 50% active. A large-scale experiment was carried out and the enzymatically synthesized γ-methylglutamine was isolated. This product was found to be completely oxidatively deaminated by L-amino acid oxidase indicating that the product was an L-isomer. Further characterization of the enzymatically synthesized γ-methylglutamine was performed by carrying out the reactions shown in Fig. 5. The final product obtained was shown to be L-α-methylsuccinic acid indicating that the active isomer is *threo*-γ-methyl-L-glutamic acid.

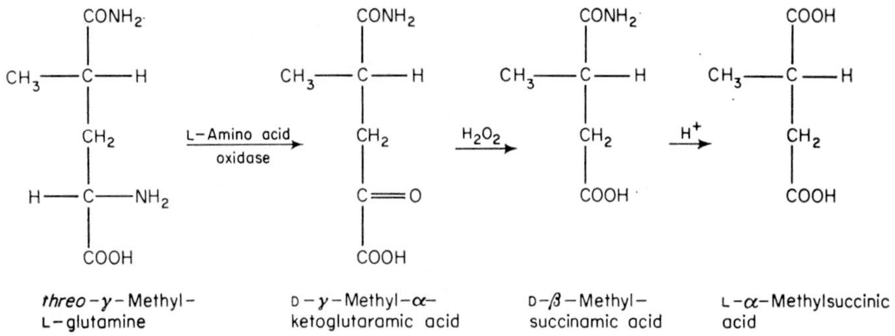

FIG. 5. Conversion of enzymatically synthesized γ-methyl-L-glutamine to L-α-methyl-succinic acid.

Values for the apparent K_m and relative maximal velocity for a number of the substrates of glutamine synthetase are given in Table 1, which also gives values for the four γ-hydroxyglutamic acids. Although *threo*-γ-hydroxy-L-glutamic acid is the most active of the four γ-hydroxyglutamic acids, substantial rates of reaction were observed with *erythro*-γ-hydroxy-L-glutamic acid. It is of interest that *erythro*-γ-hydroxy-D-glutamic acid is also appreciably active. Examination of Fig. 2 indicates that the hydroxyl groups of the L- and D-isomers of *erythro*-γ-hydroxyglutamic acid are similarly located. However, the threo-γ-hydrogen atom of D-glutamic acid is on the opposite side of the molecule. It therefore appears that there is sufficient space in the region of the erythro-γ-hydrogen atom of L-glutamic acid for a hydroxyl group but that a methyl group is of such size as to provide steric hindrance inconsistent with enzymatic susceptibility. Since substitution of the threo-γ-hydrogen atom of D-glutamic acid by either a methyl group or a hydroxyl group leads to inactivity or to a substrate of very low activity, the "available" space in this region must be quite limited and the substrate must therefore be very close to the enzyme at this point.

As indicated in Table 1, the reactivity of D-glutamic acid with hydroxylamine is much greater than with ammonia. *threo*-β-Methyl-D-glutamic acid reacts even less readily with ammonia than with hydroxylamine. To explain

TABLE 1. Values for apparent K_m and relative maximal velocity[a, c]

Amino acid substrate	Relative maximal velocity		$K_m \times 10^3$ (moles l^{-1})	
	With NH$_2$OH	With NH$_3$	With NH$_2$OH	With NH$_3$
L-Glutamic acid	100[b]	100[b]	3·3	3·9
D-Glutamic acid	54	27	3·8	13
α-Methyl-L-glutamic acid	67	75	6·4	6·7
threo-β-Methyl-D-glutamic acid	46	2·2	5·9	25
threo-γ-Methyl-L-glutamic acid	63	27	2·6	3·6
threo-γ-Hydroxy-L-glutamic acid	89	100	1·7	2·4
threo-γ-Hydroxy-D-glutamic acid	1·6	<0·08	22	—
erythro-γ-Hydroxy-L-glutamic acid	64	81	4·0	5·6
erythro-γ-Hydroxy-D-glutamic acid	29	38	13	22

[a] Obtained by the method of Lineweaver & Burk (1934). The reaction mixtures consisted of imidazole–HCl buffer (50 μmoles; pH 7·2), 2-mercaptoethanol (25 μmoles), MgCl$_2$ (20 μmoles), ATP (10 μmoles), NH$_2$OH.HCl adjusted to pH 7·2 with NaOH, or NH$_4$Cl (100 μmoles), amino acid, and enzyme in a final volume of 1 ml; 37°C.

[b] All values are relative to that of L-glutamic acid with NH$_2$OH (200 μmoles of L-γ-glutamylhydroxamate formed per mg of enzyme per 15 min).

[c] Kagan & Meister (1966b).

these phenomena, we have postulated that ammonia is bound to a specific site on the enzyme and that although hydroxylamine may also bind at this site, it may also directly attack the activated carboxyl carbon atom. Study of the models indicates that the γ-carboxyl atom of D-glutamic acid is oriented somewhat differently than that of L-glutamic acid; it might therefore be in a less favorable location for reaction with enzyme-bound ammonia. The much lower reactivity of threo-β-methyl-D-glutamic acid with ammonia may in addition reflect steric hindrance offered by the methyl group. It is notable that threo-γ-methyl-L-glutamic acid reacts about twice as readily with hydroxylamine than with ammonia; the methyl group of this substrate is located in a position similar to that of threo-β-methyl-D-glutamic acid and it seems possible that the methyl group of threo-γ-methyl-L-glutamic acid might also provide hindrance to the attack by ammonia. These considerations suggest that the ammonia binding site on the enzyme lies just above the position of the γ-carbon atom of L-glutamic acid; thus, an unfavorable orientation of the carboxyl carbon atom (as in D-glutamic acid) or the presence of a γ-methyl group (as in threo-γ-methyl-L-glutamic acid) might hinder the attack of enzyme-bound ammonia on the γ-carboxyl carbon atom. The very low reactivity of threo-β-methyl-D-glutamic acid with ammonia as compared to hydroxylamine may reflect the combined effect of both phenomena.

Additional evidence that seems to bear on this question has come from studies on the optical isomers of α-aminoadipic acid (Wellner et al., 1966). It has been known for some time that the glutamine synthetases from peas and ovine brain are active toward L- and D-α-aminoadipic acid. Values for apparent K_m and relative maximal velocity for these substrates are given in Table 2. It

TABLE 2. Values for apparent K_m and relative maximal velocity[a]

Reaction	L-α-Aminoadipate		D-α-Aminoadipate	
	Relative V_{max}[b]	$K_m \times 10^3$ (moles l^{-1})	Relative V_{max}[b]	$K_m \times 10^3$ (moles l^{-1})
δ-(α-Aminoadipyl)hydroxamate synthesis	22	48	11	14
Homoglutamine synthesis	0·63	50	0·19	26

[a] Obtained by the method of Lineweaver & Burk (1934). The concentrations of NH_4Cl and NH_2OH were 0·1 M; other experimental details are given elsewhere (Wellner et al., 1966).

[b] Relative to a value of 100 for L-glutamate with NH_2OH.

is of significance that both isomers of α-aminoadipate exhibit substantial activity in hydroxamate synthesis, but that they are less than 3% as active in homoglutamine synthetase. The ability of α-aminoadipic acid to serve as a substrate suggests that the amino and carboxyl groups of this molecule can attach to the enzyme at the same respective sites as those of L-glutamic acid and other substrates that have carbon chains of five atoms. When a model of L-α-aminoadipic acid was constructed it was found possible to orient the carboxyl carbon atoms in space in a manner similar to those of L-glutamic acid. To accomplish this a model of the fully extended form of L-α-amino-adipic acid is rotated between the γ- and δ-carbon atom so as to bring the center of the ω-carboxyl carbon atom to a position that is very close to 5 Å from that of the α-carboxyl carbon atom; this is about the same inter-carboxyl carbon distance as for L-glutamate. Figure 6 presents a comparison between L-glutamic acid (also shown in Figs. 1 and 2) and the proposed conformation of L-α-aminoadipic acid. The γ-hydrogen, β-hydrogen, α-hydrogen and α-amino nitrogen atoms of both models are in similar positions relative to the α-carboxyl groups. On the other hand, the δ-methylene moiety of α-aminoadipic acid occupies a position corresponding in space to that of the ω-carboxyl groups of L-glutamic acid. Thus, the ω-carboxyl group of L-α-aminoadipic acid is displaced downward as compared to L-glutamic acid. This suggests that the δ-methylene moiety of

L-α-aminoadipic acid might interfere with the attack of ammonia from the enzyme or with the binding of ammonia to the enzyme, or both. The finding that the apparent K_m values for ammonia with α-aminoadipate are higher than those for ammonia with glutamate is consistent with, but does not prove, that the affinity of the enzyme for ammonia is reduced in the presence of α-aminoadipate. We have also constructed a model of D-α-aminoadipic acid following the same general considerations adopted with the L-isomer. Comparison of this model with that of D-glutamic acid shows that there is close correspondence between the relative positions of the carboxyl groups. In addition, the δ-hydrogen atoms of D-α-aminoadipic acid are in about the same relationship to the δ-carboxyl group as in L-α-aminoadipic acid. We have also found that although methylamine is active with glutamic acid (leading to synthesis of the corresponding γ-N-methylamide) this ammonia analog is inactive with α-aminoadipic acid. This suggests that methylamine may not effectively bind to the enzyme in the presence of α-aminoadipic acid, or if bound is very greatly hindered in its attack on the activated carboxyl carbon atom. We hope that investigations with other ammonia analogs and various amino acid substrates may provide further information concerning the conformational relationships between the enzyme and its substrates.

The studies described above support the view that the amino acid substrate of glutamine synthetase is in an extended conformation when attached to the active site of the enzyme and that the side of this substrate molecule bearing the amino group (Fig. 2; right-hand side) and the undersurface of this molecule are in close contact with the enzyme and nucleotide. We have begun to speculate about the steric relationships between substrate and ATP on the active site. Assuming that a γ-glutamyl phosphate linkage is formed and that the α-amino nitrogen atom is involved in a metal chelate–nucleotide complex, plausible models can be constructed involving amino acid, metal ion, and the β- and γ-phosphate moieties of ATP.

In addition to the studies described above, which are concerned with the conformation of the substrate on the active site and with the relationships between the binding sites for ammonia and glutamate, we have begun to gain insight into the structure of the enzyme itself. Earlier work (Meister, 1962; Pamiljans et al., 1962) indicated that the sedimentation coefficient of the enzyme from peas was 13·9 s; a value of 14·9 s was found later for the ovine brain enzyme. Our first value for the molecular weight of the latter enzyme was about 450,000. A more recent determination of the molecular weight (525,000 ± 50,000) was carried out by Dr Rudy H. Haschemeyer, who has been able to dissociate the enzyme into eight apparently identical subunits by treatment with sodium dodecyl sulfate, 8 M urea, or 5 M guanidine hydrochloride (Haschemeyer, 1965). Studies on the binding of ATP and ADP to the enzyme (Wellner & Meister, 1966) indicate that about 32 molecules of

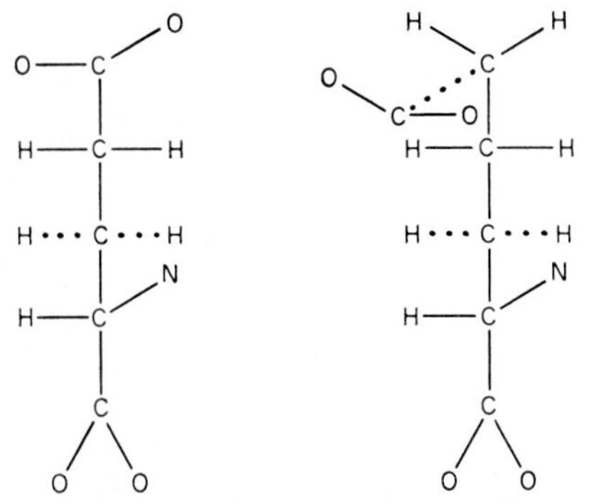

FIG. 6. For explanation see text.

ADP are bound maximally per mole of enzyme; however, the enzyme can bind no more than about 16 moles of ATP per mole. The affinity of the enzyme for ATP and for ADP is about the same at low concentrations of nucleotide. However, at higher concentrations of nucleotide about twice as much ADP as ATP is bound. These findings suggest that the binding of some ADP (or ATP) to the enzyme lowers the affinity of the enzyme for additional nucleotide. Thus, about 16 moles of ADP are readily bound to enzyme but the enzyme binds additional ADP with less affinity. The inability of the enzyme to bind more than about 16 moles of ATP per mole of enzyme suggests that the affinity for additional ATP is much less than that for ADP. We have considered the possibility that the active sites on the enzyme occur in pairs and that acceptance of a nucleotide molecule by one site of a pair reduces the affinity of the neighboring site for nucleotide. Such a model would appear to explain the equal affinity of the enzyme for ATP and ADP at lower nucleotide concentrations. The higher affinity of the enzyme for ADP than ATP at higher nucleotide concentrations might then be ascribed to the greater effect of the somewhat bulkier ATP molecule in reducing the affinity of the second site for nucleotide. The studies on the binding of nucleotides and those of Haschemeyer on the subunit structure of the enzyme suggest that there are four sites for nucleotide on each subunit. Very recently, Haschemeyer (1966) has examined the enzyme with the electron microscope and has obtained evidence that the eight subunits lie in positions that are arranged in a manner analogous to the corners of a cube. One can then visualize the enzyme as consisting of eight more or less spherical subunits each containing four active sites; the relationships between the subunits could be such as to permit interaction between pairs of active sites. It is interesting to speculate, on the basis of our present knowledge, as to how these sites might be arranged on the subunits. A possible arrangement is described in Fig. 7. The sites for nucleotide in this model are identical in each subunit, and the orientation of the subunits shown brings each site into close relationship with a site on an adjacent subunit. Obviously there are other possible explanations for the findings, and the present speculation requires further study. Additional physical and enzymatic investigations are now in progress.

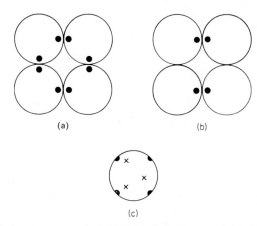

(a)   (b)

(c)

FIG. 7. Speculative arrangement of ADP binding sites on glutamine synthetase. The model consists of eight identical spherical subunits (each with four sites) arranged as the corners of a cube; there are 32 sites situated in pairs, 16 of which are located on two sides (a) and 16 of which are on four sides (b) of the cube. (c) Subunit (four sites for ADP). ×, Subunit binding sites.

REFERENCES

Haschemeyer, R. H. (1965). Paper presented before the Division of Biological Chemistry of the American Chemical Society, Sept. 13–17, Atlantic City, N.J., Abstract 68.

Haschemeyer, R. H. (1966). Paper presented before the Division of Biological Chemistry of the American Chemical Society, Sept. 12–16, New York, N.Y., Abstract 46.

Kagan, H. M., Manning, L. R. & Meister, A. (1965). *Biochemistry* **4**, 1063.

Kagan, H. M. & Meister, A. (1966a). *Biochemistry* **5**, 725.

Kagan, H. M. & Meister, A. (1966b). *Biochemistry* **5**, 2423.

Khedouri, E. & Meister, A. (1965). *J. Biol. Chem.* **240**, 3357.

Khedouri, E., Wellner, V. P. & Meister, A. (1964). *Biochemistry* **3**, 824.

Levintow, L. & Meister, A. (1953). *J. Am. chem. Soc.* **75**, 3039.

Levintow, L., Meister, A., Hogeboom, G. H. & Kuff, E. L. (1955). *J. Am. chem. Soc.* **77**, 5304.

Lineweaver, H. & Burk, D. (1934). *J. Am. chem. Soc.* **56**, 658.

Meister, A. (1962). *Enzymes* **6**, 443.

Pamiljans, V., Krishnaswamy, P. R., Dumville, G. & Meister, A. (1962). *Biochemistry* **1**, 153.

Wellner, V. P. & Meister, A. (1966). *Biochemistry* **5**, 872.

Wellner, V. P., Zoukis, M. & Meister, A. (1966). *Biochemistry* **5**, 3509.

Structural Alterations of Enzyme Ribonuclease A in Aqueous Solution at Acidic and Alkaline pH Regions

P. J. Vithayathil, A. S. Acharya and B. N. Manjula

Department of Biochemistry, Indian Institute of Science
Bangalore, India

Aqueous solutions of ribonuclease A have been maintained for different intervals of time in acidic and alkaline environments and changes in activity and chromatographic behaviour of the products have been studied. It was found that in 0·5 M HCl at 30°C, ribonuclease A (10^{-3} M) undergoes structural alterations without loss in activity during the initial 20 h of reaction. Neither peptide-bond cleavage nor gross changes in amino acid composition could be detected in this period. In 10 h, nearly 90% of ribonuclease A was converted to a product that was not eluted from CM-cellulose columns. In later stages of reaction, this product was found to give rise to two chromatographically distinct active components. The product formed in the initial stages was isolated by chromatography on IRC-50 as a fraction distinct from ribonuclease A. This new derivative was found to possess the same activity as ribonuclease A.

In the alkaline region, above pH 10·5, at 25°C ribonuclease A was found to show relatively rapid changes in activity with time. It was observed that at pH 11·0 ribonuclease A undergoes inactivation in the beginning and is subsequently reactivated as the reaction proceeds. The rates of these consecutive reactions were found to depend on ribonuclease A concentration. At $3·5 \times 10^{-4}$ M ribonuclease A concentration, the products exhibiting minimum and maximum activity are obtained in 9 and 18 min of reaction, respectively. The products were found to show increased activity when assayed in presence of S-peptide. Chromatographic analysis of the products of reaction have been made on IRC-50 columns at pH values of 6·1, 6·2, 6·3 and 6·4. The results indicate that ribonuclease A is converted initially to a less active material that is subsequently converted by reactions with itself or with ribonuclease A to an active "complex". These products appear as incompletely resolved two-component peak fractions in chromatographic runs. The chromatographic mobility of the reaction product was found to be more sensitive to changes in pH (in the region of 6·1 to 6·3) than ribonuclease A. On the basis of these findings, it is suggested that, at pH 11·0, transformation of ribonuclease A to a "resistant" product takes place in the initial 20 min of reaction.

1. Introduction

Enzyme ribonuclease A,† in aqueous solution at temperatures 20–40°C, is known to undergo irreversible structural alterations when maintained at pH regions below 1 and above 9. In a highly acidic or alkaline environment,

† The following abbreviations are used: RNase A, the major chromatographic component of bovine pancreatic ribonuclease; RNase S, S-protein, and S-peptide are the subtilisin-modified derivatives of RNase A (Richards & Vithayathil, 1959); FDNB, 1-fluoro-2,4-dinitrobenzene.

there is rapid fragmentation of the macromolecular structure of the protein and total loss of its catalytic function. Such a degradation is rather slow in the pH ranges 0·1–2 and 9–12·5, and physicochemical studies have shown that in these pH regions the primary reactions, such as abnormal ionization lead to subtle irreversible conformational changes of the protein. The present investigation has been directed towards the isolation of structurally altered forms of RNase A that are produced in these pH regions with a view to obtaining information on the influence of protein–protein interactions on the stability of catalytically active protein structures.

Preparations of structurally altered forms of RNase A by acid and alkali treatments have been reported in a few instances. RNase A when heated at 100°C for 2 min at pH 8·0 was found to yield a product exhibiting the same chromatographic pattern on CM-cellulose as that of crystalline RNase but having only 75% of the initial activity (Shapira & Parker, 1960). Bigelow (1961) studied the titration properties of the product formed from RNase maintained at pH 1·0 and 100°C for 2 h and was able to show that structural characteristics that were quite distinct from those of the starting material were present in the product. Richards & Vithayathil (1960) studied the kinetics of inactivation of RNase A exposed to 0·1 M NaOH, and have postulated the existence of an intermediate in the early stages of the reaction, which possessed structural characteristics different from those of RNase A and the final denatured product. This intermediate could be distinguished from the native as well as from the final denatured product by activity studies with subtilisin-modified derivatives of RNase A. By using this method of activity measurements for detecting structural alterations as well as chromatographic procedures for separating the derivatives, it has now been possible to isolate structurally altered derivatives of RNase A formed during the initial stages of reaction in acidic and alkaline environments. The present paper describes the detection, isolation and some structural characteristics of these derivatives.

2. Materials and Methods

(a) Materials

The RNase, Type 1A (Sigma Chemical Company, lot 65B–0350), was a gift from Mr Dan Broida. This commercial sample was chromatographed on CM-cellulose according to the procedure of Taborsky (1959). RNase A preparations were subjected to extensive dialysis, lyophilized and stored at 4°C until needed.

RNase S was prepared by the method of Richards & Vithayathil (1959) and purified by chromatography on CM-cellulose (Allende & Richards, 1962). S-Protein and S-peptide were prepared by the trichloracetic acid precipitation procedure (Richards & Vithayathil, 1959). S-Peptide as well as S-protein prepared in this manner were found to have no activity towards RNA when assayed separately at concentration levels up to $40 \mu g$. Equivalent amounts of S-peptide and S-protein regenerated full RNase A activity.

CM-cellulose was obtained from Sigma Chemical Company (lot 34B–1790, medium mesh, capacity 0·62 meq/g). Amberlite IRC–50 (H) was a product of Rohm & Haas Co. (Batch No. S.W.5288/51019), which was converted to smaller particle size by grinding and fractionated by the method of Hamilton (1958). All chromatographic columns were prepared with the material in the 200 to 300 mesh range.

Hydrochloric acid used was of analytical grade and was twice distilled in nitrogen atmosphere. All other reagents used were of analytical grade and were used without further purification. Only freshly distilled hydrochloric acid was used in experiments dealing with the reactions of RNaseA at acidic pH values.

(b) *Methods*

(i) *Activity measurements*

RNase A activity was followed by the release of acid-soluble nucleotides from RNA by the uranyl acetate–TCA procedure (Klee & Richards, 1957). For measuring changes of activity of protein solutions in presence of S-protein and S-peptide, appropriate amounts of these derivatives, representing nearly 1·5 equivalents, were added to the assay sample. For calculation of percentage activity of the protein solutions, the concentration of the protein was determined from absorbance measurements, a molar extinction coefficient of 9740 at 278 mμ being assumed (Saroff & Carroll, 1962).

(ii) *Spectrophotometric measurements*

These were made with a Beckman Model DU Spectrophotometer.

(iii) *pH measurements*

All pH measurements were carried out in a Radiometer type PHM 4 pH Meter, care being taken to see that the accuracy is of the order of at least ± 0.01 pH units.

(iv) *End-group analysis*

Amino terminal group analysis was performed with the FDNB technique of Sanger (1945) as modified by Levy (1955).

(v) *Performic acid oxidation*

This was carried out as described by Hirs (1956).

(vi) *Amino acid analysis*

Amino acid composition was determined by the method of Spackman *et al.* (1958) with an automatic recording analyser at an operating temperature of 50°C.

(vii) *Chromatography on Amberlite IRC–50*

Columns of this resin (0·9 × 30 cm) were prepared after equilibration with 0·2 M phosphate buffer of desired pH and operated at the same pH. All runs were made in the cold room at 5°C at a flow rate of 5 ml per hour. Standard runs with known amounts of RNase A in the pH region of 6·1–6·50 gave a recovery of 85–95 % at consistently reproducible peak positions.

(viii) *Chromatography on CM-cellulose*

Chromatographic experiments with CM-cellulose were carried out in the cold room at 5°C according to the procedure of Taborsky (1959). A 500-ml. closed mixing chamber was initially filled with 0·005 M tris–HCl buffer, pH 8·0. The reservoir contained the same buffer made up to 0·25 M with NaCl. By using this chromatographic procedure, a consistent recovery of 90 to 95 % of RNase A could be obtained.

(ix) *Experimental procedures for studies at acidic pH regions*

To samples of RNase A, usually 10–80 mg, in a glass tube (1·2 × 8 cm) was added 5 ml of HCl of required molarity, and the tube was tightly stoppered after being flushed with pure nitrogen. The tube was kept in a constant-temperature water-bath maintained at 30° ± 0·2°C. At different intervals of time, aliquots of the protein solution were removed for assay and isolation, care being taken to flush the tube with nitrogen every time. For activity determinations, the protein solutions were first diluted to approximately 0·01 M HCl concentration, neutralized with 0·01 M NaOH to pH 7·0 and made up to a definite volume with 0·2 M sodium acetate buffer of pH 5·1. Aliquots from this solution were subsequently used for RNase assay. For isolation purposes, aliquots from the reaction tube were diluted 20 fold with distilled water and immediately lyophilized. The product obtained was lyophilized thrice more after the addition of 20 ml of distilled water at the end of each lyophilization. The final product was always a white, fluffy material.

(x) *Experimental procedures for studies at alkaline pH regions*

The reactions were carried out in a thermostated 10-ml glass vessel having provision for introduction of electrodes, inlet and outlet for nitrogen, stirring and removal of samples. Solutions of RNase A in 0·05 M NaCl were placed in the vessel and set aside for 15 min to attain a temperature of 25 ± 0·2°C.

After the tube had been flushed with nitrogen for 10 min, the protein solution was quickly brought to the desired pH by the addition of 0·1 M NaOH. Known volumes of the solutions were removed from the reaction mixture at different intervals of time and placed in 0·1 M sodium acetate buffer (pH 5·0) to arrest the reaction. These solutions were subsequently analysed for their activity. For isolation of the protein, the buffered solutions were dialysed against distilled water and lyophilized. Only products obtained in this manner were analysed on CM-cellulose columns. In some chromatographic experiments with IRC-50, the buffered protein solution itself was directly placed on the columns.

3. Results

(a) Studies at acidic pH region

When RNase A was maintained in 0·1 M HCl at 30°C, at a protein concentration of 10^{-3} M, no significant changes in activity were observed even after 96 h. At an acid concentration of 0·5 M, however, gradual decrease in activity occurred after 20 h of reaction indicating the possible breakdown of the protein molecule (Fig. 1, insert). It was, however, not possible to detect any structural breakdown and release of new N-terminals by end-group analysis up to a period of 60 h. Hence, it appeared likely that alteration in the structure without involving peptide-bond cleavage has occurred in the early stages of the reaction. To verify this, the 60-h sample (0·5 M HCl reaction) was dialysed, lyophilized and its amino acid composition determined. The results are shown in Table 1. It may be seen that the amino acid composition is very similar to that of RNase A.

Results of a detailed chromatographic examination of the products that were obtained at 0, 10, 20, 40 and 60 h of reaction in 0·5 M HCl are presented in Fig. 1. In these experiments same amounts of protein (4·6 mg) were loaded on the column. It may be seen from Fig. 1, that of the original RNase only 15% was present in the 10-h sample, the remaining amount was not eluted up to a volume of 170 ml. In the 20-h sample, however, no unreacted RNase A was present, but two other fractions eluting at 10 to 40 ml. and 55 to 100 ml. were present. Increased amounts of these latter two fractions were present in the 40- and the 60-h samples. An approximate calculation of the yield of these various fractions from absorbance measurements is given in Table 2. It could be readily seen from the Table that approximately 85% of the RNase A has been converted into a product not chromatographing under these conditions in the initial 10 h of the reaction in 0·5 M HCl. In subsequent stages of reaction, this material appears as two distinct fractions. Both these fractions were found to be enzymatically active, though not to the same extent as RNase A.

TABLE 1. Amino acid composition† of derivatives of RNase A
obtained from reactions at acid and alkaline pH regions

	Theoretical value‡	RNase A‡	Derivative of RNase A from 60 h reaction in 0·5 M HCl	Derivative of RNase A from 60-min reaction at pH 11·0‡
Cysteic acid	8·0	7·9	—	7·9
Methionine sulphone	4·0	4·2	—	3·9
Aspartic acid	15·0	15·3	14·5	15·3
Threonine	10·0	10·4	10·2	10·5
Serine	15·0	14·8	15·3	14·9
Glutamic acid	12·0	11·9	11·9	12·3
Proline	4·0	3·8	4·0	3·9
Glycine	3·0	2·6	2·1	3·2
Alanine§	12·0	12·0	12·0	12·0
Half cystine	—	—	7·8	—
Valine	9·0	8·1	8·1	8·7
Methionine	—	—	3·6	—
Isoleucine	3·0	1·7	1·8	2·1
Leucine	2·0	2·0	1·8	2·1
Tyrosine	6·0	5·4	5·3	5·3
Phenylalanine	3·0	3·2	2·8	3·2
Lysine	10·0	10·4	10·0	10·3
Histidine	4·0	3·8	3·8	3·9
Arginine§	4·0	4·0	4·0	4·0

† Expressed as moles of amino acid per mole of protein. No corrections have been applied in the calculations either for destruction or incomplete release of amino acids during hydrolysis.
‡ Values given are for the performic acid oxidized samples.
§ Alanine and arginine contents were taken as reference for calculations of the acidic and neutral amino acids, and of basic amino acids, respectively.

The product obtained in the 10-h reaction in 0·5 M HCl (8 mg) was chromatographed on Amberlite IRC-50, at pH 6·42. The chromatographic pattern is shown in Fig. 2. It may be seen from this chromatography that all of the product has been eluted in two fractions, one of which represents unreacted RNase A (15%) and the other, eluting at 13·5 ml., represents the remaining 85% of the total material. The activity of this new RNase A derivative was found to be the same as that of RNase A itself (Fig. 2). Fractions containing this derivative were pooled, dialysed and lyophilized. The product obtained as a very light, white powder amounted to 5·5 mg.

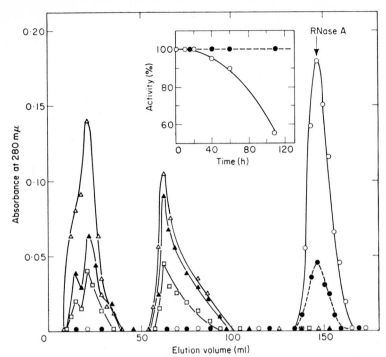

Fig. 1. Chromatography on CM-cellulose column of RNase A (10^{-3} M) maintained in 0·5 M HCl at 30°C for different intervals of time. Samples (4·6 mg in each case) were applied to columns of CM-cellulose (0·9 × 20 cm). Elution pattern of reaction products at: ○, 0 h; ●, 10 h; □, 20 h; ▲, 40 h; and △, 60 h are shown by the separate curves.

Insert shows the changes in activity of RNase A (10^{-3} M) when maintained in: ●, 0·1 M HCl; and ○, 0·5 M HCl at 30°C for different intervals of time.

TABLE 2. Composition of the products obtained from RNase A during the reactions in 0·5 M HCl at 30°C as determined by CM-cellulose chromatography

Reaction time, hr	Composition†			Protein not chromato-graphed§
	RNase A	Fraction I‡	Fraction II‡	
0	95	0	0	5
10	15	0	0	85
20	0	18	32	50
40	0	30	45	25
60	0	50	40	10

† Expressed as % of the amount of protein placed on the columns.
‡ Fraction I and fraction II represent the protein components eluting between 10 and 40 ml. and between 55 and 100 ml., respectively (Fig. 1).
§ Values given are the difference in total amount of protein that was recovered in various fractions and the total amount of protein placed on the columns.

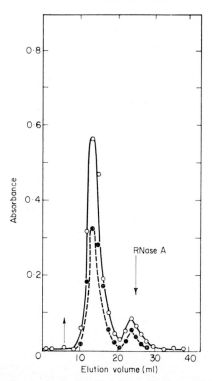

FIG. 2. Chromatography on Amberlite IRC-50 at pH 6·42 of RNase A (10^{-3} M) maintained in 0·5 M HCl at 30°C for 10 h. An 8-mg portion of the reaction product was applied to the column (0·9 × 30 cm) and the elution pattern is given by the continuous-line curve, absorbance at 280 mμ, and the activities of the fractions are shown by the broken-line curve.

The ultraviolet-absorption spectra of the above derivative, RNase A, S-protein and alkali-denatured RNase A are presented in Fig. 3. A close similarity of the spectral characteristics of the derivative with that of RNase A is apparent.

(b) *Studies at alkaline pH region*

Changes in activity of RNase A maintained for different intervals of time in the alkaline pH region are shown in Fig. 4. As will be seen from Fig. 4(c), the enzyme retains its original activity without any detactable changes for at least 80 min at pH 10·5, whereas there is a regular decrease in its activity when kept at pH 12·2 and 13·0. In the intermediate pH region of 11·0 and 11·5, the activity curve shows an initial dip, a rise and a final slow fall. Of particular interest in the present study are the changes that take place in this intermediate pH region where the activity changes are indicative of subtle molecular re-arrangements.

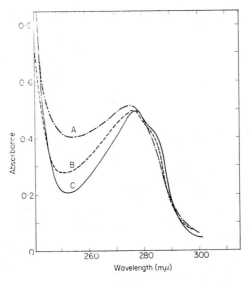

Wavelength (mμ)

Fig. 3. Ultraviolet-absorption spectra (curve C) of RNase A and of its derivative (isolated by IRC-50 chromatography from 0·5 M HCl reaction) in 0·2 M phosphate buffer, pH 6·42, continuous line. The spectra of alkali-denatured RNase A (prepared by keeping RNase A in 0·1 M NaOH for 2 hr, curve A, and of S-protein, curve B, in 0·2 M phosphate buffer, pH 6·42 are given for comparison.

At pH 11·0 the activity reaches a minimum point after 16 min and returns to nearly 100% after 32 min. These minimum and maximum points in the activity curve have been changed to 9 and 18 min in the reaction at pH 11·5, most probably reflecting increased rates of the re-arrangement reactions. At pH 11·0, the initial concentration of protein has been found to have an influence on the maximum and minimum points (Fig. 4(b)) in the activity curve. On increasing the concentration from $1·75 \times 10^{-5}$ M to $3·5 \times 10^{-5}$ M, the minimum point increases from 8 to 16 min, whereas the maximum point decreases from 64 to 32 min. In this concentration region, the inactivation reaction proceeds at a faster rate at the lower concentration and the activation reaction at a slower rate. Above this range, both inactivation and activation reaction rates are enhanced with increase in concentration up to 7×10^{-5} M. Increasing the concentration further to $3·5 \times 10^{-4}$ M was found to have little effect on these rates. It may be noted that at higher concentrations the activity increases up to a level of 110% in 20 min but, however, returns to the original value in 60 min of reaction. This type of increased activity of RNase has been observed in a few instances (Kalnitsky & Rogers, 1956; Allende & Richards, 1962) and a possible reason is given by Allende & Richards (1962).

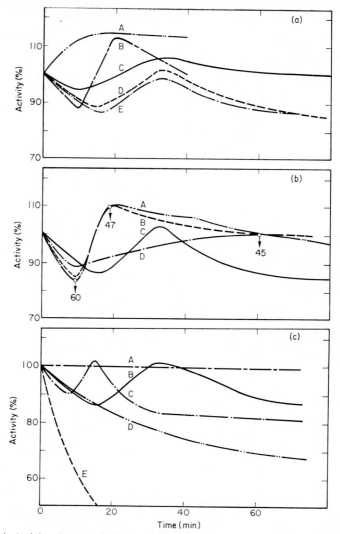

FIG. 4. Activity changes of RNase A maintained in aqueous solutions at alkaline pH regions.

(a) The influence of S-peptide and S-protein on the activity of products formed from RNase A maintained at pH 11·0 and 25°C for different intervals of time. The activity changes of RNase A at a concentration of $3·5 \times 10^{-5}$ M are given by the curves indicated: D, when assayed alone; C, when assayed in presence of S-peptide; and E, when assayed in presence of S-protein. The changes in activity of RNase A at a concentration of $3·5 \times 10^{-4}$ M are given by the curves indicated: B, when assayed alone; and A, when assayed in presence of S-peptide.

(b) The effect of RNase A concentration on the changes in activity when maintained at pH 11·0 and 25°C. Concentrations: curve A, $3·5 \times 10^{-4}$ M; curve B, $7·0 \times 10^{-5}$ M; curve C, $3·5 \times 10^{-5}$ M; and curve D, $1·75 \times 10^{-5}$ M. The percentage recovery of RNase A from CM-cellulose chromatography of the samples at 10, 20 and 60 min of reaction (RNase A concentration $3·5 \times 10^{-4}$ M) is indicated by the numbers given.

(c) Changes in activity of RNase A ($3·5 \times 10^{-5}$ M) maintained at 25°C and pH values of: curve A, 10·5; curve B, 11·0; curve C, 11·5; curve D, 12·2; and curve E, 13·0.

The effect of added S-protein and S-peptide on the activity of the products formed during reaction at pH 11·0 is shown in Fig. 4(a). Addition of S-peptide increased the activity of the products at all stages of reaction whereas addition of S-protein resulted in a slight, but noticeable, decrease in activity. At higher RNase A concentrations, the maximum increase in activity with added S-peptide is attained in the region of minimum activity.

The products obtained from the reaction at pH 11·0 at an RNase A concentration of $3·5 \times 10^{-4}$ M were chromatographed on CM-cellulose. The percentage recovery of RNase A from the samples at 10, 20 and 60 min is indicated in Fig. 4(b). It may be seen that the reaction at pH 11·0 has contributed to a decrease of 40% of RNase A during the initial 10 min. A further decrease of 13 and 15% can be observed in 20 and 60 min of reaction, respectively. Some amounts of inactive protein materials that eluted unadsorbed from the columns were also found to be present. The amino acid analysis of the 60-min sample after dialysis and performic acid oxidation has been carried out and the results are given in Table 1. No significant changes in the amino acid composition from that of RNase A could be observed.

A detailed study was made of the distribution of the components present in the products of reaction at pH 11·0 by chromatographic analysis on Amberlite IRC-50 with 0·2 M phosphate buffer as eluent. The results of these experiments are represented schematically in Figs. 5–7.

In Fig. 5(a) is given the chromatographic pattern of the 60-min reaction products on IRC-50 at pH 6·4. Nearly quantitative recovery of the protein was obtained in the initial 40 ml of eluent. The major peak eluting very close to the position of RNase A was found to be preceded by two smaller peaks. This observation in conjunction with the finding that only 45% of RNase A was recoverable on CM-cellulose chromatography was indicative of inhomogeneity of the peak at RNase A position.

The chromatographic pattern on IRC-50, at pH 6·3 of the 5-, 10- and 20-min reaction products, after dialysis and lyophilization, is shown in Fig. 5(b). It may be clearly seen that nearly half of the products of the 5-min reaction consist of RNase A, the other half being represented by two components chromatographing in peak positions 15 and 25 ml, respectively, eluting earlier than RNase A. In the 10-min reaction product, there is considerable decrease in RNase A peak with concomitant increase in the 25-ml peak component. Some decrease in the 15-ml component may also be observed. The overall yield of protein in these three peaks is less than that of the 5-min sample. This loss of protein was not observed in the 20-min sample where the general pattern is similar to that of the 10-min sample.

The chromatographic pattern at pH 6·2 of the 10- and 20-min reaction products is given in Fig. 5(c). In this experiment, the products of reaction

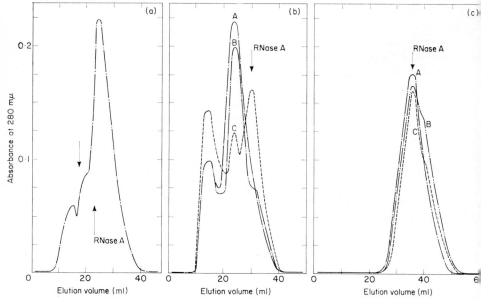

FIG. 5. Chromatography on Amberlite IRC-50 column (0·9 × 30 cm) of RNase A (3·5 × 10⁻⁴ M) maintained at pH 11·0 and 25°C.

(a) Elution pattern at pH 6·42 of products (6·5 mg) after 60 min of reaction. The peak position of RNase A is indicated by ↑, and the region giving increased activity with added S-peptide is marked by ↓.

(b) Elution pattern at pH 6·3 of the products (6·5 mg each) after reaction times of: curve C, 5 min; curve B, 10 min; and curve A, 20 min.

(c) Elution pattern at pH 6·2 of RNase A (6 mg), curve A, and for the products (6 mg each) after reaction times of: curve C, 10 min; curve B, 20 min.

were directly placed on the columns. It may be seen that in the 10-min sample the recovery is not quantitative, just as for pH 6·3 chromatography. However, in this chromatographic run, only two components seem to be present in both 10- and 20-min samples. Moreover, the major peak corresponding to RNase A is now followed by a minor component represented as a shoulder in the chromatographic pattern.

Fig. 6(a) and (b) shows the chromatographic pattern at pH 6·1 of 5-, 10-, 20- and 40-min samples. In this chromatography, RNase A itself shows the presence of a minor component chromatographing at a peak position of 28 ml (Hirs, 1962). There is no marked change in the amount of this component in any of the reaction products; only the major RNase A component shows changes in composition with reaction. After 5 min of reaction there is a decrease of RNase A peak and the formation of a shoulder in the region of 48–55 ml. After 10 min, the overall yield is reduced, and a two-component peak is observed in the region of 40–50 ml. In the 20-min sample the recovery

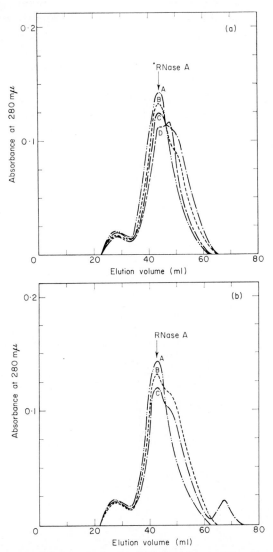

FIG. 6. Chromatography on Amberlite IRC-50 columns (0·9 × 30 cm) at pH 6·1 of RNase A maintained at pH 11·0 and 25°C (RNase A concentration, 3·5 × 10⁻⁴ M).

(a) Elution pattern of RNase A, 5·6 mg, curve A, and of the products (5·6 mg each) after reaction times of: curve B, 5 min; curve D, 10 min; and curve C, 20 min.

(b) Elution pattern of RNase A, 5·6 mg, curve A, and of the products after 40 min of reaction. Curve B shows the pattern when the product of reaction (5·6 mg) is applied to the columns directly, and curve C shows the pattern of the same product when applied to the columns after dialysis and lyophilization.

is nearly quantitative, and the shape of the chromatogram is similar to that of the 5-min sample; however, the quantities of protein represented by RNase A and the shoulder-peak components are different. The 40-min sample was found to chromatograph in nearly the same manner as the 20-min sample. To see whether any change in composition occurs during dialysis and lyophilization, the 40-min sample was subjected to this treatment and chromatographed. The pattern obtained is included in Fig. 6(b). It is seen that losses in the amount of 40- to 60-ml peak components do take place resulting in the formation of a component eluting in the 68-ml peak position.

RNase A activity measurements of all the fractions represented in the chromatograms (Fig. 7) have been carried out, and all the protein-containing

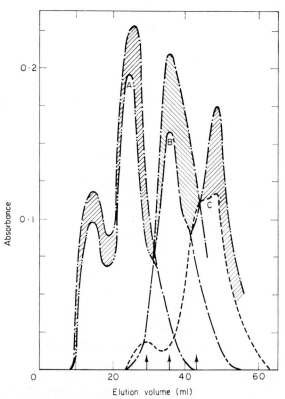

Fɪɢ. 7. Chromatography on Amberlite IRC-50 columns (0·9 × 30 cm) of RNase A (3·5 × 10⁻⁴ ᴍ), maintained at pH 11·0 and 25°C for 10 min, and then chromatographed at pH values of: curve A, 6·3; curve B, 6·2; curve C, 6·1. Positions of RNase A peak when chromatographed at pH values of 6·3, 6·2 and 6·1 are indicated by the arrows at 29·5, 35·5 and 43·5 ml. elution volumes, respectively. The fractions showing increased activity in the presence of S-peptide are indicated by the shaded areas in each elution pattern for purposes of comparison of changes in their mobilities with that of RNase A.

fractions were observed to have nearly the same activity as the RNase A fraction. However, there was significant changes in the activity shown by the different fractions when assayed in presence of S-peptide. These are shown in Fig. 7, in which the changes in activity pattern of the fractions of 10-min reaction sample at pH 6·3, 6·2 and 6·1 are given. Similar activity patterns were observed for the 20- and 40-min reaction products. The increased activity of the fractions in presence of S-peptide is schematically represented by the shaded portions in the figure. In this Figure are also indicated the expected positions for RNase A. It may be noted that RNase A and the peak giving increased activity with S-peptide have significantly different mobilities with changes in pH; this latter peak, which precedes RNase A at pH 6·3, takes a position very much after RNase A in the pH 6·1 chromatography.

4. Discussion

The results given above deal with the chromatographic analysis of the products obtained from RNase A maintained in acidic and alkaline environments.

It was shown that in 0·5 M HCl RNase A does not show changes in amino acid composition for 60 h of reaction. Further, no decrease in activity could be observed for 20 h of reaction although no RNase A was found to be present by CM-cellulose chromatography. It was also shown that within 10 h of reaction, almost 90% of RNase A has been converted to chromatographically homogeneous (IRC-50) and completely active product.

It may be inferred from these results that structural alterations of RNase A, not involving gross changes in its primary structure have contributed to the formation of this new RNase A derivative. From the present study it is not possible to say whether reactions such as amide-bond hydrolysis, disulphide interchange (Anfinsen, 1957), N–O acyl shift or aggregation (Crestfield et al., 1962) have taken place during this reaction. In the absence of information regarding these types of structural changes, it is difficult to consider the question of whether the acid treatment is capable of unfolding the protein molecule in such a manner as to lead to enzymatically active altered folding in RNase A. The RNase A derivative that is formed during the initial stages is subsequently converted to other enzymatically active products during the course of the reaction by processes not involving peptide-bond cleavage.

In the alkaline region, RNase A was shown to undergo changes in its activity and in its IRC-50 chromatographic pattern that reflect the structural alterations of the protein. The experiments in which a detailed study has been made involve the reactions at pH 11·0 in the concentration region of $3·5 \times 10^{-4}$ M at a temperature of 25°C. The reaction has been followed by activity measurements and chromatographic analysis for the initial reaction period of 60 min. Structural changes of RNase A in this period can reasonably be restricted to unfolding and refolding reactions of the peptide chain and protein–protein interactions. No changes in the amino acid composition of the protein were observed in this period of reactions indicating the absence of protein fragmentation. Desulphuration reactions of the nature observed at higher pH values (Brown et al., 1959) are also not apparent from the amino acid composition. The possibility of reactions involving racemization, de-amination (Brown et al., 1959), etc., can be considered only when information is available regarding their existence under the experimental conditions of the present study.

In the pH 11·0 reaction, RNase A was found to give derivatives of minimum and maximum activity in the initial period of 10 and 20 min, respectively. After 20 min of reaction, the activity changes were comparatively small. Similarly, chromatographic analysis on CM-cellulose revealed that the RNase A content was rapidly decreased in the initial 20 min to nearly 50% of the original, the changes after this period being relatively small. It may be concluded from these results that the initial fast reactions taking place at pH 11·0 are more or less completed in the first 20 min of the reaction. Subsequent reactions probably represent the slow decomposition of a structural form of RNase A that is more resistant to irreversible changes at pH 11·0.

On the basis of the results of the present study, it is suggested that at pH 11·0 RNase A takes part in an initial unfolding reaction of the nature postulated by Richards & Vithayathil (1960). The product of this reaction takes part in a subsequent reaction either with itself or with unreacted RNase A to form "stable", enzymatically active product in 20 min of reaction. A few evidences give validity to the above postulations. They are:

(a) That an irreversible reaction takes place from the beginning is evident from the decrease in activity and the changes in chromatographic pattern of RNase A after 5 and 10 min of reaction. Moreover, ionization of abnormal tyrosine residues has been observed in titration studies (Tanford et al., 1955) in this pH region at 25°C. Influence of S-peptide on RNase A activity is apparent from the beginning of reaction (Fig. 4(a)).

(b) That the initial reaction is followed by a subsequent reaction involving the initial product is apparent from the rise in the activity curve after 10 min of reaction. In case such a reaction was not present, the activity curve should have continued to show a fall with time. The relatively retarded influence of S-peptide on the total activity after the first 10 min of reaction also point to the decrease of the initial product of reaction earlier to 20 min of reaction.

Some characteristics of the products of the above indicated consecutive reactions, are apparent from the chromatographic analysis. Product I (initially formed) and/or product II (derived from product I) are not stable under conditions of CM-cellulose chromatography, by which only RNase A and inactive materials could be isolated. The possibility of RNase A being a constituent part of product II cannot be ruled out in this analysis.

Analysis of the products obtained at different reaction time on IRC-50 reveals the complete loss of fraction chromatographing in RNase A peak position in 20 min of reaction (Fig. 5(b)). The loss of RNase A is now represented by a new fraction with a peak at 25 ml in the chromatogram. The protein material represented by this peak is eluted in incompletely separated two-component peak fractions when chromatographed at pH values of 6·2 (Fig. 5(c)) and 6·1 (Fig. 6). Formation of products chromatographing in this fashion is strongly indicative of protein–protein interactions in them. This being very likely in the present instance, it is suggested that product II is formed from interactions of the following type:

$$\text{Product I} + \begin{array}{c}\text{RNase A}\\ \text{or}\\ \text{Product I}\end{array} \rightarrow \text{Product II}$$

The observed properties of product II may be summarized in the following way: (a) formed from pH 11·0 "resistant" structure; (b) shows increased activity than RNase A; (c) relatively less influence of S-peptide on activity than product I; (d) can be dissociated to give 50% of RNase A on CM-cellulose chromatography; (e) can be chromatographed on IRC-50 as a "complex" showing signs of dissociation.

The faster rate of formation of the maximum active component with increasing concentrations of RNase A (Fig. 4(b)) is also indicative of "complex" formation involving the initial product. Such treatments as dialysis and lyophilization, possibly lead to the disruption of the complex and subsequent formation of components that are chromatographically distinct from RNase A (Fig. 6(b)).

The heterogeneous nature of the peaks obtained on IRC-50 chromatography is also apparent from the results presented in Fig. 7. The different fractions from the products of the 10-min reaction show varying degrees of increased activity with S-peptide (the initial peak shown in the pH 6·3 chromatography is probably a degradation product of the "complex" represented by the major peak—this preparation was obtained only after dialysis and lyophilization). In both pH 6·3 and 6·1 chromatography, there does not seem to be any appreciable increase in activity with added S-peptide in the fraction eluting in the peak position represented by RNase A. The material that shows enhanced activity with S-peptide migrates at a slower rate at pH 6·1 and at a faster rate at pH 6·3 than RNase A. It appears, therefore, that the "complex" formed is much more sensitive to pH changes than RNase A in the pH region 6·1 to 6·3.

A possible explanation for the above indicated behaviour seems to be that either the "complex" or the products formed from it by dissociation (conditions of activity measurements probably favour dissociation), or both, have an "S-protein type of conformation", in which the orientation of the S-peptide part is different from that in RNase A or RNase S. Added S-peptide can either reverse the "S-protein conformation" to the original RNase A conformation or bind to the protein to exhibit the observed enhanced activity. It has been observed that the histidine residues in S-protein were not reactive towards carboxymethylation, and this was explained as due to conformational differences of RNase A and S-protein (Vithayathil & Richards, 1961). The greater sensitivity of the products formed in the pH 11·0 reaction towards chromatographic mobility in the 6·1–6·3 pH region probably reflect changes in configuration of one or more histidine residues of RNase A.

The present studies on RNase A point to an apparently new phenomenon associated with its structure, namely, its capacity to preserve a catalytically active structure by subtle conformational changes when exposed to environmental conditions of high acidity and alkalinity.

ACKNOWLEDGMENT

We wish to thank Professor P. S. Sarma for his continued interest in these studies. The studies in the acidic and alkaline regions form part of the thesis work of B. N. Manjula and A. S. Acharya, respectively.

REFERENCES

Allende, J. E. & Richards, F. M. (1962). *Biochemistry* **1**, 295.
Anfinsen, C. B. (1957). *Fedn Proc. Fedn Am. Socs exp. Biol.* **16**, 783.
Bigelow, C. C. (1961). *J. biol. Chem.* **236**, 1706.
Brown, R. K., Delaney, R., Levine, L. & Van Vunakis, H. (1959). *J. biol. Chem.* **234**, 2043.
Crestfield, A. M., Stein, W. H. & Moore, S. (1962). *Arch. biochem. Biophys. Suppl.* **1**, 217.
Hamilton, P. B. (1958). *Analyt. Chem.* **30**, 914.
Hirs, C. H. W. (1956). *J. biol. Chem.* **219**, 611.
Hirs, C. H. W. (1962). *Brookhaven Symp. Biol.* **15**, 154.
Kalnitsky, G. & Rogers, W. I. (1956). *Biochim. biophys. Acta* **20**, 378.
Klee, W. A. & Richards, F. M. (1957). *J. biol. Chem.* **229**, 489.
Levy, A. L. (1955). *Meth. biochem. Analysis* **2**, 359.
Richards, F. M. & Vithayathil, P. J. (1959). *J. biol. Chem.* **234**, 1459.
Richards, F. M. & Vithayathil, P. J. (1960). *Brookhaven Symp. Biol.* **13**, 115.
Sanger, F. (1945). *Biochem. J.* **39**, 507.
Saroff, H. A. & Carroll, W. R. (1962). *J. biol. Chem.* **237**, 3384.
Shapira, R. & Parker, S. (1960). *Biochem. biophys. Res. Commun.* **3**, 200.
Spackman, D. H., Stein, W. H. & Moore, S. (1958). *Analyt. Chem.* **30**, 1190.
Taborsky, G. (1959). *J. biol. Chem.* **234**, 2652.
Tanford, C., Hauenstein, J. D. & Rands, D. G. (1955). *J. Am. chem. Soc.* **77**, 6409.
Vithayathil, P. J. & Richards, F. M. (1961). *J. biol. Chem.* **236**, 1386.

Studies on the Structural Requirements of the Substrate of Protein Kinase

A. R. Pawse, K. Sankaran and K. S. V. Sampath Kumar

Biochemistry and Food Technology Division
Bhabha Atomic Research Centre, Trombay, Bombay, India

The hen egg yolk phosphoprotein, phosvitin and the milk phosphoprotein, casein, are phosphorylated by the action of protein kinase (ATP: protein phosphotransferase, EC 2.7.1.37). Other protein substrates tested so far are not phosphorylated. The characteristics of the substrates that accept phosphate were investigated with a view to explaining the unique specificity of the enzyme. Heated substrates accept more phosphate, whereas the substrates exposed to 8 M urea do not function effectively. The enzyme can transfer phosphate even to peptides derived from casein by the action of pepsin and trypsin. The peptide substrate exposed to 8 M urea also loses its ability to incorporate phosphate. These results are discussed in relation to the peculiarities of the substrate molecule.

1. Introduction

Investigations on phosphoproteins have been confined for a long time only to storage proteins, such as casein of milk and phosvitin of egg yolk, with particular reference to their nutritive value and the type of linkages by which the phosphorus is bound to the protein molecule (Perlmann, 1955). The demonstration of the existence of a distinct cellular phosphoprotein fraction and the ability of this protein fraction to incorporate radioactive phosphate very rapidly in various cells (Davidson *et al.*, 1951; Williams-Ashman & Kennedy, 1952; Johnson & Albert, 1953; Kennedy & Smith, 1954) have stimulated considerable investigations on the mechanistic, functional and chemical features of this protein fraction. These investigations have implicated a role for the phosphoprotein fraction in various metabolic reactions, for example in enzyme catalysis (Engstrom, 1961), in phosphorylation of membrane-bound proteins in metal-ion transfer (Heald, 1962; Ahmed *et al.*, 1963), in electron transfer (Boyer, 1963) and in energy storage (Rabinowitz & Lipmann, 1960). More recently, a possible role in cellular regulation processes has been brought to light by the investigations of Langan and Smith (quoted from Kleinsmith *et al.*, 1966) who have shown that a phosphoprotein isolated from rat liver nuclei overcomes the inhibition by histone of DNA-dependent RNA polymerase.

In phosphoproteins, phosphate is mostly esterified to the hydroxyl groups of serine (Lipmann & Levene, 1932; Lipmann, 1933). Phosvitin has most of its serine hydroxyl groups esterified, phosphoserine accounting for more than 50% of the amino acid residues in the protein (Taborsky & Allende, 1962; Allerton & Perlmann, 1965; N. Ramachandran & K. S. V. Sampath Kumar, unpublished). The metabolically active phosphoprotein fractions in normal and tumour tissues have their serine residues phosphorylated during their turnover (Agren et al., 1954; Kennedy & Smith, 1954). Only traces of phosphothreonine have been reported so far in casein (de Verdier, 1953), and in phosvitin (Allerton & Perlmann, 1965).

The mechanism by which the phosphorus gets into the protein molecule has been the subject of many recent studies. Burnett & Kennedy (1954) made an observation of conceptual significance that an enzyme in normal rat liver mitochondria, protein kinase, can phosphorylate proteins through the mediation of ATP. This enzyme uses as its substrate only casein or enzymatically dephosphorized casein and, to a very limited extent, ovalbumin. The site of phosphorylation in these substrates has been again shown to be a serine residue. This enzyme has now been purified partially from several sources (Rabinowitz, 1962).

The specificity of this enzyme was investigated by Burnett & Kennedy (1954) using rat liver mitochondrial enzyme, by Rabinowitz & Lipmann (1960) using yeast enzyme, and by Sundararajan et al. (1958, 1960a) using the enzyme from lactating mammary gland of rabbit. Their observations could by summarized as follows: (i) casein and phosvitin are the only substrates for this enzyme; (ii) partially dephosphorized proteins are better acceptors; (iii) serine as a free amino acid is not phosphorylated; and (iv) the intactness of the protein moiety is not an obligatory requirement, since certain peptides derived from these proteins could accept phosphate.

With these observations in view, we have investigated certain mechanistic features of this phosphorylation reaction in an effort to explain the unique preference of this enzyme to phosphorylate only casein and phosvitin. The experimental details presented in this discussion pertain to the observations made with enzyme preparations from livers of tumour-bearing animals.

2. Protein Kinase from Tumour-bearing Animals

The high metabolic activity of phosphoprotein fraction in ascites tumour cells (Kennedy & Smith, 1954), the capability of a non-specific tissue phosphoprotein fraction to function as a substrate for protein kinase (Schmidt & Davidson, 1956) the general distribution of this enzyme in a wide variety of cells with different functions (Rabinowitz, 1962) and the presence of this enzyme in tissues, such as mammary gland, in which an active phosphoprotein synthesis is taking place (Sundararajan et al., 1958), prompted us to investigate the role, if any, for this enzyme in the metabolism of phosphoproteins. These studies led us to the observation that the activity of the enzyme in tumour cells is the same as that of normal liver, but the enzyme is present in much higher concentrations in the livers of the animals bearing tumours like Yoshida ascites or fibrosarcoma (Pawse *et al.*, 1966). Further, the enzyme is localized both in the mitochondria and in the cytoplasmic supernatant of liver homogenates. Both the subcellular enzymes have been purified partially (A. R. Pawse and K. S. V. Sampath Kumar, unpublished). The mitochondrial enzyme purified by sonication, ammonium sulphate precipitation and calcium phosphate gel adsorption, and the supernatant enzyme concentrated by salt fractionation and calcium phosphate gel adsorption have been used in these investigations. Essentially similar results are obtained with both the preparations.

3. Substrate Specificity of Protein Kinase

The experimental conditions for the assay of protein kinase have been described in an earlier paper (Pawse *et al.*, 1966). The phosphorylation of the protein is followed by measuring the radioactivity incorporated into the substrate when $AT^{32}P$ labelled at both terminal positions (Pressman, 1960) is used as phosphate donor. Phosvitin prepared by butanol treatment of the lipovitellin fraction of egg yolk (Sundararajan *et al.*, 1960*b*; N. Ramachandran & K. S. V. Sampath Kumar, unpublished) was routinely used as a substrate for the enzyme. The results presented in Table 1 confirm our earlier findings and those of others (Burnett & Kennedy, 1954; Rabinowitz, 1962;

TABLE 1. Phosphorylation of various proteins by protein kinase†

Protein	Radioactivity incorporated (counts/min)	Protein	Radioactivity incorporated (counts/min)
Phosvitin	2121	Haemoglobin	37
Casein	1415	Histone	140
Cytochrome *c*	17	Polyserine	0
Serum albumin	88	Polyserine + phosvitin	1820

† The reaction mixture consisting of 1 mg of substrate, $AT^{32}P$ (1 μmole containing $1 \cdot 2 \times 10^5$ counts/min in the terminal phosphate), 50 μmoles of tris (hydroxymethylaminomethane) pH 7·4, 5 μmoles of $MgCl_2$ and 30 μmoles of KCl and the enzyme in a total volume of 2·0 ml was incubated at 37°C for 15 min. The protein precipitated with trichloroacetic acid was washed thoroughly, and the radioactivity in the precipitate was measured. Appropriate enzyme and substrate blanks were also set up. The incorporation in the acid-soluble polyserine was followed by hydrolysing the excess of $AT^{32}P$ with M HCl and separating the polyserine from inorganic phosphate on a Sephadex G-10 column.

Rodnight & Lavin, 1964) that casein and phosvitin function as acceptors. Other proteins, such as serum albumin, haemoglobin, cytochrome c are not effective. Proteins such as trypsin, chymotrypsin, ribonuclease and pepsin have been shown earlier to be not amenable for phosphorylation (Burnett & Kennedy, 1954). Histone incorporates very little phosphate under the experimental conditions tested. These results indicate that a unique configuration of the protein molecule is indeed needed in a functional substrate.

Williams & Sanger (1959) have reported that in phosvitin and casein phosphoserine occurs in blocks of four or more residues, and similar phosphoseryl clusters have been reported in the tissue phosphoprotein fraction of ascites tumour cells (Moret *et al.*, 1962). The presence of repeating seryl units may represent a unique structure that might explain the suitability of these proteins as acceptors. This specific structural requirement may not be present in proteins that do not accept phosphate. Synthetic poly-L-serine tested in our system failed to incorporate phosphate. Also polyserine in the presence of phosvitin was not phosphorylated, nor was there any increase in the incorporation of phosphate into phosvitin in the presence of polyserine. It has been reported earlier that completely dephosphorylated phosvitin failed to function as an acceptor, whereas partially dephosphorylated protein proved to be more effective. It appears likely therefore that poly-L-serine with some of its residues phosphorylated might function as an acceptor.

4. Phosphorylation of Peptide Fragments

The complete structural integrity of the protein molecule is not an essential prerequisite for phosphorylation. This has been demonstrated first by Sundararajan *et al.* (1958) that the enzyme isolated from mammary gland can utilize paranuclein, the peptic-resistant core derived from casein, as a substrate. Similar results have been obtained with paranuclein in the present investigation (Table 2). Rabinowitz & Lipmann (1960) demonstrated that even small fragments, phosphopeptides derived from tryptic digests of casein, can be phosphorylated by the yeast enzyme. In the present investigation, we used fragments derived from paranuclein as a substrate. Paranuclein was digested with trypsin, and the phosphopeptides were precipitated as barium salt by the addition of alcohol to 50% concentration. The precipitate represents a mixture of phosphopeptides, but in the present study, this peptide mixture was used as a substrate without the individual peptides being purified. Barium was removed from the peptide mixture by treatment with Dowex-50×8, and the results obtained with this phosphopeptide mixture are presented in Table 2.

The experimental method followed for detecting the phosphate incorporation into the acid-soluble phosphopeptide mixture is as follows. After incubation at $37°C$ for 20 min with the enzyme and AT^{32}P, the reaction

TABLE 2. Phosphorylation of peptides derived from casein†

Substrate	Radioactivity incorporated (counts/min)
Paranuclein	1830
Phosphopeptide fraction	1361

† The incorporation into trichloroacetic acid precipitable paranuclein was followed as described under Table 1. Details for following the incorporation in the acid-soluble peptide fraction are described in the text and in Fig. 1.

mixture was acidified with HCl to M acid concentration and heated in a boiling-water bath for 10–12 min to hydrolyse completely the terminal radio-active phosphates of $AT^{32}P$. The resulting solution was chromatographed on a 66 cm × 1 cm column of Sephadex G-10 equilibrated with water as the eluant. The peptide fraction was tested by the method of Lowry et al. (1951) and the colour was read on a Klett–Summerson colorimeter. The peptide fraction was resolved completely from radioactive inorganic phosphate. The peptide fractions were pooled again, lyophilized and re-chromatographed on the same system to ensure that there is no overlap of ^{32}P peak. A typical elution pattern is given in Fig. 1. These results indicate that certain unique peptide fragments derived from casein have the necessary structural requirement in them to function as a substrate of protein kinase.

5. Phosphorylation of Heated Substrates

In order to determine whether secondary and tertiary structural characteristics in the substrate have any role to play in the phosphorylation reaction, substrates subjected to different treatments were tested in the assay system. Phosvitin and paranuclein were heated at 130°C for 1 h at pH 5·5 in 0·2 M acetate buffer. Under these conditions, phosvitin remained soluble. As indicated in Table 3, these substrates incorporate 50% more radioactivity than control samples. It is unlikely that the increase is mainly due to conformational alterations in the molecule, which make available more sites for phosphorylation, since heating can cause partial dephosphorylation of phosphoproteins (Belec & Jenness, 1962) and the higher incorporation of radioactivity in the heated samples may thus be due to the phosphorylation of the sites made available as a result of dephosphorylation. Partially dephosphorized proteins have been shown earlier to accept more phosphate (Sundararajan et al., 1960; Rabinowitz & Lipmann, 1960). With our enzyme system, we have shown that phosvitin and paranuclein subjected to the action of wheat germ phosphatase can incorporate more radioactivity (Table 3).

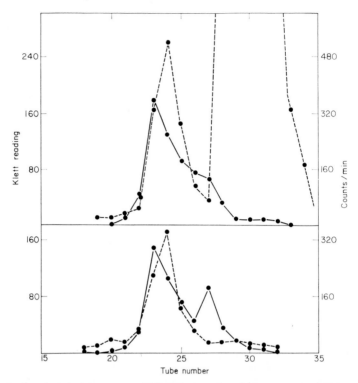

FIG. 1. A typical elution pattern of labelled phosphopeptide on Sephadex G-10 column. Details of the reaction mixture are given in Table 1. Radioactivity is indicated by the broken line. The upper traces represent the elution pattern of the labelled phosphopeptide from the incubation mixture. The contents of the tubes containing the peptide were pooled and lyophilized. The lower traces represent the elution pattern obtained on re-chromatography of a portion of the peptide on the same column.

TABLE 3. Effect of heat and phosphatase on the substrate of protein kinase†

Treatment	Radioactivity incorporated (counts/min)		
	phosvitin	paranuclein	phosphopeptide
Control	1028	1276	1360
Heated substrate	1507	1806	2004
Phosphatase-treated substrate	1712	2000	1818

† Assay conditions as described in Table 1 and in the text.

The effect of heating of the tryptic peptide fraction was also investigated. As for the proteins, there is an increase in the ability of the peptide to accept phosphate. A higher incorporation of radioactivity in the peptide was observed when the peptide was treated with wheat germ phosphatase (Table 3).

To confirm that heating can cause dephosphorylation, phosvitin labelled with ^{32}P in the conventional assay system was heated at 130°C at pH 5·5 and also at 100°C at pH 5·5, and the radioactivity left on the protein was measured at regular intervals. The results shown in Table 4 indicate that heating of

TABLE 4. Effect of heat on phosphorylated phosvitin

Time of heating (min)	Radioactivity on the protein after heating (counts/min)	
	100°C	130°C
0	2517	2641
5	2130	2503
15	2049	1898
30	1705	1450
45	1281	1137
60	1004	780

these proteins can solubilize the phosphate, and that this dephosphorylation is temperature dependent in agreement with the findings of Belec & Jennes (1962). It remains to be established whether heating can effect dephosphorylation of the phosphopeptides also.

6. Effect of Urea on the Substrates

Even though it has been established that a complete integrity of the protein moiety is not a prerequisite for functioning as a substrate, it was of interest to determine whether any specific conformational characteristics, not present in the proteins that do not accept phosphate, determine the suitability of those proteins that do accept phosphate. Phosvitin and paranuclein were exposed to 8 M urea for 1 h at pH 7·5 at room temperature or 0°C, and then dialysed exhaustively against repeated changes of water in the cold. The urea-treated samples incorporate much less phosphate, amounting to only 50% of the control samples not exposed to urea (Table 5). The inactivation by urea seems to vary with concentration, the inhibition brought about by 2 M and 6 M urea under the same conditions being 25% and 45% respectively. Heated phosvitin or phosphatase-treated phosvitin, when subjected to 8 M urea lose almost 70% of their original incorporation, thereby indicating that probably some conformational characteristics in these molecules determine their efficiency as a substrate. These results are difficult to reconcile with the

TABLE 5. Effect of urea on the substrates†

| Treatment | Radioactivity incorporated (counts/min) | | |
	Phosvitin	Paranuclein	Phosphopeptide
Control	2616	2353	817
Urea treated	1386	1200	118

† Experimental details are described in the text.

observations that certain peptide fractions derived from the protein can function as acceptor. The tryptic peptide fractions that can serve as a substrate (Table 2) were exposed to 8 M urea at 0°C at pH 7·5 for 1 h, and the urea was subsequently removed by chromatography on Dowex-1-chloride column. The peptides are eluted from the column with 0·5 M HCl, lyophilized and then used as a substrate in the regular assay system. Surprisingly, the peptide fraction also failed to incorporate any phosphate, only 15% of the control radioactivity being observed in the urea-treated peptide fraction (Table 5). Traces of ammonium cyanate that might be present in urea solution can alter the substrate by modifying the amino groups (Stark & Smyth, 1963), and so the experiments were repeated at pH 4·5 with freshly prepared urea solutions. A similar decrease (about 50%) in the incorporations was observed in phosvitin treated with urea at pH 4·5.

To eliminate the possibility of trace quantities of adsorbed urea on the substrate inhibiting the enzyme activity, corresponding to 0·2 ml of substrate solution that is added in the conventional assay, 0·2 ml of urea was added to the incubation medium in varying concentrations. Even when the concentration of the added urea solution was 2 M, there was no inhibition in the uptake of radioactivity by phosvitin, thus precluding the possibility of an inhibition of phosphorylation reaction by any adsorbed urea.

Ultraviolet spectroscopy when used to detect difference between control and urea-treated phosvitin failed to reveal any difference within the range studied (220–310 mμ). Similarly, no change could be detected in the urea-treated paranuclein or tryptic peptide fraction. These studies indicate that the differences observed in the phosphorylation reaction between the control and urea-treated samples, if due to any conformational alterations, could not be detected by the method employed.

Oxazoline formation between a hydroxyl group of serine and a peptide linkage can conceivably take place in urea-treated samples, thereby masking a potential site of phosphorylation. When the peptide fraction or phosvitin was treated with 8 M urea at pH 4·0 and pH 8·0, no spectral characteristic of the oxazoline ring could be detected in the ultraviolet region.

7. Discussion

The specificity of protein kinase is unique, in that the enzyme phosphorylates only casein and phosvitin and not any other protein. Casein and phosvitin occur already in nature as phosphoproteins, and the additional phosphorylation observed with the enzyme system employed is due to a substitution of the remaining potential sites of phosphorylation. The phosphorylation observed with these substrates by an enzyme present in mitochondria may not have a direct relation to their biosynthesis, but it is pertinent to mention that it has been shown that phosphorylation of an intact protein is the ultimate step in the biosynthesis of casein in the lactating mammary gland (Sampath Kumar et al., 1960) and in the biosynthesis of ovalbumin (Sanger & Hosquard, 1962). The ubiquitous distribution of this enzyme probably indicates a role in the phosphorylation of the tissue phosphoprotein fraction.

The ability of protein kinase to use as substrates only naturally occurring phosphoproteins was examined with a view to explain the inertness of other proteins that do not accept phosphate. The role, if any, of a definite configurational environment in the substrate moiety was investigated.

The intactness of the molecule is not an obligatory requirement as it is shown that paranuclein, the peptic-resistant core derived from casein, and a phosphopeptide fraction derived from paranuclein function as acceptors (Table 2).

Attempts were made to induce conformational alterations in the protein by heat and by urea. Since phosvitin remained soluble on heating, it proved amenable for studies of this type. These experiments were carried out at pH 5·5. A higher pH was avoided, as it might favour dephosphorylation because the phosphate of phosphoprotein can be solubilized by alkali treatment (Posternak & Posternak, 1928). The increased phosphorylation observed after heating at pH 5·5 may not be entirely due to secondary alterations in the molecule exposing more sites for phosphorylation. It has been observed by Belec & Jenness (1962) and also in the present investigation that heating at pH 5·5 can bring about dephosphorylation (Table 4). The higher incorporation observed in the heated samples may thus be due to the availability of more sites as a result of dephosphorylation, although the role for configurational changes in the molecule contributing to an enhanced incorporation cannot be precluded. A higher incorporation is observed in the heated tryptic fraction, possibly involving the same mechanism by which the parent protein incorporates more radioactivity after a similar treatment.

The effect of urea on these molecules illustrates an interesting problem. That the enzyme can use a small peptide substrate—a peptide having only 12 amino acids has been found to be effective (Rabinowitz & Lipmann,

1960)—is only suggestive of a particular environment in the substrate that activates the potential site of phosphorylation. It was indeed surprising that the protein substrate treated with 8 M urea could incorporate only 50% of the radioactivity of the control samples. The result is even more striking with phosvitin or paranuclein, which are heated first and then exposed to urea. In all these experiments, the observed inhibition does not appear to be due to any adsorbed urea on the substrate affecting the enzyme action. Even with extraneously added urea well in excess of that which might be present in urea-treated substrate after dialysis, the enzyme can still function effectively without any loss in activity. The u.v. spectra of phosvitin and urea-treated phosvitin are exactly identical. It is even more surprising that the tryptic peptide fraction after exposure to 8 M urea does not accept phosphate. Whatever the conformational prerequisite in the protein substrate or a peptide fraction derived from it is, urea has an inhibitory effect and the mechanism by which this is brought about is not clear.

Preliminary studies have been carried out to evaluate the role of different amino acid side chains in the phosphorylation of the protein or peptide substrate. It has been claimed that peptide fragments devoid of histidine and arginine have been found to be acceptors (Rabinowitz, 1962), although the detailed analytical data on these have not been published. We investigated the action of cyanogen bromide on paranuclein and phosvitin. Under the experimental conditions used, this had no effect on the substrates. The tryptic peptide fraction treated with hydrogen peroxide lost almost all its ability to incorporate phosphate. However, the same tryptic peptide fraction on acetylation could still incorporate about 75% of the original activity. In all these different modifications, the extent to which the various amino acid side chains have been modified remains to be established.

The unique and interesting properties of the enzyme should prompt further investigations on the purification of the peptide substrate, on the peculiarity of the serine hydroxyl group that is phosphorylated, and on the evaluation of the conformational prerequisites for the parent protein or even on its derived fragment to function as a substrate for protein kinase.

REFERENCES

Agren, G., de Verdier, C. H. & Glomset, J. (1954). *Acta chem. scand.* **8**, 503, 1570.
Ahmed, K., Judah, K. D. & Wallgren, H. (1963). *Biochim. biophys. Acta*, **69**, 428.
Allerton, S. E. & Perlmann, G. E. (1965). *J. biol. Chem.* **240**, 3892.
Belec, J. & Jenness, R. (1962). *Biochim. biophys. Acta*, **63**, 512.
Boyer, P. D. (1963). *Science, N.Y.* **141**, 1147.
Burnett, G. & Kennedy, E. P. (1954). *J. biol. Chem.* **211**, 969.
Davidson, J. N., Frazer, S. C. & Hutchinson, W. C. (1951). *Biochem. J.* **49**, 311.
de Verdier, C. H. (1953). *Acta chem. scand.* **1**, 196.
Engstrom, L. (1961). *Biochim. biophys. Acta*, **54**, 179.

Heald, P. J. (1962). *Nature, Lond.* **193**, 451.

Johnson, R. N. & Albert, S. (1953). *J. biol. Chem.* **200**, 335.

Kennedy, E. P. & Smith, S. W. (1954). *J. biol. Chem.* **207**, 153.

Kleinsmith, L. J., Allfrey, V. G. & Mirsky, A. E. (1966). *Proc. natn. Acad. Sci. U.S.A.* **55**, 1182.

Lipmann, F. (1933). *Biochem. Z.* **262**, 3.

Lipmann, F. & Levene, P. A. (1932). *J. biol. Chem.* **98**, 109.

Lowry, O. H., Rosebrough, N. J., Farr, A. L. & Randall, R. J. (1951). *J. biol. Chem.* **193**, 265.

Moret, V., Sperti, S. & Siliprandi, N. (1962). *Biochim. biophys. Acta*, **62**, 196.

Pawse, A. R., Sankaran, K. & Sampath Kumar, K. S. V. (1966). *Indian J. Biochem.* **3**, 205.

Perlmann, G. (1955). *Adv. Protein Chem.* **10**, 1.

Posternak, S. & Posternak, T. (1928). *C.r. hebd. Séanc. Acad. Sci., Paris*, **187**, 313.

Pressman, B. E. (1960). *Biochem. Prep.* **1**, 14.

Rabinowitz, M. (1962). *In* "The Enzymes", ed. by P. D. Boyer, H. Lardy and K. Myrback, Vol. 6, p. 119. New York: Academic Press.

Rabinowitz, M. & Lipmann, F. (1960). *J. biol. Chem.* **235**, 1043.

Rodnight, R. & Lavin, B. E. (1964). *Biochem. J.* **93**, 84.

Sampath Kumar, K. S. V., Sundararajan, T. A. & Sarma, P. S. (1960). *J. biol. Chem.* **235**, 679.

Sanger, F. & Hoequard, E. (1962). *Biochim. biophys. Acta*, **62**, 606.

Schmidt, G. & Davidson, H. M. (1956). *Biochim. biophys. Acta*, **19**, 116.

Stark, R. & Smyth, D. G. (1963). *J. biol. Chem.* **238**, 214.

Sundararajan, T. A., Sampath Kumar, K. S. V. & Sarma, P. S. (1958). *Biochim. biophys. Acta*, **29**, 449.

Sundararajan, T. A., Sampath Kumar, K. S. V. & Sarma, P. S. (1960*a*). *Enzymologia* **21**, 314.

Sundararajan, T. A., Sampath Kumar, K. S. V. & Sarma, P. S. (1960*b*). *Biochim. biophys. Acta*, **38**, 360.

Taborsky, G. & Allende, C. C. (1962). *Biochemistry*, **1**, 406.

Williams-Ashman, H. G. & Kennedy, E. P. (1952). *Cancer Res.* **12**, 415.

Williams, J. & Sanger, F. (1959). *Biochim. biophys. Acta*, **33**, 294.

A Fluorescent Probe at the Active Site of α-Chymotrypsin

RICHARD P. HAUGLAND AND LUBERT STRYER

Department of Chemistry, Stanford University, and the
Department of Biochemistry, Stanford University School of Medicine
Palo Alto, California, U.S.A.

A highly fluorescent anthraniloyl group has been inserted at the active site of α-chymotrypsin. The anthraniloyl acyl enzyme is indefinitely stable at neutral pH, allowing a detailed spectrofluorimetric study of the mobility and polarity of the active site. The acylating reagent, *p*-nitrophenyl anthranilate, is very selective in its reactivity. Only one anthraniloyl chromophore is introduced into chymotrypsin, rendering the enzyme inactive. Chymotrypsinogen, di-isopropylphosphoryl chymotrypsin, trypsinogen, lysozyme and serum albumin do not react at all, while trypsin reacts slowly.

The anthraniloyl chromophore in the acyl enzyme can be selectively excited since its absorption (342 mμ) and emission (422 mμ) maxima are distinct from those of the aromatic residues of the protein. The absorption and emission spectra of methyl anthranilate and other anthraniloyl model compounds vary with solvent polarity. This sensitivity to solvent makes it feasible to determine the polarity of the immediate environment of the acyl group in the enzyme. From the positions of the absorption and emission maxima, as well as from the broadening of those spectra, it is concluded that the environment of the anthraniloyl group at the active site is highly polar. The fluorescence polarization and emission kinetics in the nanosecond range were measured to determine the flexibility of the active site. The rotational relaxation time of the anthraniloyl group is 49 nsec,[†] indicating that the active site of the acyl enzyme is rigid. The anthraniloyl chromophore has no rotational mobility independent of the motion of the whole chymotrypsin molecule. Emission and excitation spectra reveal that energy is transferred from the tryptophan residues of the acyl enzyme to the anthraniloyl group with an efficiency of 65%.

1. Introduction

Fluorescence spectroscopy has proven to be a valuable technique in the study of protein structure and interactions in solution (Velick, 1961; Steiner & Edelhoch, 1962). The method can provide detailed information concerning the active sites of enzymes if a suitable fluorescent chromophore is located near the active center. The fluorescent group should have an absorption and emission maximum distinct from that of the aromatic residues of the protein, and its excited state lifetime should be sufficiently long so that the rotational

---

† Abbreviations used: A, emission anisotropy; NPA, *p*-nitrophenyl anthranilate; nsec, nanosecond (10^{-9} sec); ρ, rotational relaxation time; τ, excited state lifetime.

mobility of the active site can be determined (Weber, 1953). In addition, it is desirable if the emission properties are sensitive to the polarity of the environment of the chromophore (Stryer, 1965). Finally, the fluorescent probe should be highly selective in terms of its site of attachment to the protein.

We report here a spectrofluorimetric study of the active site of α-chymotrypsin, using a fluorescent probe which meets these criteria. The p-nitrophenyl ester of anthranilic acid (1) reacts specifically with the active site of α-chymotrypsin to form a highly fluorescent anthraniloyl chymotrypsin (2).

This derivative is stable for months at neutral pH, allowing a detailed study of its spectroscopic properties. Absorption and fluorescence studies of anthraniloyl chymotrypsin have provided a measure of the polarity and rotational mobility of the active site of the acyl enzyme.

2. Experimental Methods

(a) Materials

The synthesis of p-nitrophenyl anthranilate (NPA, I) has been described by Staiger & Miller (1959). We obtained, however, a product which melts at a significantly higher temperature than previously reported. Commercial grade isatoic anhydride (29·9 g, 0·183 mole), p-nitrophenol (25·4 g, 0·183 mole) and powdered sodium hydroxide (1·5 g) were heated with 150 ml dioxane on a steam bath. Carbon dioxide evolution proceeded briskly above 75°. After 45 min, the dark reaction mixture was poured into 75 ml warm water and cooled, yielding 27·5 g yellow crystals, m.p. 127–128° (cf. Staiger and Miller, m.p. 108°). An additional 10·4 g, m.p. 126–128°, was obtained by concentrating the filtrate to near dryness and recrystallizing the residue from absolute ethanol. The analytical sample recrystallized from methanol in wide yellow sheaths, m.p. 127·8–128·3°. Analysis–calcd for $C_{13}H_{10}N_2O_4$: C, 60·46; H, 3·90; N, 10·85; found C, 60·28; H, 3·80; N, 10·95.

Chymotrypsinogen, α-chymotrypsin (3 × recrystallized), di-isopropyl-phosphorylchymotrypsin, trypsinogen, and trypsin were obtained from Worthington, while bovine serum albumin and lysozyme were purchased from Armour.

(b) Anthraniloyl chymotrypsin

Anthraniloyl chymotrypsin (2) was prepared by addition of 1 ml of $4\cdot8 \times 10^{-3}$ M NPA ($4\cdot8$ μmoles) in acetonitrile to 20 ml of $2\cdot0 \times 10^{-4}$ M α-chymotrypsin ($4\cdot0$ μmoles) in $0\cdot1$ M phosphate buffer, pH $6\cdot8$, at $5°$. The NPA was added in five aliquots at three hour intervals. After an additional 15 h at 5°C, the yellow solution was filtered to remove excess NPA that had precipitated and then dialysed for 2 days against several changes of water.

(c) Absorption and fluorescence spectra

Absorption spectra were obtained on a Cary model 14 recording spectro-photometer using 1 cm cell paths. Fluorescence emission, excitation, and polarization measurements were performed on a recording spectrofluori-meter described previously (Stryer, 1965). The emission spectra reported here are the direct recorder tracings which have not been corrected for the variation with wavelength in the sensitivity of the detection system. The relative sensitivity of the 1P28 photomultiplier-grating monochromator system has been experimentally determined to be $3\cdot68$, $3\cdot34$, $2\cdot97$, $2\cdot69$, $2\cdot55$, $2\cdot29$, $1\cdot91$, $1\cdot78$, $1\cdot59$, $1\cdot40$, $1\cdot31$, $1\cdot20$, $1\cdot08$, $0\cdot99$, $0\cdot89$, $0\cdot81$ and $0\cdot72$ at 10 mμ intervals from 340 mμ to 500 mμ. The corrected fluorescence excitation spectra and polarization measurements were recorded directly using a ratio amplifier. Corning CS 3–73 filters were used to isolate the emission in both the excitation and polarization measurements. Fluorescence spectra were taken at $20\cdot0 \pm 0\cdot2$°C.

The fluorescence polarization is expressed in terms of the emission aniso-tropy, A. Jablonski (1960) has emphasized the advantage of using A rather than p, the customary measure of polarization. The emission anisotropy is defined as

$$A = \frac{F_x - F_y}{F_x + 2F_y}, \quad \text{while} \quad p = \frac{F_x - F_y}{F_x + F_y}.$$

(d) Nanosecond fluorescence kinetics

The excited state lifetime of the anthraniloyl group was measured on a nanosecond fluorimeter designed by L. Hundley, R. Coburn, E. Garwin, and L. Stryer (unpublished). A flash lamp operated at 12 kV and a repetition rate of about 1 kc provides light pulses which have a width at half-height of less than 3 nsec. The emission was detected by an RCA 1P21 photo-multiplier tube operated at $1\cdot3$ kV and a Tektronix sampling oscilloscope.

Multiple scans (typically 64) of the sampling oscilloscope output are averaged on a LINC computer, which then writes a magnetic tape for detailed analysis on the IBM 7090. Computer analysis of the nanosecond data is necessary because the duration of the light pulse is comparable to the excited state lifetime of many chromophores of biological interest. The observed time course of fluorescence, $R(t)$, is related to the light pulse and instrument response time $L(t')$, by the expression

$$R(t) = \int_0^t L(t')\,e^{-(t-t')\tau}\,dt'$$

if the emission is characterized by an exponential decay of lifetime τ. $R(t)$ and $L(t')$ are experimentally observed. τ is then determined by evaluating $\sum L(t')\,e^{-(t-t')/\tau}$ for various trial values of τ and finding the one that gives the best least-squares fit to $R(t)$. When the emission is partially polarized, as in anthraniloyl chymotrypsin, the lifetimes of the parallel and perpendicularly polarized components differ (Jablonski, 1960). The mean lifetime depends on the kinetics of the sum of the components, $F_x + F_y + F_z$. When the exciting light is y-polarized, the total emission is proportional to $F_y + 2F_x$, since $F_x = F_z$. As noted by Jablonski (1960), the emission polarized at 55° to the direction of excitation is in fact proportional to $(F_y + 2F_x)$. In the present study, a Polaroid-type HNB sheet polarizer was used to obtain y-polarized excitation. The emission was observed at right angles to the direction of excitation, with a Polaroid HN 32 sheet polarizer oriented at 55° to y. A Corning CS 7–60 filter was used for excitation, while the HN 32 polarizer served as the emission filter.

3. Results

(a) *Reaction of p-nitrophenyl anthranilate with α-chymotrypsin*

Spectrophotometric and spectrofluorimetric measurements reveal that *p-nitrophenyl anthranilate reacts specifically and stoichiometrically with α-chymotrypsin*. When excess *p*-nitrophenyl anthranilate is added to α-chymotrypsin, 1·0 equivalent *p*-nitrophenol is released per equivalent of enzyme, as determined by following the absorbance of the *p*-nitrophenolate ion at 410 mμ. The reaction is complete within 90 min and no additional *p*-nitrophenol is formed during the next several hours. The fluorescence emission spectrum (Fig. 1) provides further information. Addition of 1·3 equivalents NPA to 10^{-5} M α-chymotrypsin leads to a large decrease in the 333 mμ emission peak and to a large increase in the 422 mμ emission maximum. The half-time of the reaction is about 25 min. The 333 mμ peak is due to the fluorescence of the tryptophan residues in α-chymotrypsin, while the 422 mμ emission comes from the anthraniloyl chromophore. The decrease

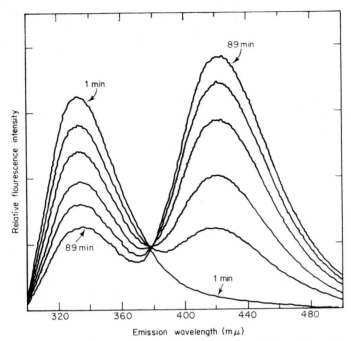

FIG. 1. The reaction of *p*-nitrophenyl anthranilate ($1 \cdot 4 \times 10^{-5}$ M) with α-chymotrypsin ($1 \cdot 0 \times 10^{-5}$ M) is shown by changes in the emission spectrum on excitation at 290 mμ. The tryptophan emission at 333 mμ decreases due to energy transfer to the anthraniloyl group, while the anthraniloyl fluorescence at 422 mμ increases because of release of *p*-nitrophenol.

of the 333 mμ peak is due to energy transfer from the tryptophan residues to the anthraniloyl group. The increase in fluorescence at 422 mμ is the result of the release of the *p*-nitrophenol group, which had completely quenched the fluorescence of the anthraniloyl chromophore in NPA. It is evident that anthranilic acid is not released in the course of the reaction. There is no peak or shoulder at 393 mμ, the emission maximum of anthranilic acid. Furthermore, the existence of an isoemissive point (Anderson & Weber, 1965) at 379 mμ confirms that only two fluorescent species are present.

The constancy of the emission and absorption spectra of the anthraniloyl chymotrypsin following extensive dialysis and gel filtration chromatography indicates that *the anthraniloyl group is covalently bonded to the enzyme.* Moreover, the complex is stable for months at pH 6·8. The stability of the anthraniloyl chymotrypsin makes it feasible to carry out extensive spectro-fluorimetric studies of the modified enzyme.

The enzymatic activity of α-chymotrypsin is virtually completely inhibited by reaction with p-nitrophenyl anthranilate. At pH 6·8, anthraniloyl chymotrypsin has less than 5% of the activity of the native enzyme. The assay was carried out with glutaryl-L-phenylalanine *p*-nitroanilide as substrate (Erlanger *et al.*, 1964).

(b) *Specificity of p-nitrophenyl anthranilate as a fluorescent labeling reagent*

Chymotrypsinogen, di-isopropylphosphoryl chymotrypsin, bovine serum albumin, and lysozyme do not react with NPA. Excess NPA was added to 10^{-5} M solutions of these protein. There was no change in absorbance at 410 mμ or in the fluorescence emission spectrum after 24 h.

Trypsin, but not trypsinogen, does react with NPA, though at a slower rate than chymotrypsin.

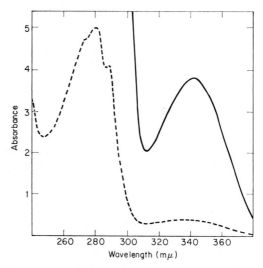

Fig. 2. Absorption spectrum of anthraniloyl chymotrypsin in 0·1 M phosphate buffer, pH 6·8. An absorbance of 1 corresponds to an extinction coefficient of 10,000 cm²/mmole for the broken line spectrum or 1000 cm²/mmole for the full line spectrum.

(c) *Absorption and emission spectra of anthraniloyl chymotrypsin*

The absorption spectrum of anthranilyol chymotrypsin is given in Fig. 2. The extinction coefficient is $5·0 \times 10^4$ cm²/mmole at 280 mμ and $4·0 \times 10^3$ cm²/mmole at 342 mμ. The concentration of the solution was determined by amino acid analysis. The observed extinction coefficient at 342 mμ is consistent with a stoichiometry of one anthraniloyl group per chymotrypsin, since the extinction coefficient of methyl anthranilate in a variety of solvents ranges from $3·8 \times 10^3$ to $5·4 \times 10^3$ cm²/mmole.

The emission spectrum (Fig. 3) shows a maximum at 422 mμ. The absolute quantum yield of the anthraniloyl chromophore when attached to chymotrypsin is 0·53. The emission was excited at 336 mμ, where all of the absorption is due to the anthraniloyl group.

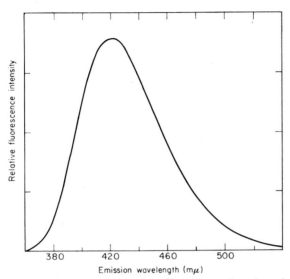

FIG. 3. The emission spectrum of the anthraniloyl chromophore in anthraniloyl chymotrypsin. The excitation wavelength was 336 mμ.

(d) *Absorption and emission spectra of model compounds*

Absorption and emission spectra of methyl anthranilate, *p*-cresyl anthranilate, and anthranilamide were obtained in solvents of varying polarity. The solvents were cyclohexane, dioxane, acetonitrile, methanol and water. The absorption and emission maxima are given in Tables 1 and 2.

The emission maxima of these compounds are markedly dependent on the polarity of the solvent. There is a shift of some 40 mμ to the red as the solvent polarity increases from cyclohexane to water. In contrast, the solvent depend-

TABLE 1. Absorption maxima (mμ) of model compounds

| | Solvent | | | | |
	Water[a]	Methanol	Acetonitrile	Dioxane	Cyclohexane
Methyl anthranilate	327	336	335	335	332
Anthranilamide	316	328	327	331	330
p-Cresyl anthranilate	334	343	341	340	337
Anthraniloyl chymotrypsin	342				

[a] 0·1 M phosphate buffer, pH 6·8.

TABLE 2. Emission maxima (mµ) of model compounds

	Water[a]	Methanol	Acetonitrile	Dioxane	Cyclohexane
Methyl anthranilate	420	405	391	390	380
Anthranilamide	418	406	393	390	386
p-Cresyl anthranilate	428	418	402	401	386
Anthraniloyl chymotrypsin	422				

[a] 1·0 M phosphate buffer, pH 6·8.

ence of the absorption maxima is complex. A small shift to the red is observed in going from cyclohexane to dioxane (Table 1). A significant shift to lower wavelengths is, however, observed in going from dioxane to water. In fact, the absorption maxima in water are at lower wavelengths than in cyclohexane.

The emission spectra of methyl anthranilate in cyclohexane, dioxane and water are shown in Fig. 4. As the solvent polarity increases, there is a broadening of the spectrum as well as a red shift of 2500 cm^{-1}. The width of the emission spectrum at half-height is 3100 cm^{-1}, 3400 cm^{-1} and 3600 cm^{-1} in cyclohexane, dioxane and water, respectively. A similar

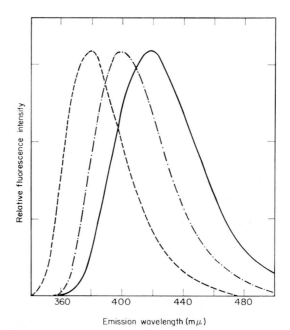

Relative fluorescence intensity

Emission wavelength (mµ)

FIG. 4. The solvent-dependence of the emission spectrum of methyl anthranilate. As the solvent polarity increases from cyclohexane (broken line) to dioxane (dot-dash line) and water (full line), there is a large shift to the red in the emission spectrum. In addition, the emission spectrum becomes broader as solvent polarity increases.

broadening of the emission spectrum is observed for the other model compounds. It is of interest to note that for anthraniloyl chymotrypsin (Fig. 3), the width at half-height is 3700 cm^{-1}.

The width of the near-ultraviolet absorption band of the model compounds varies with solvent polarity in the same manner. The width at half-height in the absorption spectrum of methyl anthranilate is 3200 cm^{-1}, 3600 cm^{-1} and 4400 cm^{-1} in cyclohexane, dioxane and water, respectively. The corresponding width in the absorption spectrum of anthraniloyl chymotrypsin is 4200cm^{-1}.

(e) *Energy transfer*

The excitation and emission spectra demonstrate that energy is transferred from the tryptophan residues to the anthraniloyl group. The emission spectrum (Fig. 1) shows that the tryptophan fluorescence is quenched, while the excitation spectrum (Fig. 5) reveals that the energy is in fact transferred to the anthraniloyl group. These spectra provide independent measures of the efficiency of energy transfer.

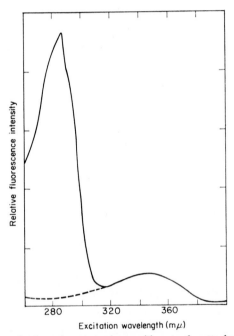

FIG. 5. Energy transfer from the tryptophan residues to the attached anthraniloyl group is shown by this excitation spectrum. The observed excitation spectrum (full line) has a peak of high magnitude at 280 mμ, where nearly all of the absorption is due to the aromatic residues of the protein. The calculated excitation spectrum corresponding to an absence of energy transfer (broken line) is strikingly different at wavelengths below 300 mμ. The efficiency of energy transfer is 67%.

The efficiency of transfer, T, is related to the intensity of tryptophan emission in native chymotrypsin, F_0, and in anthraniloyl chymotrypsin, F, by the expression

$$T = 1 - (F/F_0).$$

From the emission spectrum, F/F_0 is 0·37, and so the transfer efficiency is 63%.

The transfer efficiency can also be obtained from the excitation spectrum of the anthraniloyl fluorescence, using the relationships

$$E_{280} = \varepsilon_{280}^a + T\varepsilon_{280}^p$$

$$E_{342} = \varepsilon_{342}^a$$

where E_{280} and E_{342} are the magnitudes of the excitation spectrum at 280 and 342 mμ, ε_{280}^p is the extinction coefficient of the protein alone, and ε_{280}^a and ε_{342}^a are the extinction coefficients of the anthraniloyl group at 280 and 342 mμ. On rearranging terms,

$$T = \left[\frac{E_{280}}{E_{342}} - \frac{\varepsilon_{280}^a}{\varepsilon_{342}^a}\right] \times \frac{\varepsilon_{342}^a}{\varepsilon_{280}^p}.$$

E_{280}/E_{342} is 8·47 (from Fig. 4), while ε_{280}^a, ε_{342}^a and ε_{280}^p are $1·0 \times 10^3$, $4·0 \times 10^3$ and $49·0 \times 10^3$ cm^2/mmole, respectively. These values give a transfer efficiency of 67%.

(f) Fluorescence polarization and excited state lifetime

The fluorescence polarization of anthraniloyl chymotrypsin was measured in order to determine the rotational relaxation time of the active site. On excitation at 360 mμ, the emission anisotropy, A, is 0·211 in 0·1 M phosphate buffer, pH 6·8, at 20°C. The enzyme concentration was $3·75 \times 10^{-5}$ M. A plot of the reciprocal of the emission anisotropy as a function of T/η (Fig. 6) gives a straight line which extrapolates to a value of 3·29 at $T/\eta = 0$. This corresponds to a limiting emission anisotropy, A_0, of 0·304. T/η was varied by changing the viscosity, η, while the temperature, T, was kept constant at 20°C. The viscosity was varied by addition of glycerol to a solution of the enzyme in 0·1 M phosphate buffer.

The rotational relaxation time, ρ, is related to A, A_0 and τ, the excited state lifetime, by the expression (Weber, 1953)

$$\rho = 3\tau \frac{A}{(A_0 - A)}.$$

From nanosecond pulse measurements (Fig. 7), a value of 7·2 nsec was obtained for τ. These values give a rotational relaxation time of 49·4 nsec.

Sephadex G–75 chromatography of anthraniloyl chymotrypsin was carried out in order to determine whether the modified protein is monomeric or

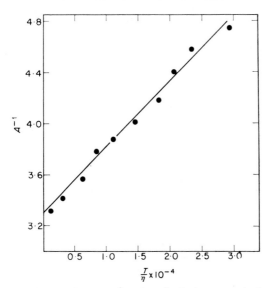

FIG. 6. Fluorescence polarization of anthraniloyl chymotrypsin in aqueous glycerol solutions. The reciprocal of the emission anisotropy, A^{-1}, is plotted as a function of T/η, to extrapolate to a limiting emission anisotropy, A_0, at $T/\eta = 0$. The emission was excited at 360 mμ. The temperature was 20°C.

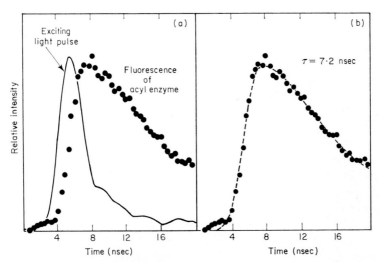

FIG. 7. Nanosecond fluorescence kinetics of anthraniloyl chymotrypsin: (a) the intensity of the exciting light pulse (full line) and of the fluorescence of the anthraniloyl group (●) are shown as a function of time; (b) a least-squares fit (broken line) to the observed fluorescence (●) yields a lifetime of 7·2 nsec.

dimeric at the concentration used in these fluorescence polarization measurements. The elution pattern of $3 \cdot 75 \times 10^{-5}$ M anthraniloyl chymotrypsin corresponds closely to that of α-chymotrypsin at the same concentration $(V/V_0 = 1 \cdot 6)$. The elution volume of ovalbumin, which has a molecular weight nearly twice that of chymotrypsin, was $V/V_0 = 1 \cdot 25$. Thus, anthraniloyl chymotrypsin, like α-chymotrypsin (Safare et al., 1966), is almost entirely monomeric at this concentration.

4. Discussion

A highly fluorescent anthraniloyl group has been inserted at the active site of α-chymotrypsin. *The striking experimental finding is that the anthraniloyl acyl enzyme is indefinitely stable at neutral pH, allowing a detailed spectrofluorimetric study of some features of the active site.* The acylating reagent, *p*-nitrophenyl anthranilate, is very selective in its reactivity. Only one anthraniloyl chromophore is introduced into chymotrypsin, rendering the enzyme inactive. Chymotrypsinogen, trypsinogen, lysozyme and serum albumin do not react at all. Enzymatically active chymotrypsin appears to be essential for the reaction, since di-isopropylphosphoryl chymotrypsin is not labeled by the reagent. Numerous studies have shown that acylation, carbamylation and sulfonylation, as well as phosphorylation, all occur at a highly reactive serine residue in the active site (for a review, see Bruice & Benkovic, 1966). It seems likely that the anthraniloyl group also is esterified to this serine residue.

Of the proteins studied, trypsin is the only other one which reacts with *p*-nitrophenyl anthranilate, though it does so at a considerably slower rate than chymotrypsin. The acylation of trypsin by this reagent is not unexpected, since trypsin and chymotrypsin have overlapping specificities (Inagami & Sturtevant, 1960). It is of interest to know whether other serine proteases react with *p*-nitrophenyl anthranilate.

The indefinite stability of anthraniloyl chymotrypsin at neutral pH is also a characteristic of sulfonyl, carbamyl and phosphoryl derivatives of the enzyme. In contrast, most carboxylic acid derivatives of chymotrypsin deacylate rather rapidly at neutral pH. The most stable acyl enzyme previously reported (Balls et al., 1958) is trimethylacetyl chymotrypsin, which has a half-life of about an hour under these conditions. It remains to be determined whether the stability of anthraniloyl chymotrypsin is typical of anthraniloyl esters *per se* or whether it is due to a particular interaction of this acyl group with the active site of chymotrypsin.

Hartley & Massey (1956) have sulfonylated the active site of α-chymotrypsin with a fluorescent chromophore. They found that dansyl chloride (1-dimethylaminonaphthalene-5-sulfonyl chloride) reacts preferentially with a residue at the active site. In comparing dansyl chloride with *p*-nitrophenyl anthranilate, we find that the latter reagent is more suitable as a fluorescent probe of the active site of chymotrypsin. An advantage of *p*-nitrophenyl anthranilate is that it reacts only at the active site, while dansyl chloride reacts with other residues as well. This makes it more difficult to obtain a homogeneous derivative in which all of the chymotrypsin molecules contain a fluorescent group at only a single residue.

The fluorescence polarization and nanosecond kinetic studies of anthraniloyl chymotrypsin (Figs. 6 and 7) provide a measure of the rotational mobility of the active site. The observed rotational relaxation time ρ of 49 nsec can be compared with ρ calculated for a model structure. The rotational relaxation time of an anhydrous, rigid sphere is given by

$$\rho_0 = \frac{3\eta V}{RT} = \frac{3\eta M \bar{v}}{RT}$$

where V is the volume of the sphere, M is its molecular weight, $\bar{v}$ is its partial specific volume, η is the viscosity of the solution, R is the gas constant, and T is the absolute temperature. For a sphere of molecular weight 25,000 and a $\bar{v}$ of 0·73, ρ_0 is calculated to be 22 nsec, in aqueous solution at 20°C. The observed rotational relaxation time of a rigid protein molecule will be greater than ρ_0 if the protein is hydrated or if its shape is not spherical. On the other hand, if the protein is not rigid, the observed ρ will be less than ρ_0. For anthraniloyl chymotrypsin, ρ/ρ_0 is 2·2. It can be concluded that *the active site of the acyl enzyme is rigid. The anthraniloyl chromophore has no rotational mobility independent of the motion of the whole chymotrypsin molecule, which behaves as a rigid particle.* This conclusion is consistent with previous spectroscopic studies of different acyl chymotrypsins (Massey *et al.*, 1955; Berliner & McConnell, 1966).

The absorption and emission spectra of anthraniloyl derivatives vary with solvent polarity (Tables 1 and 2). This dependence makes it possible to infer the polarity of the immediate environment of the acyl group in anthraniloyl chymotrypsin. The interpretation of the emission spectra (Table 2) is straightforward. The emission maximum of anthraniloyl chymotrypsin is at 422 mμ, while methyl anthranilate emits at 420 mμ in water and at 380 mμ in cyclohexane (Fig. 4). The other model compounds show the same red shift in the emission maximum with increasing solvent polarity, an effect generally observed for fluorescent molecules that possess a substantial dipole moment in the excited state (Lippert, 1957). *Thus, it can be concluded from the position of the emission maximum that the environment of the anthraniloyl group at the active site is highly polar.*

The absorption spectra are more complex, since there appear to be two distinct solvent effects (Table 1). The absorption maxima of the model compounds shift to the red in going from cyclohexane to dioxane. In going from dioxane to water, however, there is a significant shift to the blue, so that the absorption maxima in water are actually at lower wavelengths than in cyclohexane. The red shift is most likely a solvent polarity effect. The blue shift may be due to hydrogen bonding between the anthraniloyl chromophore and the solvent, but it must be stressed that this interpretation is by no means unique. The absorption maxima of anthraniloyl chymotrypsin, 342 mμ, is at a longer wavelength than that of any of the model compounds in water. This finding suggests that *the environment of the acyl group is highly polar but that water is excluded from it.*

The polarity of the environment of the acyl group can also be assessed from the breadth of the absorption and emission spectra of anthraniloyl chymotrypsin. The theoretical basis of the relationship between solvent polarity and spectral broadening has recently been given by Marcus (1965). In polar solvents, the absorption and emission spectra of the anthraniloyl model compounds are considerably broader than in non-polar solvents. For example, methyl anthranilate has an absorption bandwidth of 3200 cm^{-1} in cyclohexane and 4400 cm^{-1} in water, while its emission bandwidth is 3100 cm^{-1} in cyclohexane and 3600 cm^{-1} in water. Anthraniloyl chymotrypsin has an emission bandwidth of 4200 cm^{-1} and an absorption bandwidth of 3700 cm^{-1}. These spectral broadening data provide independent confirmation that the environment of the anthraniloyl group at the active site is highly polar.

It is of interest to compare our conclusions concerning the polarity of the active site with those derived by other investigators who have used different probes. The absorption spectrum of *trans*-cinnamoyl chymotrypsin indicates that the environment of that group is more polar than water (Bender *et al.*, 1962). The high polarity was attributed to the carboxylate group of an aspartate residue adjacent to the reactive serine. In contrast, Kallos & Avatis (1966) reported that the absorption spectrum of *p*-nitrobenzenesulfonyl chymotrypsin indicates that the chromophore is situated in a hydrocarbon-like environment. A similar conclusion was reached for the binding site of proflavine (Bernhard *et al.*, 1966). The finding of a hydrocarbon-like environment with some chromophores and a highly polar environment with others is not surprising since the active site of chymotrypsin consists of distinct binding loci (Hein & Niemann, 1961), which probably differ greatly in polarity. Thus, each of the probes samples a particular region of the active site.

Electronic excitation energy is transferred from the tryptophan residues to the anthraniloyl group in the acyl enzyme, as demonstrated by the quenching of tryptophan fluorescence (Fig. 1), as well as by the excitation spectrum (Fig. 5). The transfer efficiency is 65%. The spectroscopic conditions for dipole–dipole resonance transfer (Förster, 1947) are fulfilled here. Using

Förster's equations, it is possible to calculate a distance R_0 at which the efficiency of transfer is 50%, assuming that the chromophores are randomly oriented with respect to each other. For tryptophan to anthraniloyl transfer, R_0 is calculated to be 20 Å. In Förster's treatment, the rate constant for energy transfer is proportional to the inverse sixth power of the distance between the energy acceptor and donor, so that the transfer efficiency is expected to be 75% at 17 Å, and 25% at 24 Å. Since there are eight tryptophan residues in α-chymotrypsin, it is not possible to interpret the observed transfer efficiency in terms of a distance between the donor and acceptor groups. Rather, when the coordinates of the tryptophan residues become known from an X-ray crystallographic analysis, it will be of considerable interest to determine whether Förster's theory gives good quantitative agreement with the observed transfer efficiency.

ACKNOWLEDGMENT

We wish to thank Miss Verena Kurer for her expert technical assistance. We are indebted to Dr. George Stark for stimulating discussions. This work was supported by grants from the National Aeronautics and Space Administration (NGR–05–020–137) and from the National Institutes of Health (GM–11783–02).

REFERENCES

Anderson, S. R. & Weber, G. (1965). *Biochemistry, N.Y.* **4**, 1948.
Balls, A. K., McDonald, C. E. & Brecher, A. S. (1958). *Proc. Int. Symp. Enzymes Chem.*, Tokyo, Kyoto, p. 392.
Bender, M. L., Schonbaum, G. R. & Zerner, B. (1962). *J. Am. chem. Soc.* **84**, 2540.
Berliner, L. J. & McConnell, H. M. (1966). *Proc. natn. Acad. Sci. U.S.A.* **55**, 708.
Bernhard, S. A., Lee, B. F. & Tashjian, Z. H. (1966). *J. molec. Biol.* **18**, 405.
Bruice, T. C. & Benkovic, S. J. (1966). "Bio-organic Mechanism", Vol. 1, pp. 212–258. New York: W. A. Benjamin.
Erlanger, B. F., Cooper, A. G. & Bendich, A. J. (1964). *Biochemistry, N.Y.* **3**, 1880.
Förster, T. (1947). *Annln. Phys.* **2**, 55.
Hartley, B. & Massey, V. (1956). *Biochim. biophys. Acta*, **21**, 58.
Hein, G. & Niemann, C. (1961). *Proc. natn. Acad. Sci. U.S.A.* **47**, 1341.
Inagami, T. & Sturtevant, J. M. (1960). *J. biol. Chem.* **235**, 1019.
Jablonski, A. (1960). *Bull. Acad. pol. Sci. Sér. Sci., math. astr. phys.* **8**, 259.
Kallos, J. & Avatis, K. (1966). *Biochemistry, N.Y.* **5**, 1979.
Lippert, E. (1957). *Z. Elektrochem.* **61**, 962.
Marcus, R. A. (1965). *J. chem. Phys.* **43**, 1261.
Massey, V., Harrington, W. & Hartley, B. (1955). *Discuss. Faraday Soc.* **20**, 24.
Safare, P. S., Kegeles, G. & Kwon-Rhee, S. J. (1966). *Biochemistry, N.Y.* **5**, 1389.
Staiger, R. P. & Miller, E. B. (1959). *J. org. Chem.* **24**, 1214.
Steiner, R. F. & Edelhoch, H. (1962). *Chem. Rev.* **62**, 457.
Stryer, L. (1965). *J. molec. Biol.* **13**, 482.
Velick, S. F. (1961). *In* "Light and Life", ed by W. D. McElroy and B. Glass, p. 108. Johns Hopkins, Baltimore.
Weber, G. (1953). *Adv. Protein Chem.* **8**, 415.

PROTEINS AND POLYPEPTIDES

D. Statistical Mechanical Studies

Configurational Statistics of Polypeptide Chains

Paul J. Flory

Department of Chemistry, Stanford University, California, U.S.A.

Recent investigations on the configurational statistics of poly-L-alanine, poly-glycine, and their copolymers are reviewed and interpreted in terms of residue structure and the conformational energy computed previously by semi-empirical, approximate methods as a function of rotations φ and ψ about skeletal bonds adjoining the α-carbon atom of the residue. The characteristic ratio $\langle r^2 \rangle_0 / x l_u^2$ of the mean-square end-to-end length for the unperturbed random coil to the product of the number x of units and the square of the virtual bond length $l_u = 3 \cdot 8 \, \text{Å}$ calculated for polyglycine ($\sim 2 \cdot 0$) is much smaller than the charac-teristic ratio for poly-L-alanine (~ 9) owing to the symmetry of the glycyl residue, permitting occurrence of rotations of opposite signs for successive units at random. The marked reduction of the characteristic ratio by minor proportions of either glycyl or D-alanyl residues polymerized with L-alanine admits of similar inter-pretation.

Criteria for the occurrence of macromolecules in globular states characterized by irregular skeletal conformation and high density (i.e. virtual exclusion of solvent from the domain of the macromolecule) are discussed. Avoidance of superposition of two units of the chain in the same space is estimated to reduce the expectation of an acceptable globular conformation to a value much less than unity for a molecule having the conformational rigidity of a polypeptide. Occurrence of an acceptable globular conformation implies a special residue sequence. Absence of intermediate, competitive states follows naturally from these considerations. It is appropriate therefore to treat the transition between native and random coil (denatured) forms as an equilibrium between two states, or structurally differentiated forms. The helix–coil transition is not a proper prototype of this process. Non-helical portions of the conformation in the native globular state are not random coils, and should not be so designated.

1. Introduction

The structure of a portion of a polypeptide chain comprising residues of the type –NH—CHR—CO– is shown in Fig. 1. As is well established,† the peptide unit embracing the sequence of skeletal atoms from one α-carbon to the next is planar *trans*, except in the case of residues of the type of L-proline in which the side chain R is the diradical $-(CH_2)_3-$ which joins nitrogen with C^α to form a five-membered ring. We shall assume residues of the proline type to be absent except as noted otherwise.

---

† The terminology used to describe the structure of the polypeptide chain accords with the recommendations of Edsall *et al.*, 1966.

The torsional rigidity of the amide bond (barrier in excess of 15 kcal mole^{-1}) is sufficient to warrant treatment of the polypeptide chain as a succession of virtual bonds of fixed length $l_u = 3\cdot80$ Å, each connecting an α-carbon with the next in the chain. The virtual bonds spanning units i and $i+1$ are shown by broken lines in Fig. 1. The spatial orientation of a virtual bond $i+1$ with respect to its predecessors in the chain is determined by the pair of rotation angles φ_i and ψ_i about the N—C$^\alpha$ and C$^\alpha$—CO bonds adjoining C$_i^\alpha$; see Fig. 1. Its orientation with respect to succeeding bonds is determined equivalently by φ_{i+1} and ψ_{i+1}. In accordance with convention (Edsall et al., 1966), these angles are assigned values of zero in the planar trans form of the chain shown in Fig. 1, and they are reckoned as positive for right-handed rotations. The spatial configuration, or conformation, of the chain as a whole is determined by the set of all such rotation angles, which we denote by $\{\varphi, \psi\}$.

Most of the configuration hyperspace $\{\varphi, \psi\}$ will be precluded by steric overlaps. These overlaps can be conveniently classified in two categories: (a) short range interactions involving adjoining peptide units, and (b) interactions of longer range involving units more remote than second neighbors. The omission of interactions involving second neighbors is justified by the chain geometry, as may be confirmed by inspection of scale models (Brant & Flory, 1965a). Thus, if one pair of rotation angles φ_i, ψ_i is varied while values of zero (planar trans) are maintained for all others, it will be observed that atoms and groups preceding C$_{i-1}^\alpha$ (R$_{i-1}$ included; see Fig. 1) do not for any values of φ_i and ψ_i come sufficiently close to atoms and groups beyond C$_{i+1}^\alpha$ (R$_{i+1}$ included) for an appreciable interaction to occur between a member of one set and those of the other. If the φ_i, ψ_i pair is varied over the ranges not excluded by steric overlaps between atoms of the peptide units spanned by virtual bonds i and $i+1$, and if at the same time the $\varphi_{i+1}, \psi_{i+1}$ pair is permitted to vary correspondingly, no combination of the four rotations will be found which brings peptide unit i into interaction with unit $i+2$. Interactions between units i and $i+3$ can be brought about by similarly varying the sequence of three consecutive rotation pairs over their individually allowed ranges, but they occur for only a very small fraction of the associated angle space. Thus, the distinction between overlaps in category (a) and those of longer range (in a topological sense) in category (b) is well defined.

Three classes of conformations should be clearly distinguished: helical, random coil, and compact or globular. Those of the former class result from assignment of the same set of rotation angles for every repeating sequence consisting of an integral number of the chemical units (residues), which by repetition generate the chain as a whole. For polypeptide helices of interest, the number of chemical units in this repeating sequence (not to be confused with the helix repeat) is one; i.e. the same bond rotation angles φ and ψ apply to every amino acid residue, and Liquori's (Desantis *et al.*, 1963) principle of equivalence of all chemical repeat units applies. Usually residues at periodic intervals—three in the case of the α-helix—are juxtaposed in close proximity in the helical conformation. Non-bonded interactions between the several units over the range of at least one turn of the helix must be taken into account for the purpose of evaluating the conformational energy of a helical form.

In the random coil state the rotation angles at successive α-carbon atoms adopt values which are essentially uncorrelated from one pair to the next. The resulting irregular form of the random coil coupled with its low density reduce interactions of category (b), which involve more distantly related units, to low incidence. Although the preponderance of the units in a very long chain escape such interactions, the liability of an occasional long-range overlap may affect the dimensions of the random coil appreciably, and a vast literature on the influence of such interactions has evolved over the last twenty years under the title of the effect of volume exclusion. All this can be circumvented by observing that the effects of these long range interactions can be reduced to nullity by conducting measurements at the ideal point, or theta point, at which the co-volume of a chain unit is zero, as signified by a second virial coefficient of zero in the usual expansion of the osmotic pressure (Flory, 1949,1953; Fox & Flory, 1949); or, if conduct of experiments under these conditions is impractical (as will nearly always be so for polypeptides and proteins), measurements made in "good" solvents may be corrected to the condition of ideality (Orofino & Flory, 1957). Interactions of category (b) may then be dismissed, and attention can be devoted to the short range interactions (a), which for polypeptides are confined to first neighbor units.

In dense or globular conformations, exemplified by the conformations of most native proteins (except fibrous proteins) copious interactions occur between units which are long range in the chain sequence. Optimization of local interactions is overshadowed by the much more demanding requirement that the chain be so arranged as to render it space filling without superimposing atoms or groups within the same space, the integrity of the structure of the chain being respected. The helical conformations and those of the random coil can by analysed satisfactorily in terms of appropriate steric maps, or conformation energy diagrams. But the globular conformations cannot be comprehended in terms of such diagrams alone, owing to the overriding importance that attaches to longer range interactions which occur in profusion whenever a very long chain is forced to fill three-dimensional space to high density or when a system of many chains is so packed in space.

The treatment of random coil conformations of simple polypeptides, of copolymeric polypeptides, of racemic copolymers, and of proteins will be reviewed in this paper and a rational integration of present results will be attempted. Some comments on the conformations of globular proteins will be included.

2. Estimation of the Conformational Energy

The fact pointed out above that short range interactions in polypeptide chains are confined to units which are first neighbors implies that the conformational energy of the chain as a whole may be expressed as the sum of the energies $E_i(\varphi_i, \psi_i)$ associated with the rotations φ_i and ψ_i about each bond. Whereas the energy associated with rotation about one angle of a pair is strongly affected by the other angle, $E_i(\varphi_i, \psi_i)$ can be treated as independent of all other rotational pairs. Moreover, this function is characteristic of the residue i and in good approximation it is independent of the kinds of residues which happen to be its neighbors. As has been pointed out above, the side chains R_{i-1} and R_{i+1} characterizing these residues are not, in general, subject to interactions which depend upon φ_i and ψ_i. A conformational energy function $E(\varphi, \psi)$ characteristic of each residue of the kind –NH—CHR—CO– may therefore be defined. It may be represented as a contour diagram using φ and ψ as coordinates.

The dominant interactions determining the nature of $E(\varphi, \psi)$ for a given residue are repulsions between non-bonded atom pairs when the distance between them is less than the sum of their van der Waals radii. Recognizing this fact, Ramachandran and his co-workers (Ramachandran et al., 1963,1965; Ramakrishnan & Ramachandran, 1965) have constructed diagrams showing the ranges of φ and ψ which a residue of given type may assume without incurring steric overlaps. These diagrams (Ramachandran et al., 1963,1965; Ramakrishnan & Ramachandran, 1965; Gibson & Scheraga, 1966; Leach et al., 1966) afford a good correlation of the conformations observed for various residues in peptides and polypeptides whose structures have been determined by X-ray diffraction, including the residues of the native protein myoglobin (Ramachandran et al., 1963,1965; Ramakrishnan & Ramachandran, 1965). The boundary between allowed and disallowed conformations is not, of course, sharply defined. Occasional minor transgressions of the boundaries of the excluded regions of the Ramachandran diagram are attributable to compression of atoms somewhat below their normal van der Waals radii and to deformation of the valence angles from their preferred values.

Treatment of the random coil configurations requires a more refined assessment of the conformations within the allowed regions. It is obvious that bond torsional potentials and London dispersion interactions (attractions) will render some of the allowed regions of the Ramachandran map more favorable than others. The resulting discriminations within a given region and between competitive regions can be expected to affect averages over the chain configurations, and these differences may be of critical importance. From this standpoint the requirements for analysis of the configurational statistics appear to be more stringent. On the other hand, a sharp distinction between permitted regions and those which are disallowed is not required for analysis of the configurational statistics. Moreover, the effects of variations in bond angles may be ignored, inasmuch as they are largely eliminated in the act of averaging over all configurations of the system.

Semi-empirical procedures for estimating conformational energies of chain molecules are fairly well known (Birshtein & Ptitsyn, 1964). Combining contributions from (i) bond torsional potentials with barrier heights E_φ° and E_ψ° for the respective bonds of a given residue, (ii) interactions $E_{kl}(\varphi, \psi)$ between pairs of atoms k, l from within the units adjoining the given residue, and (iii) the Coulombic interaction E_C resulting from the electrical asymmetry (group dipole moment 3·7 debye) of the amide group (Brant & Flory, 1965a), we have for the appropriate function for a peptide residue

$$E(\varphi, \psi) = \left(\frac{E_\varphi^\circ}{2}\right)(1 - \cos 3\varphi) + \left(\frac{E_\psi^\circ}{2}\right)(1 - \cos 3\psi) + \sum_{k,l} E_{kl}(\varphi, \psi) + E_C \quad (1)$$

The summation term includes interactions for every non-bonded atom pair whose distance of separation depends on φ_i and ψ_i exclusively, i.e. atoms within the span from C_{i-1}^α to C_{i+1}^α, inclusive; the serial index i is omitted for simplicity. The non-bonded interactions may be represented by a pair potential of the Lennard–Jones form

$$E_{kl}(\varphi, \psi) = \frac{a_{kl}}{r_{kl}^{12}} - \frac{c_{kl}}{r_{kl}^6} \quad (2)$$

where r_{kl}, the distance between atoms k and l, is a function of φ and ψ; a_{kl} and c_{kl} are parameters. Alternatively, a pair potential of the Buckingham type may be adopted, in which the repulsive term is replaced by an exponential expression $a'_{kl} \exp(-br_{kl})$. If b is taken to be $\sim 4 \cdot 5$, results do not differ discernibly from those obtained through use of equation 2, provided of course the parameters are determined in a consistent manner.

Details on the computations can be found in the original papers (Brant & Flory, 1965a; Brant et al., 1967; Scott & Scheraga, 1966). The large dipole moment of the amide group renders account of E_C imperative for the comprehension of the configuration statistics of the random coil, as was brought out by Brant & Flory (1965a). This contribution may be estimated through approximation of the electrical asymmetry by a point dipole situated as indicated in Fig. 1, or by a system of four-point monopoles situated on the N, H, C and O atoms of the amide group, which together reproduce the

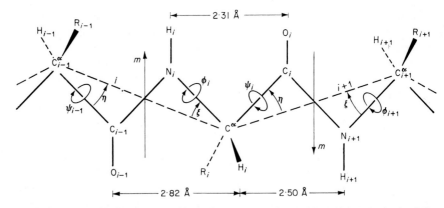

FIG. 1. Geometrical representation of a portion of a polypeptide chain in its fully extended conformation for which bond rotation angles φ and $\psi = 0$. Other conformations are generated by alteration of these rotation angles. Successive amino acid residues are indexed $i - 1$, i and $i + 1$. Virtual bonds connecting the α-carbon atoms of these residues are shown by dashed lines. Group dipole moments are indicated by vertical arrows. Interatomic distances shown refer to the planar conformation. Principal structural parameters: N—C^α, 1·47 Å; C^α—C, 1·53 Å; C—N, 1·32 Å; angle $CNC^\alpha = 123°$; angle $NC^\alpha C = 70°$ angle $C^\alpha CN = 66°$.

group dipole moment, the value of which is well known (Brant et al., 1967; Scott & Scheraga, 1966). The latter procedure seems the more satisfactory. The effective dielectric constant ε to be used in such calculations is problematical, but fortunately not critical (Brant & Flory, 1965a; Brant et al., 1967). Inasmuch as the interactions between a neutral set of charges is short range, and in the polypeptide they are shielded from the bulk solvent, a value of ε more nearly representative of the polypeptide is indicated. We have used $\varepsilon = 3·5$ (Brant & Flory, 1965a; Brant et al., 1967).

The c_{kl} may be estimated from atomic polarizabilities (Brant & Flory, 1965a; Birshtein & Ptitsyn, 1964; Scott & Scheraga, 1966). The contributions governed by them, namely the van der Waals attractions, are least important of all. Assignment of the a_{kl} is critical. They can be so chosen as to reproduce the van der Waals radii for the various pairs (Brant & Flory, 1965a; Brant et al., 1967).

We have taken the torsion potentials to be threefold with minima for both bonds occurring at $0°$ and $\pm 120°$, as specified in equation 1. These choices are supported by conformations assumed by low molecular analogs in crystals. Potentials V_φ° and V_ψ° of 1·5 and 1·0 kcal mole^{-1} respectively were used. Scott & Scheraga (1966) chose lower potential barriers of 0·6 and 0·2 kcal mole^{-1} respectively with the minima for the former (V_φ°) displaced by $60°$ to $\pm 60°$ and $180°$ positions.

Calculations of this nature, being mainly empirical in basis and approximate in numerical result, should be treated with circumspection. They cannot be accepted as being accurate in detail. Only those general features which persist when the parameters are varied over reasonable ranges, and when alternative methods are compared, can be regarded as reliable.

3. Glycyl and Alanyl Residues

Maps of the conformation energy for the glycyl residue ($R = H$) calculated by Brant et al., 1967, through the use of equations (1) and (2) are shown in Figs 2 and 3. Energy contours are drawn at intervals of 1 kcal mole^{-1} relative to the lowest minima marked by crosses. Contours above 5 kcal mole^{-1} are not shown. Figure 2 was calculated with neglect of the Coulombic interaction energy, i.e. with $E_C = 0$. Figure 3 was obtained by adding to this energy surface the Coulombic energy E_C computed as the energy of interaction between two sets of monopole charges (see above) embedded in the pair of adjoining peptide units. The absence of an asymmetric center in the glycyl residue requires equivalence of energy for rotations φ, ψ and $-\varphi, -\psi$ of opposite signs. The diagrams consequently are symmetric with respect to reflection through their centers at $\varphi = \psi = 180°$.

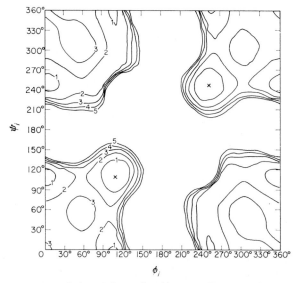

FIG. 2. Contour map of the conformational energy (Brant et al., 1967) of the glycyl residue calculated according to equations (1) and (2) with $E_C = 0$. Contours are shown at intervals of 1 kcal mole^{-1} relative to the lowest minima marked $\times$; those above 5 kcal mole^{-1} are omitted.

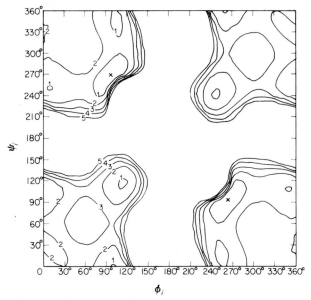

FIG. 3. Conformational energy map (Brant *et al.*, 1967) for the glycyl residue calculated according to equations (1) and (2) with E_C estimated on the basis of point monopole charges. See legend to Fig. 2.

Certain features of these conformational energy maps admit of straight-forward interpretation. As will be apparent at once from Fig. 1 (with R = H) or from a suitable model, a *cis* conformation about either of the pair of single bonds entails a very large overlap. Regions near either of the two lines $\varphi = 180°$ and $\psi = 180°$, which would bisect the diagram vertically and horizontally, respectively, are therefore strongly forbidden. The planar *trans* conformation $\varphi = \psi = 0$ is disfavored, although to a lesser degree, due to repulsive interactions between the amido H_i (attached to N_i) and O_i, these atoms being only 2·31 Å apart at $\varphi_i = \psi_i = 0$. Their mutual repulsion is readily diminished by a small rotation about either bond. Consequently, the energy in Fig. 2 diminishes in all directions from the origin (shown in quad-rants at each of the four corners of the diagram), except near the diagonal $\psi = -\varphi$. Weaker repulsions involving the H_i atoms attached to C_i^α occur for somewhat larger rotations. At $\varphi_i = \pm 60°$ the O_{i-1} atom is situated at a distance of 2·40 Å from one of these H_i. A rotation $\varphi_i = \pm 60°$ places the amido hydrogen H_{i+1} at 2·08 Å from one of the H_i. Small repulsions are to be expected in each of these conformations.

Small minima appearing along the margins of the figure bear a semblance to the $tg^\pm$ and $g^\pm t$ minima for n-alkanes (t = *trans*, $g^\pm$ = *gauche*, $\pm 120°$). These minima are due in part to the inherent torsional potentials attributed to the single bonds. Relief of the small repulsions cited above, which are maximal at φ or $\psi \cong \pm 60°$ and which diminish for $|\varphi|$ or $|\psi| > 60°$, contributes also to the $g^{\pm}t$ minima and $tg^{\pm}$ minima occurring along the margins of the diagram. Incipience of the *cis* overlaps displaces the minima for φ and ψ to values smaller than $|120°|$.

All of the repulsions cited above for the glycyl residue are relieved by simultaneously rotating both φ and ψ to angles $>|60°|$. Hence, the favored conformations in Fig. 2 are approximately g^+g^+ and g^-g^-. The g^+g^- state at $120°$, $-120°$ (and likewise its mirror image at $-120°$, $120°$) is rendered unsatisfactory by overlaps between O_{i-1} and amido H_{i+1}, which are analogous to those prevalent in polymethylene (Hoeve, 1961; Abe *et al.*, 1966) and other simple polymeric chains (Flory *et al.*, 1964; Mark & Flory, 1965). However, the trend toward a minimum is evident in this region of Fig. 2; in its stead a saddle occurs at about $95°$, $-95°$ and a trough extends from it in either direction.

The energy surface of the φ, ψ map is affected also by non-bonded attractions, but to a lesser degree. These are invariably small for any given pair but, being of longer range, the number of them contributing in a given conformation is greater. For the same reason, the sum of these London dispersion energies is subject to a smaller variation with φ and ψ.

In the planar *trans* conformation shown in Fig. 1 the group dipole moments are favorably oriented antiparallel to one another, with each dipole perpendicular to the line between them (Brant & Flory, 1965a). At the minima in Fig. 2—a conformation corresponding approximately to the α-helix—they are very nearly parallel and inclined somewhat to the line between them. In this arrangement the dipole energy is positive (repulsive). Along the diagonal $\varphi + \psi = 0$, the dipole directions are predominantly antiparallel, but their distance apart decreases with increase in $|\varphi|$ from $0°$ to $180°$. In the vicinity of this line the Coulombic interaction remains favorable (Brant & Flory, 1965a; Brant *et al.*, 1967). The negative Coulombic energy along the line $\varphi + \psi = 0$ causes the saddle point in Fig. 2 to be replaced by a minimum in Fig. 3 (Brant *et al.*, 1967). The positive electrostatic energy in the g^+g^+ region (and also in the g^-g^- region) raises the minimum in Fig. 2 above that of the new minimum in Fig. 3. Although the energy of the new pair of equivalent minima is only a little lower than that of the g^+g^+ and g^-g^- minima, the troughs of low energy occurring near the g^+g^- and g^-g^+ minima enhance the weighting of this region as a whole, which consequently will account for the major contribution to the partition function.

Diagrams computed in corresponding manner (Brant *et al.*, 1967) for the L-alanyl residue are shown in Figs. 4 and 5. The presence of the R group renders right- and left-handed rotations non-equivalent. The diagrams therefore are not symmetric. Positive rotations φ_i about the N—C$^{\alpha}$ bond are preferred over negative ones owing to the repulsion between $(CO)_{i-1}$ and R_i (see Fig. 1). For rotations of small magnitude about the C^α—C bond, negative values of ψ_i are preferred over positive ones in consequence of the interaction of $(NH)_{i+1}$ with R_i; at larger angles $|\psi_i|$ this preference vanishes. In other respects, the rules enunciated above for the glycyl residue obtain.

Because of the asymmetry manifested in the preferences for rotations of one sign over the other, the g^+g^+ minimum I in Fig. 4 takes precedence over the g^-g^- minimum II. The conformations of the right- and left-handed α-helices lie close to these respective minima. The preference for the right-handed α-helix usually exhibited by an L-polypeptide is thus seen to follow from rudimentary considerations of the asymmetry of rotations about the pair of bonds adjoining the α-carbon atom in an amino acid residue having the L configuration. This preference is manifest also in the Ramachandran steric maps (Ramachandran *et al.*, 1963,1965; Ramakrishnan & Ramachandran, 1965).

The diffuse region III in Fig. 4 is the domain in which the interactions encountered in the *tt* state, and cited in the foregoing account of the glycyl residue, are alleviated by rotations of both angles in their preferred directions. The repulsions associated with a g^+g^- pair delimit this region and raise its energy relative to I. The energies at the minima in I and III do not differ decisively; the accessible range in III considerably exceeds that of I, however.

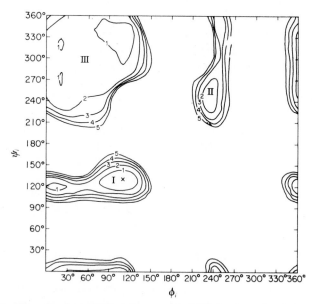

FIG. 4. Conformational energy map (Brant *et al.*, 1967) for the L-alanyl residue calculated according to equations (1) and (2) with $E_C = 0$.

Addition of E_C moves the minimum from region I to III, as shown in Fig. 5. The latter domain includes the β-form and related conformations which, if repeated regularly throughout sequences of many successive units, may yield sheet-like structures wherein parallel chains are hydrogen bonded intermolecularly. The large area of region III in Fig. 5 invests it with a considerable advantage over region I, which may be more significant than the small difference in energy.

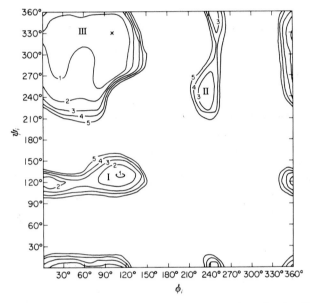

FIG. 5. Conformational energy map (Brant *et al.*, 1967) for the L-alanyl residue calculated according to equations (1) and (2) with E_C estimated on the basis of point monopole charges (see text; $\varepsilon = 3\cdot5$ as in preceding calculations). Contours drawn as stated in the legend to Fig. 2.

Diagrams for a D-alanyl residue are obtained by reflecting those of Figs. 4 and 5 through their centers; this operation is tantamount to reversing signs of rotation angles. Figures 4 and 5 may be assumed to be representative also of other α-amino acid residues in which R is a longer, unbranched side chain of the kind $-CH_2-X$. For bulkier side chains, additional interactions must be considered (Ramachandran *et al.*, 1963,1965; Ramakrishnan & Ramachandran, 1965; Gibson & Scheraga, 1966; Leach *et al.*, 1966).

The similarity of Figs. 2 and 4 to the Ramachandran steric maps will be apparent, and much of the content of the more detailed results can be gleaned from the simpler steric diagrams. Steric overlaps are of overriding importance.

The more elaborate calculations offer a measure of refinement needed for analysis of the configurational statistics, however; the principal gradations of energy within the "allowed" regions of Figs. 2–5 can be seen to be genuine by critical examination of models. The effects of dipolar interactions, also important, are beyond the scope of the steric map. They materially affect both the stabilities of helical forms of polyamides in general, as first pointed out by Arridge & Cannon (1964), and also the random coil configuration statistics of polypeptides (Brant & Flory, 1965a; Brant et al., 1967).

4. Random Coil Statistics of Stereoregular Chains

The partition function for a residue, formally defined as

$$z = \int \int \exp \left[\frac{-E(\varphi, \psi)}{RT} \right] d\varphi \, d\psi, \tag{3}$$

may be approximated as the sum of Boltzmann factors, taken at equal intervals of φ and ψ throughout their ranges. That is,

$$z \cong \sum_{\varphi} \sum_{\psi} \exp \left[\frac{-E(\varphi, \psi)}{RT} \right]. \tag{4}$$

Energies $E(\varphi, \psi)$ are furnished by the computed conformation energy crudely represented by the contours in Figs. 2–5. The average energy and configurational entropy per residue are

$$\langle E \rangle = RTz^{-1} \sum_{\varphi} \sum_{\psi} E(\varphi, \psi) \exp \left[\frac{-E(\varphi, \psi)}{RT} \right] \tag{5}$$

and

$$S = R \left(\ln z + \frac{\partial \ln z}{\partial \ln T} \right)$$
$$= R \ln z + \langle E \rangle / T. \tag{6}$$

The value of the entropy depends of course on the interval chosen for φ and ψ for the evaluation of the summations in these equations; i.e. the entropy is subject inevitably to an additive constant, and hence its absolute value has no significance. Entropies of conformational transitions (e.g. helix–coil) cannot be derived in this manner, as has frequently been attempted.

The vector connecting the terminal α-carbons of a polypeptide chain consisting of x units is

$$\mathbf{r} = \sum_{i=1}^{x} \mathbf{l}_{u;i} \tag{7}$$

where $\mathbf{l}_{u;i}$ is the vector representing virtual bond i. The average square of the magnitude of r, unperturbed by long range interactions (as $\langle r^2 \rangle$ determined, for example, at the theta point; see above), is

$$\langle r^2 \rangle_0 = \sum_{i,j} \langle \mathbf{l}_{u;i} \cdot \mathbf{l}_{u;j} \rangle$$
$$= x l_u^2 + 2 \sum_{i<j} \langle \mathbf{l}_{u;i} \cdot \mathbf{l}_{u;j} \rangle \tag{8}$$

where angle brackets denote the statistical mechanical average over all configurations of the chain.

Persuant to the evaluation of $\langle r^2 \rangle_0$, let a coordinate system be affixed to each virtual bond. The x-axis of this reference frame will be taken in the direction of the virtual bond, the y-axis will be placed in the plane of the peptide unit with its direction making an acute angle with the amide C—N bond of the same unit, and the z-axis will be taken in the direction required for completion of a right-handed orthogonal reference frame. The bond vector $\mathbf{l}_{u;i}$ is represented in its coordinate system by

$$u = l_u \begin{bmatrix} 1 \\ 0 \\ 0 \end{bmatrix}$$

or by its transpose

$$\mathbf{l}_u^T = l_u[1\ 0\ 0].$$

Henceforth we assume all virtual bonds to be of the same length, $3 \cdot 80 \text{ Å}$, in keeping with limitation of the treatment to residues of the type –NH—CHR—CO–. If the transformation from coordinate system $i+1$ to i is represented by $\mathbf{T}_i$, then

$$\langle \mathbf{l}_{u;i} \cdot \mathbf{l}_{u;j} \rangle = l_u^2 \langle \mathbf{T}_i \mathbf{T}_{i+1} \dots \mathbf{T}_{j-1} \rangle_{11} \tag{9}$$

where the subscript denotes the 1,1 element of the averaged matrix. Now $\mathbf{T}_i$ is a function of the fixed structural parameters and of φ_i and ψ_i. (The formulation of $\mathbf{T}$, here omitted, is given in full elsewhere (Brant & Flory, 1965a; Birshtein & Ptitsyn, 1964; Brant et al., 1967; Abe et al., 1966). Since the total energy is separable into the sum of independent contributions $E_i(\varphi_i, \psi_i)$ for the various residues, it follows that the averaged product of the transformation matrices can be replaced (for the polypeptide chain, in contrast to most polymer chains) by the product of averages. Hence

$$\langle \mathbf{l}_{u;i} \cdot \mathbf{l}_{u;j} \rangle = l_u^2 \left(\prod_i^{j-1} \langle \mathbf{T}_h \rangle \right)_{11}. \tag{10}$$

If all units are identical

$$\langle \mathbf{l}_{u;i} \cdot \mathbf{l}_{u;j} \rangle = l_u^2 (\langle \mathbf{T} \rangle^{j-i})_{11}. \tag{11}$$

Substitution of (11) in (8) yields

$$\frac{\langle r^2 \rangle_0}{x l_u^2} = 1 + \frac{2}{x} \left(\sum_{i<j} \langle \mathbf{T} \rangle^{j-i} \right)_{11}$$

$$= 1 + \frac{2}{x} \left[\sum_{k=1}^{x-1} (x-k) \langle \mathbf{T} \rangle^k \right]_{11} \tag{12}$$

which for infinite chains reduces to

$$\left(\frac{\langle r^2 \rangle_0}{x l_u^2} \right)_\infty = [(\mathbf{E} + \langle \mathbf{T} \rangle)(\mathbf{E} - \langle \mathbf{T} \rangle)^{-1}]_{11} \tag{13}$$

where $\mathbf{E}$ is the matrix identity. The quantities on the left of equations (12) and (13) are the characteristic ratios for finite and for infinite chains respectively. The expression which for finite chains replaces equation (13) is here omitted.

For the numerical evaluation of $\langle \mathbf{T} \rangle$, the matrix is computed at equal intervals of φ and ψ and multiplied by the Boltzmann factor, $\exp(-E(\varphi, \psi)/RT)$, of the conformational energy at each point. Intervals of 30° were used in the calculations cited here (Brant & Flory, 1965a; Brant et al., 1967) making a total of 144 "states" over the conformation map. The sum of the resulting terms is then divided by the residue partition function z, the latter being evaluated according to equation (4) by summing over the same intervals. Matrices evaluated in this way for the glycyl, L-alanyl and D-alanyl residues are the following (Brant et al., 1967).

$$\langle \mathbf{T}_{Gly} \rangle = \begin{bmatrix} 0\cdot36 & -0\cdot077 & 0 \\ -0\cdot092 & -0\cdot037 & 0 \\ 0 & 0 & 0\cdot12 \end{bmatrix} \tag{14}$$

$$\langle \mathbf{T}_{L-Ala} \rangle = \begin{bmatrix} 0\cdot51 & 0\cdot20 & 0\cdot59 \\ -0\cdot046 & -0\cdot61 & 0\cdot21 \\ 0\cdot65 & -0\cdot23 & -0\cdot30 \end{bmatrix} \tag{15}$$

$$\langle \mathbf{T}_{D-Ala} \rangle = \begin{bmatrix} 0\cdot51 & 0\cdot20 & -0\cdot59 \\ -0\cdot046 & -0\cdot61 & -0\cdot21 \\ -0\cdot65 & 0\cdot23 & -0\cdot30 \end{bmatrix} \tag{16}$$

The computation of $\langle \mathbf{T} \rangle$ could be refined by choice of an interval smaller than 30°, with consequent increase in the number of states. Exploratory calculations (Brant & Flory, 1965a) indicate, however, that the value for the characteristic ratio would be little affected by reducing the interval below 30°. The refinement attainable in this manner is certainly within the limits of reliability of the conformation energy calculations.

Values of the characteristic ratio in the limit $x = \infty$ calculated according to equation (13) are given in Table 1 for polyglycine, poly-L-alanine and for poly-L-lactide.

TABLE 1. Calculated characteristic ratios $(\langle r^2 \rangle_0 / x l_u^2)_\infty$

	Free rot.	$E_C = 0$	E_C (dipole)	E_C (monopole)
Polyglycine[a]	1·93	1·79	1·89	2·16
Poly-L-alanine[a]	1·93	2·97	12·18	9·27
Poly-L-lactide[b]	1·92	1·24	2·13	3·13

[a] Brant et al. (1967).
[b] Brant & Flory (1965a,b).

Included for comparison in the second column are values calculated for free rotation. Results in the third and fifth columns for polyglycine and poly-L-alanine were calculated using the $\langle T \rangle$ matrices given in equations (14) and (15). Those in the fourth column were obtained similarly, but with E_C estimated in the point dipole approximation of the electrical asymmetry of the amide group.

The structural geometry of the poly-L-lactide chain resembles that of poly-L-alanine, apart from the substitution of O for NH; dimensions differ only in detail. Absence of the amido hydrogen removes certain of the local interactions (see above) affecting the energy in the neighborhood of tt conformation, and the smaller valence angle at O (113°) compared to that at NH (123°) accentuates repulsions in the $\varphi > 180°$ half of the conformation map. The smaller dipole moment (by one half) and the lower electrostatic interactions (less than one fourth owing to the direction of the dipole) introduces the most significant difference which distinguishes this chain from poly-L-alanine.

The characteristic ratio for poly-L-alanine given in the last column of Table 1 agrees very well with experimental results (Brant & Flory, 1965b) for four polypeptides having side chains R as follows: $-CH_2COOCH_2C_6H_5$, $-CH_2CH_2COOCH_2C_6H_5$, $-CH_2CH_2COO^-$ and $-CH_2CH_2CH_2CH_2NH_3{}^+$. Each is of the type $-CH_2-R'$ which should resemble CH_3 in its effect on the conformational energy. For all four polypeptides, investigated in as many different solvents, $(\langle r^2 \rangle_0 / x l_u^2)_\infty = 9·0 \pm 0·5$ (Brant & Flory, 1965b). The virtual coincidence with the calculated value given in the last column of Table 1 is fortuitous to a degree; uncertainties in the van der Waals radii used to evaluate the parameters (Brant & Flory, 1965a; Brant et al., 1967) a_{kl} in equation (2) would admit of a range of about 20% in the calculated characteristic ratio. The same set of parameters was used consistently in other calculations, those for polyglycine and poly-L-lactide included.

Characteristic ratios in Table 1 calculated with $E_C = 0$ are low for all three polymers. The effect of polar interactions on the chain dimensions is particularly striking for poly-L-alanine. Disregard of E_C (Fig. 4) renders regions I and III competitive, and thereby allows successive residue conformations to differ considerably, and at random. When E_C is included

(Fig. 5) region III is preferred, with the result that successive units tend to assume similar conformations. These conformations (III), moreover, are in the vicinity of the fully extended form.† The striking difference between the characteristic ratios calculated for poly-L-alanine with and without E_C is thus explained. It is significant that when E_C is ignored no reasonable combination of parameters, a_{kl}, raises the value calculated for the characteristic ratio above about 4·5 (Brant & Flory, 1965a), which is well below the experimental observations. Variation of these parameters governing the repulsions between non-bonded atoms affects each of the minima I, II and III similarly, and hence has only a minor effect on the value calculated for $\langle r^2 \rangle_0$. Coulombic interactions, which cause region III to be favored over I, appear to be mainly responsible for the large characteristic ratio for polypeptides in which the side chain R has the steric effect of CH_3.

Equivalent electrostatic interactions operative in polyglycine affect its conformational energy similarly; g^+g^- and g^-g^+ domains of the conformation map replace g^+g^+ and g^-g^- as the preferred regions. The interchange of roles of these two pairs of domains has little effect however on the chain dimensions of polyglycine. The fact of importance is the retention of two equally accessible states, which is a consequence, of course, of the symmetry of glycine. Random occurrence of g^+g^- and g^-g^+ conformations for successive residues maintains the characteristic ratio near its value for free rotation.

5. Average Dimensions of Copolypeptides

Let us consider a random copolypeptide comprising two kinds of residues, a and b. In keeping with the limitations to residues of the kind –NH—CHR—CO–, we ascribe identical geometric parameters, including l_u, to them. The average projection of virtual bond j on i, these being separated by the series of residues $ba...b$, will be

$$\mathbf{l}_u^T \langle \mathbf{T}_b \rangle \langle \mathbf{T}_a \rangle \ldots \langle \mathbf{T}_b \rangle \mathbf{l}_u. \tag{17}$$

We require the sum of such terms for each and every sequence of $j-i$ residues, each weighted according to its frequency of occurrence. If the distribution of a and b units is random, it follows at once that the required sum is given by a binomial raised to the power $j-i$. That is, the transformation from j to i, averaged over all sequences of units is

$$\langle (\langle \mathbf{T}_i \rangle \langle \mathbf{T}_{i+1} \rangle \ldots \langle \mathbf{T}_{j-1} \rangle) \rangle = \langle\!\langle \mathbf{T} \rangle\!\rangle^{j-i} \tag{18}$$

where

$$\langle\!\langle \mathbf{T} \rangle\!\rangle = w_a \langle \mathbf{T}_a \rangle + (1 - w_a) \langle \mathbf{T}_b \rangle. \tag{19}$$

† Even if every residue were constrained to assume a conformation within region III, the chain as a whole could scarcely be described in terms of any simple geometrical form, helical or planar. The range of rotation angles permitted in this region is too great to enforce a uniform spatial configuration. A semblance to the β-form, or some nearby conformation, would be discernible over the range of several units, but random variations within region III would dissipate all vestiges of order overlong sequences.

w_a being the fraction of units of kind a in the copolymer. Hence, the characteristic ratio for the infinite copolypeptide may be calculated by resort to equation (13) with $\langle\!\langle T\rangle\!\rangle$ replacing $\langle T\rangle$.

Results of calculations carried out in this manner (Miller *et al.*, 1967) for random copolymers of glycine with L-alanine are shown by the solid curve in Fig. 6, which is plotted against the mole fraction w_{Gly} of glycine. (The use of matrices differing slightly from those given in equations (14) and (15) causes the limiting ratio calculated for poly-L-alanine $w_{Gly} = 0$ to be 8·9 instead of 9·27 as quoted in Table 1.) The characteristic ratio decreases rapidly with w_{Gly} near $w_{Gly} = 0$; a small proportion of glycine exerts a disproportionately large effect. The curve decreases more gradually, but monotonically, with further increase in w_{Gly}; a minor proportion of alanine exerts only a small effect on $\langle r^2\rangle_0/xl_u^2$ for polyglycine.

The dashed curve in Fig. 6 represents corresponding calculations for random copolymers of D- and L-residues of the alanyl type. A small proportion of the enantiomorphic alanyl residue is even more effective than an equal proportion of glycyl in lowering the characteristic ratio. For equimolar proportions ($w = 0.50$) the random–coil dimensions for the two copolymers of L-alanine are similar. The curve for D,L-alanine copolymers is necessarily symmetric about $w = 1/2$.

Perpetuation of the quasi-helix generated by adherence of successive residues to conformations within the domain of region III of Fig. 5 for L-alanyl may be interrupted by interposition of either a glycyl or a D-alanyl

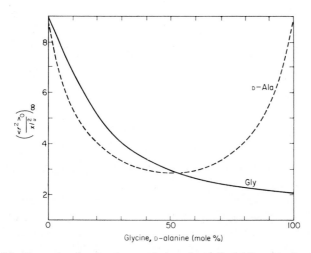

FIG. 6. Limiting value for the characteristic ratio $(\langle r^2\rangle_0/xl_u^2)_\infty$ calculated for random copolymers of L-alanine and glycine (solid line) and for random copolymers of L- and D-alanine (broken line). From Miller *et al.* (1967).

residue. The former presents two equally favored minima. One member of this mirror image pair occurs in the general neighborhood of region III (cf. Figs. 3 and 5), though displaced somewhat from it. The other represents a helix of opposite screw sense. If the glycyl residue chooses the former location (approximately g^+g^-), it introduces only a small departure from the preferred quasi-helicoidal form of the L-alanyl sequence. Choice of the latter (approximately g^-g^+) disrupts the direction of the trajectory of the chain completely.

A D-alanyl residue offers one strongly-favored conformational domain. This domain corresponds to III of Fig. 5, but it occurs in the opposite quadrant of the diagram. Whereas half of the glycyl residues are expected to adopt conformations resembling the preferred one for L-alanyl, this option is strongly forbidden for D-alanyl. The latter residue will usually assume the conformation of the quasi-helix of opposite sense of rotation which, as was noted above, represents a drastic departure from the preferred conformation for the L-alanyl residue. It is on this account that a small proportion of D-alanyl is about twice as effective as glycyl in reducing the characteristic ratio for poly-L-alanine.

Experimental results (Miller et al., 1967) tend to confirm these predictions. Twenty-five mole per cent of glycine randomly copolymerized with L-glutamic acid reduces the characteristic ratio to about 4 ± 0.5. A copolymer of D- and L-glutamic acids in the proportions of 40 : 60 exhibited a similar ratio (Miller et al., 1967). A tendency to generate sequences of residues of the same kind in the copolymerization of N-carboxyanhydrides of the α-amino acids by which these copolymers were prepared would, if operative, raise the value of the characteristic ratio.

A particular class of polypeptides of interest in this connection consists of racemic copolymers of D and L residues in equal proportions copolymerized under conditions such that the probability of selection of one or the other unit depends on the one preceding it in the chain. The probability of sequence perpetuation w appearing in equation (19) is replaced by a matrix of sequence probabilities

$$\mathbf{w} = \begin{bmatrix} w_{\mathrm{DD}} & w_{\mathrm{DL}} \\ w_{\mathrm{LD}} & w_{\mathrm{LL}} \end{bmatrix} = \begin{bmatrix} w_{\mathrm{iso}} & 1 - w_{\mathrm{iso}} \\ 1 - w_{\mathrm{iso}} & w_{\mathrm{iso}} \end{bmatrix} \tag{20}$$

Details of the calculation are given elsewhere (Miller et al., 1967). Results of calculations for racemic copolymers of alanine (or alanine type) are presented in Fig. 7. The abscissa covers the range from the regularly alternating, or syndiotactic, copolymer of D and L residues, for which $w_{\mathrm{iso}} = 0$, to the polymer having indefinitely long sequences of residues of the same isomer, for which $w_{\mathrm{iso}} = 1$. For random copolymers $w_{\mathrm{iso}} = 1/2$. The solid line representing the characteristic ratio in the limit $x = \infty$ decreases with decreasing stereo-regularity from the large value for all L- or all D-polyalanine to a value less

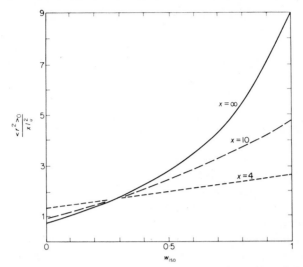

FIG. 7. Characteristic ratios calculated for racemic copolypeptides of the polyalanine type as functions of the stereoregularity index. Degrees of polymerization are indicated for the respective curves. From Miller *et al.* (1967).

than unity. Thus, the characteristic ratio predicted for the regularly alternating racemic copolymer is less than would obtain for a chain of freely jointed bonds each of length l_u. This result is unusual.

Corresponding curves in Fig. 7 for finite chains show smaller variations with w_{iso}, as might be expected. The increase in the intercept at $w_{iso} = 0$ with decrease in x is unexpected, however. It denotes a decrease in the characteristic ratio with chain length, which is without precedent in other chains which have been treated heretofore.

The low value of the characteristic ratio for the alternating D,L copolymer finds explanation in the conformation map for L-alanine and its counterpart for the D-residue (Miller *et al.*, 1967). If each residue is assigned its preferred conformation—region III in Fig. 5 for L and its inversion image for D—the resulting skeletal conformation will be found to approximate a helix of very low pitch. Strict adherence to helical form will not, of course, obtain owing to the breadth of the preferred domain III. The tendency toward a comparatively compact conformation, which nevertheless prevails, is responsible for the low values calculated for the average dimensions of the alternating copolymer.

6. Average Random Coil Dimensions for Denatured Proteins

Tanford *et al.* (1966) have examined the intrinsic viscosities of eleven proteins in a solvent, 6 M aqueous guanidinium hydrochloride, in which denaturation should be complete. Disulfide cross-linkages, present in some of the native proteins, were dissociated by the action of β-mercaptoethanol in order to assure linearity of the polypeptide chains in solution. The intrinsic viscosities of the proteins ranging in molecular weight from 15,500 to 197,000 are well represented by a single relationship, variations in residue composition and in sequence notwithstanding. This relationship,

$$[\eta] = 7 \cdot 16 \times 10^{-3} x^{0 \cdot 66} \qquad (21)$$

with $[\eta]$ expressed in decil. g^{-1}, is typical of those found for random coil polymers in general when dispersed in good solvents. As Tanford et al. point out, this observation, confirmed by investigation of sedimentation velocities (Tanford et al., 1966), demonstrates the random coil character of fully denatured proteins in solution. The characteristic ratio estimated from these results, after approximate correction for the volume exclusion perturbation (Tanford et al., 1966), is $\langle r^2 \rangle_0 / x l_u^2 = 4 \cdot 5$. The difference between this result and that cited above for the synthetic L-polypeptides (~ 9) may reasonably be attributed to the effects of glycyl and L-prolyl residues in depressing the random coil dimensions of the proteins.

Conformations of the various residues present in proteins, including L-proline in particular, require further investigation before the configurations of protein chains can be treated in a satisfactory manner. It may be necessary to take account of the amino acid sequence as well. The mathematical methods for handling this problem are well in hand.

7. Conformations and Conformational Transitions of Globular Proteins

Polypeptide and protein molecules occur in the form of random coils only in solvent media in which there is strong interaction of the amide and/or other polar groups with the solvent. Typically, as in water, this interaction involves solvation of these groups. The solvation layers are, of course, compatible with the surrounding solvent. They would be incompatible with a hydrophobic medium, or with hydrophobic side chains of the polymer. Their stabilizing effect is contingent therefore on a large excess of solvent.

A possible alternative situation for the polypeptide chain dispersed in a polar solvent is one in which its peptide units are juxtaposed in such a way as to promote contacts between hydrophobic side chains and thus to minimize their contacts with the hostile environment of the solvent. Polar side chains may, of course, find such an arrangement less satisfactory. A protein chain consisting of both polar and hydrophobic residues may conceivably achieve an optimum *modus vivendi* with its environment by adopting a compact conformation in which hydrophobic groups are placed in the interior, polar groups being relegated to the exterior where they may exist in contact with surrounding (aqueous) solvent.

The foregoing is, in brief, a rationalization of the well-documented retention of the native globular conformation when native proteins are dispersed in water. The random coil and the globular, or native, states differ drastically and a compromise between them will be seen upon further, more thorough examination to be less favored than either of these extremes. Thus, the solvation of polar groups essential for stabilization of the random coil dictates an environment for the residue which consists of solvent in large excess, and this necessitates complete unfolding of the chain; otherwise solvated groups would be forced to exist in the environment of the chain, with which their interaction in general is less favorable. On the other hand, realization of effective hydrophobic interactions (and specific interactions between polar groups as well) in the globular state required close contact between the interacting groups. Hence, the latter state can be expected to be favorable only if solvent is expelled to the point where little or none is retained within the domain of the molecule.

A necessary requirement for a conformation of the skeleton of a long chain molecule to be an admissible one is the absence of spatial overlaps between any pair of its units. Compliance with this condition can be achieved with relatively little difficulty in the random coil state where occupancy of the domain of the coil by units of the chain is quite low—in the order of a few per cent only. Even in the random coil, however, many otherwise acceptable configurations of a long chain will be disqualified by spatial conflicts between units which are well separated in sequence along the chain. These long range interactions may enlarge the average dimensions of the chain by a factor appreciably exceeding unity, as was pointed out in the introduction.

Long range interactions are multiplied profusely by increase of the density of units in the domain occupied by the molecule. With complete removal of solvent and consequent packing of the chain units to bulk density, the avoidance of spatial conflicts becomes acute. If the chain is very long, the problem bears a close resemblance to that of packing a system of many random coil molecules to high density without ordering their conformations (Flory, 1956, 1961). The lattice model affords a means of estimating the stringency of space allocation. The macromolecular chain is imagined to be subdivided into approximately isometric segments, and each is allowed a measure of choice between lattice cells surrounding the one occupied by its predecessor in the chain. This range of choice is limited by the conformational "flexibility" of the chain molecule. If the molecule were isolated from all others, the number of configurations available to it would be $\omega^{x'-1} = \omega^{x'}$ where ω is the number of neighboring lattice cells accessible to each segment, with due account of the constraints on bond rotations; x' is the number of segments in the chain. If the chain molecule is to co-exist with other like molecules in the same space (or if the various portions of the same chain molecule are to be packed to high density within the same space), only those configurations will be permitted in which none of its segments encroaches on the space occupied by other segments. Obviously, if the density is high, the overwhelming majority of the configurations for the isolated molecule will fail to meet this requirement, and the attrition of the very large stock, $\omega^{x'}$, of its otherwise eligible configurations will be severe. The statistical mechanical theory of chain molecule mixtures (Flory, 1953 Chap XII, 1956,1961) estimates the factor of attrition to be

$$[e^{-1}(1-v_2)^{1-1/v_2}]^{x'}$$

where v_2 is the volume fraction of polymer. Thus, the expected number of acceptable configurations is

$$\Omega = [(\omega/e)(1 - v_2)^{1-1/v_2}]^{x'} \qquad (22)$$

At ultimate packing density, $v_2 = 1$ and

$$\Omega = \left(\frac{\omega}{e}\right)^{x'}. \qquad (23)$$

Depending on the magnitude of ω, the expected number Ω of configurations accessible to the chain may be either greater than or less than unity; if x' is large, the departure from unity will be very great in either case. If $\Omega < 1$, the chain molecule under consideration is indicated to be incapable of assuming an irregular configuration which is devoid of overlaps throughout the domain it occupies.

The same arguments apply to a single chain molecule of great length. If its "flexibility" ω is such that $\Omega < 1$ for given density v_2 (e.g. for $v_2 = 1$), then either a larger volume must be provided by dilution (decrease of v_2), or the molecule must adopt a regular conformation which fills efficiently the space at its disposal.

Estimation of ω is contingent upon the definition of a segment. Compliance with the stipulation that the segment shall occupy one cell of the lattice requires it to be isometric. The mean diameter of a protein chain is 6–7 Å; the length of a peptide unit is 3·8 Å. Thus, a segment appropriate for a lattice description comprises the greater part of two units. The marked preference of an L-residue of the alanyl type for the conformation of region III in Fig. 5, with only relatively small contributions from other regions of the energy map, signifies that the effective number of configurations per peptide unit may not be much greater than unity; their number ω for a segment, embracing approximately two units, should on this basis be less than two, and this makes $\omega/e < 1$. We are thus led to conclude that a polypeptide chain consisting of several hundred or more amino acid residues present in the proportions usually found in globular proteins, but assembled in random sequence, would rarely be found capable of being "folded", or collapsed, to an *irregular* configuration which is at once space filling, non-overlapping and free of an excessive number of residue conformations of high energy. Only by strategically fashioning the sequence of residues according to their special conformational capacities can a globular form be assured which does not entail an excessive commitment of energy. Glycyl and L-prolyl residues in particular permit skeletal conformations that depart from those preferred for other L-residues. The spatial requirements of the side chains of the various residues must, of course, be met as well. Substitution of one residue for another having a side chain of similar size and geometrical form should be permissible, as is indeed found (Dickerson, 1964) amongst corresponding proteins from different species. But an assemblage of the same or an equivalent set of residues in random succession probably would not yield a chain capable of assuming a globular conformation of low energy, according to the present line of reasoning. The necessity for a well-defined pattern in the sequence of residues is thus explicable.

The foregoing arguments offer a rational basis for observations indicating the native conformation for polypeptide chains of a given protein to be unique. This conformation is not one of many competitive possibilities which differ marginally in energy, such differences arising for example from alterations in the interactions between residues juxtaposed as neighbors in the competing conformations. Rather, its existence is an event of rare exception, allowed to occur only by virtue of a judicious selection of the residue sequence, which conduces to fulfilment of the several requisites, enunciated above, for an acceptable globular conformation. An alternative conformation also meeting these requisites would be exceedingly unlikely. The criteria for tolerance of a globular conformation are primarily steric, in the sense of accommodation of units which are remote in sequence along the chain as spatial neighbors without inflicting overlaps; specific interactions between such neighbors play a subordinate role (Dickerson, 1964).

The globular conformation of a native protein, or that part of it which is not helical, should not be likened to a random coil. The customary differentiation of helical and "random coil" portions of a native protein is a misapplication of the latter term which can be quite misleading. From what has been said above it will be apparent that a globular conformation is highly specific and certainly not random. Such conformations are compact, whereas the random coil may occupy a domain many times the molar volume. In an assembly of many random coils at high concentration (as in total absence of solvent), these domains overlap extensively, and the random coils interpenetrate one another in profusion.

The transition from the globular (native) to the random coil (denatured) form in dilute solution must obviously be a two-state process (Brandts, 1964, 1965; Brandts & Lumry, 1963), provided, of course, that the random coil is treated collectively as one state, which is proper. It should not be confused with a helix–coil transition, irrespective of the possible occurrence of partial helicity in the native form. The helix–coil transition is basically a one-dimensional process. Intermediate states contribute significantly in the transition range. The "transition" is not discontinuous, and thus differs from classical phase transitions for systems in three dimensions (Landau & Lifshitz, 1938). It remains diffuse irrespective of the length of the molecule. Globular proteins are three-dimensional, and on this basis alone denaturation of them falls in the category of a classical transition whose finite range is a consequence of their small size. If extrapolated to larger size (molecular weight), their denaturation transitions should become discontinuous. Even for proteins of finite size, the native form is properly construed as consisting of a single state.

The globular state should be differentiated from both the helix and the random coil. It may share some of the features of each, but its differences from both necessitate its description in separate terms.

ACKNOWLEDGMENT

This work was supported by the Directorate of Chemical Sciences, Air Force Office of Scientific Research Contract No. AF49(638)–1341.

REFERENCES

Abe, A., Jernigan, R. L. & Flory, P. J. (1966). *J. Am. chem. Soc.* **88**, 631.
Arridge, R. G. C. (1965). *Proc. phys. Soc.* **85**, 1157.
Arridge, R. G. C. & Cannon, C. G. (1964). *Proc. R. Soc.* **A278**, 91.
Birshtein, T. M. & Ptitsyn, O. B. (1964). "Conformation of Macromolecules". Transl. from the Russian Edition by S. N. Timasheff and M. J. Timasheff (1966), Chap. 2. New York: Interscience.
Brandts, J. F. (1964). *J. Am. chem. Soc.* **86**, 4291.
Brandts, J. F. (1965). *J. Am. chem. Soc.* **87**, 2759.
Brandts, J. F. & Lumry, R. (1963). *J. phys. Chem.* **67**, 1484.
Brant, D. A. & Flory, P. J. (1965*a*). *J. Am. chem. Soc.* **87**, 663, 2791.
Brant, D. A. & Flory, P. J. (1965*b*). *J. Am. chem. Soc.* **87**, 2788.
Brant, D. A., Miller, W. G. & Flory, P. J. (1967). *J. molec. Biol.* **23**, 47.
DeSantis, P., Giglio, E., Liquori, A. M. & Ripamonti, A. (1963). *J. Polym. Sci.* **A1**, 1383.
Dickerson, R. E. (1964). "The Proteins", ed. by H. Neurath, Vol. 2, Chap. 11. New York: Academic Press.
Edsall, J. T., Flory, P. J., Kendrew, J. C., Liquori, A. M., Nemethy, G., Ramachandran, G. N. & Scheraga, H. A. (1966). *J. biol. Chem.* **241**, 1004.
Flory, P. J. (1949). *J. chem. Phys.* **17**, 303.
Flory, P. J. (1953). "Principles of Polymer Chemistry", Chap. XIV. New York: Cornell University Press.
Flory, P. J. (1956). *Proc. R. Soc.* **A234**, 60.

Flory, P. J. (1961). *J. Polym. Sci.* **49,** 105.

Flory, P. J., Crescenzi, V. & Mark, J. E. (1964). *J. Am. chem. Soc.* **86,** 146.

Fox, T. G. & Flory, P. J. (1949). *J. phys. Colloid Chem.* **53,** 197.

Gibson, K. D. & Scheraga, H. A. (1966). *Biopolymers,* **4,** 709.

Hoeve, C. A. J. (1961). *J. chem. Phys.* **35,** 1266.

Landau, L. D. & Lifshitz, E. M. (1938). "Statistical Physics", p. 232. London: Oxford University Press.

Leach, S. J., Nemethy, G. & Scheraga, H. A. (1966). *Biopolymers,* **4,** 369.

Mark, J. E. & Flory, P. J. (1965). *J. Am. chem. Soc.* **87,** 1415.

Miller, W. G., Brant, D. A. & Flory, P. J. (1967). *J. molec. Biol.* **23,** 67.

Orofino, T. A. & Flory, P. J. (1957). *J. chem. Phys.* **26,** 1067.

Ramachandran, G. N., Ramakrishnan, C. & Sasisekharan, V. (1963). *J. molec. Biol.* **7,** 95.

Ramachandran, G. N., Ramakrishnan, C. & Venkatachalam, C. M. (1965). *Biopolymers,* **3,** 591.

Ramakrishnan, C. & Ramachandran, G. N. (1965). *Biophys. J.* **5,** 909.

Scott, R. A. & Scheraga, H. A. (1966). In press.

Tanford, C., Kawahara, K. B. & Lapanje, S. (1966). *J. biol. Chem.* **241,** 192; and unpublished data.

Statistical Mechanics of Protein–Ligand Interactions Associated with Conformational Changes

GEORGE NÉMETHY

The Rockefeller University, New York, U.S.A.

The binding of a ligand to a protein molecule, accompanied by a conformational change of the protein can be described in terms of changes in elementary non-covalent interactions, using a statistical mechanical description. For example, the model applies to the "induced fit" theory of the binding of a substrate to an enzyme molecule, or to allosteric transitions. It is assumed that the ligand binds at several points to the protein and that binding at each point can occur only after certain intramolecular interactions in the protein have been broken. Correlations must be established between the formation or the breaking of protein–ligand and of intra-protein interactions. The formulation of the partition function depends on these correlations. The model allows partial binding of the ligand to the protein, including also stages which may not all be functionally effective. Thus the concept of "effective binding" becomes necessary. A particular theoretical example, with a strongly restricted correlation of the various interactions is worked out in detail.

1. Introduction

The important role of conformational changes in proteins is well known, both with regard to physical properties (e.g. changes during denaturation) and to regulation of their chemical or biological activity. For example, the decisive role of conformational changes has been pointed out for the action of many enzymes by Koshland (1958,1964), and for the description of allosteric transitions by Monod *et al.* (1965).

The thermodynamic and statistical mechanical study of conformational changes in proteins and polypeptides has been confined so far almost exclusively to the helix-random coil transition. This phenomenon has been treated by a great variety of methods, considering both the backbone by itself (e.g. Schellman, 1955; Zimm & Bragg, 1959; Lifson & Roig, 1961; Lifson, 1964), and the effects of side chains (Poland & Scheraga, 1965). In one treatment (Poland & Scheraga, 1965), the effect of non-covalent interactions in the random coil was included. However, more complicated conformational changes in proteins, consisting of changes in interactions other than a simple helix–coil transition, have not been treated by such methods. A completely general statistical mechanical treatment of conformational changes, applicable to any protein system, may become too unwieldy. However, some conformational changes of limited extent but of importance for biochemical reactions can be treated in a useful manner.

In the theory of induced fit (Koshland, 1958), it is postulated that the establishment of a binding site for the substrate, or the bringing into juxta-position of reactive or catalytic groups, requires a conformational change in some enzymes. The effect of non-competitive inhibitors and of activators can also be interpreted in terms of the influence exerted by bound molecules upon conformational changes (Koshland, 1964).

Allosteric transitions in proteins containing subunits involve a similar structural mechanism (Monod *et al.*, 1965; Koshland *et al.*, 1966). The binding of a ligand (substrate, activator, inhibitor) to a subunit induces a conformational change, altering the nature or the extent of non-covalent interactions between the subunits. This in turn modifies the ease with which other subunits can undergo the conformational change associated with the binding of the ligand.

When the conformational change in any of these reactions consists merely of the breaking or establishment of a single non-covalent interaction (e.g. a hydrogen bond, or a hydrophobic bond between two aliphatic groups), or when several changes of these interactions must occur concurrently, due to the rigidity of the remaining structure (the motion of two α-helical segments with respect to each other, without unfolding, would be such a process), and the binding of the ligand is an all-or-none process (as for small ligands), then the entire change can be treated in terms of a single equilibrium, and the free energy is written down easily as

$$\Delta F^\circ = \Delta F_t^\circ + \Delta F_{ES}^\circ. \tag{1}$$

Here ΔF_t° denotes the free energy of the conformational change of the protein, and ΔF_{ES}° is the free energy of binding of the ligand S to the protein E after the latter has undergone the conformational change. Koshland *et al.* (1966) have described how the free energy terms of equation (1) can be interpreted in some more complex cases.

However, in many cases of interest, both the conformational change and the binding of the ligand must consist of more complicated processes. In enzyme-catalysed reactions the substrate presumably binds at several points to the surface of the enzyme. This may be one of the prime requirements of enzyme specificity, particularly whenever there is differentiation between stereoisomeric substrates. Such is the case for the "three-point interaction" discussed by Ogston (1948) and by Hein & Niemann (1962). In addition, some of the "points" involved in binding may actually consist of extensive regions (for example, if a long non-polar side chain on the substrate is bound). In such cases incomplete binding is possible, i.e. the substrate may be in contact with the enzyme at less than the maximum number of binding "points", due to flexibility or wrong orientation. At the same time, the establishment of a large active site presumably involves a conformational change, requiring the disruption of several non-covalent interactions in the enzyme molecule. Thus a sequence of conformations may exist, each of which allows different extents of partial or complete binding of the substrate.

Similarly, in the case of enzymes containing subunits, a conformational change may consist of several elementary steps, if both the binding site and the site of interaction between subunits are composed of several groups participating in non-covalent bonding.

If one merely seeks the description of an enzymatic mechanism or of a binding equilibrium in terms of empirical equilibrium constants, such detailed considerations are superfluous. All interactions are lumped into the observed constant. If, however, it is desired to correlate the binding constant with the changes in free energy (due to alterations of non-covalent interactions) accompanying the conformational changes, it is necessary to take into account the presence of all possible modes of structures. If intermediate structures, with partial unfolding of the active site, or partial binding of the ligand, are possible, the value of the observed binding constant is affected. The evaluation of the overall free energies and of the equilibrium constants requires statistical mechanical or combinatorial methods.

The purpose of this paper is to sketch out the initial steps of such a treatment. This discussion is restricted to a consideration of the binding of a ligand to a protein molecule not containing subunits, i.e. to the induced fit mechanism in enzymes. The application to changing interactions between subunits (as they occur in allosteric interactions) is being developed now and will be reported elsewhere.

2. Description of the General Treatment

In the model used here, it is assumed that the ligand S is bound through several of its constituent groups, each interacting (p–s interaction) with a corresponding "region" of the protein surface (Fig. 1). Each region can contain one or more "binding points", representing a single non-covalent interaction. Binding can occur by various means, such as ionic interactions, hydrogen bonds, hydrophobic bonds. A given "region" can contain binding points of different types, e.g. a hydrogen bond and a series of $CH_2 \ldots CH_2$ hydrophobic contacts (Fig. 1). Specificity in binding requires that the number of points of binding, denoted by n_{ps}, be the same on the protein and on the ligand, and that their spatial arrangement match each other in the conformation in which binding can occur.

Counting in terms of binding points instead of regions is necessary if there is sufficient flexibility in the system to allow partial binding at a given region.

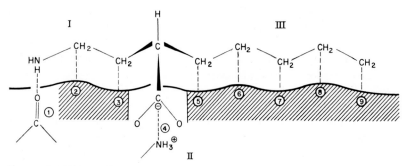

Fig. 1. Schematic diagram of protein–ligand binding by means of several points of interaction. There are three regions of binding, corresponding to the different functional groups (I, II, III). Regions I and III comprise several points of binding, and thus allow different extents of binding. The single binding points are denoted by ①,...,⑨, so that $n_{ps} = 9$. The non-polar parts of the surface of the protein molecule (available for hydrophobic bonding) are shaded.

For example, if S has a long hydrocarbon chain, bound to a non-polar surface region of the protein P by means of hydrophobic bonds, this chain may unfold gradually from the protein surface (Fig. 2). Not all the $CH_2...CH_2$ interactions have to be formed or broken simultaneously, although correlations may exist between either the strengths of interactions or the order in which they can occur. Thus, in order to be able to describe stages in which the binding at any one region is incomplete, the binding points comprising the region must be counted separately. Each interaction which can be broken non-simultaneously with other interactions is considered as a separate "binding point". The number of these points is at least as large as the number of "regions".

According to the basic postulate for the systems treated here, a conformational change of the protein is necessary for complete binding. Therefore, some or all of the n_{ps} binding points must be inaccessible to the ligand prior to the conformational change. Inaccessibility can result from two causes: (a) the functional groups involved may be buried in the interior of the protein, or (b) they may be exposed on the protein surface, but positioned wrong with respect to other binding sites. In the present discussion, these two causes can be treated in a similar way.

A conformational change in the protein molecule, making the entire binding site accessible to the ligand, presumably requires the breaking (or possibly the formation) of *several* intramolecular non-covalent interactions (denoted as p–p), with various degrees of correlation. The n_{pp} "interaction points" for intramolecular contacts in the protein (p–p interactions) are defined in analogy with the p–s binding points, discussed above. Thus in an

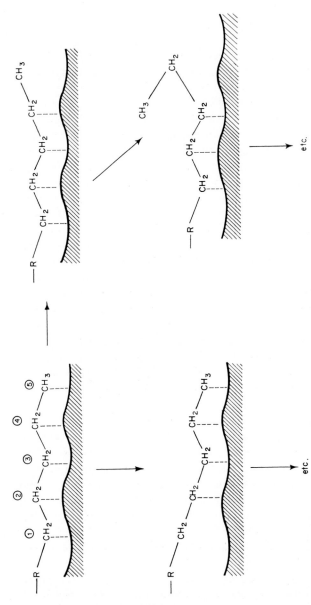

Fig. 2. Schematic example of the gradual unfolding of a hydrocarbon chain from a protein surface to which it is bound by hydrophobic bonds. The hydrophobic interactions of the individual CH₂ groups can be broken successively, starting from either end. However, the internal bonds (e.g. those formed by methylene groups ② and ③) cannot be broken unless the adjacent ones near the end (either ①, or ④ and ⑤) are broken first.

equilibrium mixture, a range of protein conformations must exist, the extrema being the conformation most stable in the absence of the ligand (= native form = form A) and the conformation in which the entire binding site is accessible (= form B). In the latter, n_{pp} interactions are altered. A description of this system requires a statistical mechanical treatment whenever n_{pp} becomes moderately large. The "native" form A and intermediate conformations may allow partial binding of the ligand at one or more points. One must also take into account the fluctuations due to incomplete binding of S to the momentarily available binding points.

For the description of conformations and binding states intermediate between forms A and B, the following approach is adopted: Let the protein have a certain conformation, such that binding by groups of the ligand is possible at a specified set of m_{ps} points of binding (selected out of the total of n_{ps} points). This set, the members of which depend on the conformation selected for the protein, is denoted by $\{m_{ps}\}$. (This notation is necessary, because, in a general case, there may be several, partly different sets containing the same *number*, m_{ps}, of allowed interactions, but selected differently, due to differences in conformation.) This set $\{m_{ps}\}$ is available only if at least a certain set of p–p interactions, denoted by $\{m_{pp}\}$, are altered from their state in conformation A.† An example will be given in the next section. This treatment can be extended beyond the simple cases discussed here. For example, binding of the ligand in incorrect orientations can be described by proper selections of the sets $\{m_{ps}\}$.

The establishment of a partition function for the protein–ligand system requires the following general steps. (a) All p–p and p–s interactions must be given in terms of either an actual list or a general rule based on the structure of the protein. (b) Rules must be set up for the correlations between the breaking or formation of the various p–p or p–s interactions, and between the sets $\{m_{pp}\}$ and $\{m_{ps}\}$. (c) The interaction energies for all p–p and p–s interaction points must be specified. Since it is assumed that each interaction point makes a separate contribution to the binding, the use of "effective" energies may be necessary. Changes in conformational freedom may require the inclusion of separate degeneracy factors. (d) The loss of translational and rotational entropy of the ligand must be included at appropriate places. (e) The partition function is set up as a summation over terms representing the various possible pairs of $\{m_{pp}\}$ and $\{m_{ps}\}$. Each term contains the Boltzmann exponential factors obtained in step (c) and, where necessary, the correction according to step (d).

† In particular cases, it is possible that $m_{pp} = 0$ for a certain set $\{m_{ps}\}$, viz. when all m_{ps} interaction sites of this particular set are exposed already in conformation A. In general, it should be noted that $\{m_{pp}\}$ is the minimum set of altered p–p interactions needed for the establishment of the given set $\{m_{ps}\}$ of p–s interactions, because some additional p–p interactions might be broken as well without altering $\{m_{ps}\}$ (see below)

The method for obtaining the sets $\{m_{pp}\}$ and $\{m_{ps}\}$ in a general case, the derivation of the most general form of the partition function, and a discussion of its physical implications are presented elsewhere. They are not being further discussed here, since the purpose of this communication is merely to present a qualitative survey of the method of approach to the problem. In the next section, a particular example is derived in detail, as an illustration.

3. Example: Enzyme–Ligand Interaction with a Single Sequence of Changing Interactions

In this section, the partition function is derived for a hypothetical example. The model used may not be very realistic, and application to any real system would presumably require the introduction of further correlations. It is used here because it provides a straight-forward illustration for the derivation of the partition function.

(a) Description of the model

The model is based on several assumptions, all of which could be made different for other examples.

(1) Both ligand S and protein P contain n_{ps} binding points. In the native conformation A of the protein, all (or most of them, see below) are buried, i.e. inaccessible.

(2) In the conformation B, all n_{ps} points are accessible. During the transition A $\rightarrow$ B, n_{pp} interactions are broken in the protein molecule.

(3) Both the p–p interaction points and the p–s binding points are arranged in a single continuous sequence. On going from conformation A to B, the protein unfolds gradually, by breaking one p–p interaction after the other. A given p–p interaction can be broken only if all the previous ones in the sequence are already broken. In the course of this process, the p–s binding points become exposed successively, i.e. when the jth p–s binding point becomes exposed, all p–s binding points numbered 1 to $j-1$ are already exposed (available for binding), but none of the p–s binding points $j+1$ to n_{ps} are exposed. The jth p–s binding point becomes available upon the breaking of the m_jth p–p interaction. For the p–p interactions, the condition of a continuous sequence requires that $m_{j+1} \geqslant m_j$. The process is illustrated schematically in Fig. 3.

(4) In order to make the jth p–s interaction possible, it is necessary that at least m_j of the p–p interactions be broken (Fig. 3). The jth p–s interaction is the last one that can form whenever the number of broken p–p interactions ranges from m_j to $m_{j+1}-1$. If $m_{j+1} > m_j+1$, several p–p interactions must be broken before a new, $(j+1)$th p–s binding point is made available.

(5) Even if j binding points are accessible, S does not have to bind to all of them. In this treatment, it is assumed that S can bind independently at any

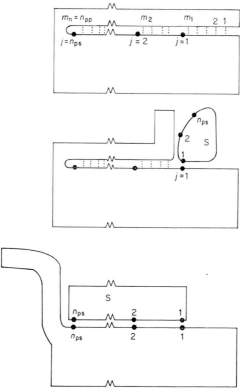

FIG. 3. Schematic illustration (not to scale) of the type of interaction described in Section 3. The protein has n_{pp} intramolecular interactions which must be broken successively in order to make the n_{ps} p–s interaction sites available one after the other. The native form, as well as the conformation with one p–s site available ($j = 1$), and the final state with all n_{ps} sites available and utilized are shown.

or all of the j exposed sites. This presupposes a very flexible ligand S. Other assumptions could obviously be made.

(6) No particular assumption is made about the functional relationship between j and m_j beyond the requirement implicit in assumption (3), i.e. if $j > i$ then $m_j \geqslant m_i$. Within this limitation, any correlation can be assumed which seems best for a given situation.

(7) The total interaction energy is separable into a sum of terms for each of the individual p–p and p–s interactions. Thus the breaking of the ith p–p interaction makes a contribution $q_{pp}(i)$ in the partition function:

$$q_{pp}(i) = Q_{pp}(i) \exp\left[+\Delta F^\circ_{pp}(i)/RT\right] \tag{2}$$

where $\Delta F^\circ_{pp}(i)$ is the free energy of formation of this p–p interaction. The free energy instead of the energy is used in the Boltzmann factor in order to take into account properly all possible types of interactions, e.g. hydrophobic bonds (Némethy *et al.*, 1963). The pre-exponential factor $Q_{pp}(i)$ is essentially an entropy term. $Q_{pp}(i) > 1$ if the breaking of the ith interaction results in an increase in the flexibility of the protein, i.e. if the resulting structure can take up several equivalent allowed conformations (Némethy *et al.*, 1966).

Similarly, for the contribution of the ξth p–s interaction,

$$q_{ps}(\xi) = Q_{ps}(\xi) \exp\left[-\Delta F^\circ_{ps}(\xi)/RT\right] \tag{3}$$

where the $\Delta F^\circ_{ps}(\xi)$ and the $Q_{ps}(\xi)$ are defined similarly to ΔF°_{pp} and Q_{pp}, respectively. Note that the two ΔF's have opposite sign in the Boltzmann factors. Both refer originally to the free energy of formation of the bond under consideration. The partition function will, however, be written in such a manner that the *breaking* of p–p bonds and the *formation* of p–s bonds are processes occuring in the same direction. The factor Q_{ps} may contain contributions from changes in flexibility of both the protein and the ligand.

(b) *Derivation of the partition function*

Based on these assumptions, the partition function can be derived easily. If the jth p–s binding point is the highest one available, we know that m_j p–p interactions must be broken (assumption (3)). Therefore, the corresponding term in the partition function must contain a factor

$$\prod_{i=0}^{m_j} q_{pp}(i). \tag{4}$$

In addition, the p–p interactions numbered m_j+1 to $m_{j+1}-1$ *may* be broken without changing the value of j (by assumption (4)). This gives rise to a series of partition function terms in which $0, 1, 2, \ldots, \Delta m_j - 1$ p–p interactions are broken beyond the m_jth one. Here $\Delta m_j = m_{j+1} - m_j$. Combining this series of terms with the common factor (equation (4)) results in the expression

$$\sum_{\lambda=m_j}^{m_{j+1}-1} \prod_{i=0}^{\lambda} q_{pp}(i). \tag{5}$$

This takes care of the broken p–p interactions. Equation (5) now has to be multiplied by the factor expressing the binding of S. Since any or all of the first j p–s interactions can be formed independently, their contribution to the partition function is expressed as a product of independent factors:

$$\prod_{\xi=0}^{j} \left[1 + q_{ps}(\xi)\right]. \tag{6}$$

Within each factor $1 + q_{ps}(\xi)$ of the product, the first and second terms represent the cases when the ξth p–s interaction is broken and formed, respectively. The jth term of the partition function is given by the product of equations

(5) and (6). The partition function for the P–S complex is obtained by summing over j:

$$Z_1 = \sum_{j=0}^{n_{ps}} \left\{ \prod_{\xi=0}^{j} [1 + q_{ps}(\xi)] \sum_{\lambda=m_j}^{m_{j+1}-1} \left[\prod_{i=0}^{\lambda} q_{pp}(i) \right] \right\} \tag{7}†$$

A further correction is needed in equation (7) for the completion of the partition function. Whenever S is not bound to P, it gains an entropy of dissociation, due to translational and rotational contributions. The ligand is dissociated in two cases: (i) Whenever $j = 0$, i.e. no binding sites are available, (ii) whenever S does not bind at any site even though $j > 0$ points are available on the protein. If the product in equation (6) is expanded into a polynomial, its first term (equal to one) corresponds to S being dissociated. Therefore, if unity is subtracted from equation (6) and thus from the corresponding product in each term of equation (7), a partition function Z_2 is obtained which represents only those states of the protein-ligand system in which the ligand is bound to the protein. The complete partition function is then obtained as

$$Z = Z_0 + Z_2. \tag{8}$$

Here Z_0 represents those states in which S is dissociated from P, irrespectively of the conformational state of the protein. It has the form

$$Z_0 = Q_s(\text{free}) \sum_{j=0}^{n_{ps}} \sum_{\lambda=m_j}^{m_{j+1}-1} \prod_{i=0}^{\lambda} q_{pp}(i)$$
$$= Q_s(\text{free}) \sum_{\lambda=0}^{n_{pp}} \prod_{i=0}^{\lambda} q_{pp}(i). \tag{9}$$

The terms of the summation represent conformational changes (due to breaking of p–p interactions) of the protein when no S is bound to it. The factor $Q_s(\text{free})$ corresponds to the entropy of dissociation of the ligand from the protein. The entropies of association reactions involving proteins have been discussed in detail by Steinberg & Scheraga (1963). In the present example, binding on specific sites is assumed, without the possibility of relative rotation of P and S. Therefore, $Q_s(\text{free})$ will include contributions for gaining both the full translational freedom (Sackur–Tetrode equation) and the full rotational freedom in the dissociation step. Since no relative rotation is assumed in the P–S complex, there is no need for the corrections discussed by Steinberg & Scheraga (1963).‡ Solvent effects, treated by them separately, are included here in the interaction free energies ΔF_{ps}° and ΔF_{pp}°.

† For $\xi = 0$, $q_{ps}(\xi) = 0$. When $j = n_{ps}$, i.e. $m_j = n_{pp}$, the summation over λ has only one term, viz. that for which $\lambda = n_{pp}$. In principle, further unfolding of the protein, without alteration of the mode of binding of S, could be treated in the partition function simply by including terms in this summation for $\lambda > m_{pp}$. This extension is not included to avoid unnecessary complications at this stage of the treatment.

‡ The correction would be required if the ligand could still rotate about an axis when it is bound at *one* point of contact. This type of binding is represented by the second term, linear in q_{ps}, of the expansion of the product in equation (6). The correction is not included in this example for the sake of simplicity.

The final partition function for the system is then written as

$$Z = Z_0 + \sum_{j=0}^{n_{ps}} \left\{ \left[\prod_{-1+\xi=1}^{j} [1 + q_{ps}(\xi)] \right] \cdot \sum_{\lambda=m_j}^{m_{j+1}-1} \left[\prod_{i=0}^{\lambda} q_{pp}(i) \right] \right\} \tag{10}$$

where the entire second term represents the Z_2 of equation (8).

(c) Equilibrium constant for the binding of S

According to the definitions given above, the equilibrium constant for binding S to P is

$$K_{PS} = \frac{(PS)}{(P)(S)} = \frac{Z_2}{Z_0}. \tag{11}$$

(d) The concept of "effective binding"

If binding of S at all n_{ps} binding points is required for some particular reaction (e.g. the enzymatic catalysis by P of some reaction of S), then not all the S bound to P is active, i.e. can take part in the reaction, but only the fraction which is bound correctly at all n_{ps} binding points. This fraction is defined as being "bound effectively". It is represented in the partition function Z_2 by the term(s) for which $j = n_{ps}$ and all n_{ps} p-s interactions exist. These terms are denoted by Z_3:

$$Z_3 = \prod_{\xi=0}^{n_{ps}} q_{ps}(\xi) \prod_{i=0}^{n_{pp}} q_{pp}(i). \tag{12}$$

The fraction of S "bound effectively", relative to the total amount bound to P is given by

$$\theta_{eff} = \frac{Z_3}{Z_2}. \tag{13}$$

The "effective equilibrium constant" for active binding of S is

$$K_{eff} = \theta_{eff} K_{PS}. \tag{14}$$

K_{eff} is equal in this case to the equilibrium constant that would be obtained if there were no intermediate states, i.e. if all n_{pp} interactions had to be broken before binding could occur and S would bind in one concerted step at all points of interaction simultaneously. Other assumptions could be made about Z_3, in which case K_{eff} would not be equal to this constant.

(e) Numerical example

In order to give a feeling for the orders of magnitude of the effects discussed here, an arbitrarily chosen numerical example is given.

The structural parameters and physical quantities involved are listed in Table 1.

It was assumed that S has three binding regions, two consisting of a hydrogen bonding group each, and one of an ethyl side chain which can form a hydrophobic bond. The free energy of a hydrophobic bond, $\Delta F_{H\phi}^{\circ} = -0.3$ kcal/

TABLE 1. *Numerical parameters for the illustrative example of the application of the partition function*

	p–s Interactions					p–p Interactions		
j	Nature of interaction	$\Delta F^{\circ}_{ps}(j)$ (kcal/mole)	$Q_{ps}(j)$	m_j	i	Nature of interaction	$\Delta F^{\circ}_{pp}(i)$ (kcal/mole)	$Q_{pp}(i)$
1	Hydrogen bond	−0·5	1	2	1	Hydrophobic bond	−0·3	1
					2	Hydrogen bond	−0·5	2
2	Hydrogen bond	−0·5	1	4	3	Hydrophobic bond	−0·3	1
					4	Hydrogen bond	−0·5	2
3	Hydrophobic bond	−0·3	$\frac{1}{2}$	5	5	Hydrophobic bond	−0·3	1
4	Hydrophobic bond	−0·3	$\frac{1}{2}$	6	6	Hydrophobic bond	−0·3	2

$n_{ps} = 4$
$n_{pp} = 6$
$Q_s(\text{free}) = 153$, corresponding to $\Delta S^{\circ}_{dissoc} = 10$ e.u.

mole per CH_2 group was taken from the work of Némethy & Scheraga (1962). For the hydrogen bond, a low value of $\Delta F_H^{\circ} = -0.5$ kcal/mole was selected, assuming aqueous environment.

Evaluation of the partition function yields the results

$$Z_0 = 422$$
$$Z_2 = 3.863$$
$$Z_3 = 0.61$$
$$K_{PS} = 9.2 \times 10^{-3} \, 1 \, \text{mole}^{-1}$$
$$\theta_{eff} = 0.16$$
$$K_{eff} = 1.5 \times 10^{-3} \, 1 \, \text{mole}^{-1}.$$

Note that Z_0 is large and hence K_{PS} is small, primarily because of the large value allotted to Q_s(free). The fraction θ_{eff} is significantly lower than unity.

4. Treatment of Flexibility in Proteins

The summation in equation (9), i.e. the quantity Z_0/Q_s(free) contains terms corresponding to various degrees of unfolding of the protein when no S is bound to it. Thus this quantity, to be denoted by Z_p, can serve as a measure of the conformational flexibility of the protein, i.e. of the tendency to undergo part or all of the conformational change A → B spontaneously, in the absence of the ligand S. This crude analysis already indicates the direction in which the present theory can be expanded to provide a statistical analysis of fluctuations in protein conformation or, more particularly, of the occurrence of deviations from the conformation of minimum free energy (cf. Scheraga et al., 1967).

If one evaluates Z_p as a function of temperature or solvent composition, under conditions where the A → B transition can take place, this treatment provides an analysis of the details of the conformational change on denaturation, etc. The individual terms of the sum in Z_p correspond to transitional structures between the two stable conformations A and B (cf. Poland & Scheraga, 1965, Part IX). Under many circumstances, either of the two terminal forms is definitely more stable than the other and than the intermediate states. This is particularly so when all or most of the n_{pp} interactions are of a similar type (hydrogen bonds or hydrophobic bonds, etc.). The two-state model for protein denaturation, proposed by Brandts (1964, 1966), corresponds to such a transition.

5. Application to Specific Proteins

In order to apply the theory in an exact form to a specific protein–ligand interaction, full information is needed about the various p–p and p–s interactions involved. An exact analysis is possible for proteins whose structure is known. Such an analysis is now being carried out for several proteins and will be reported elsewhere.

6. Discussion

The preceding discussion merely presented the basic concepts of the theory, together with a particular example of its application. The scope of applicability of this type of statistical mechanical analysis extends over a wider range of phenomena, and is now being investigated. The treatment of the binding sites in terms of points of interaction allows a convenient quantitative description of differences in enzyme specificity toward various substrates and of the action of competitive inhibitors. For example, substrate analogs with lower affinity for the enzyme than the true substrate could be substances lacking some of the n_{ps} interacting points of the substrate. Competitive inhibitors also bind to some of the n_{ps} sites, without necessarily occupying all of them, and/or may not have appropriate functional groups. Evaluation of the partition function for substrates and inhibitors with known structures can serve in the prediction of relative binding constants K_M and K_I if conformational changes of the protein are assumed to be the same for both binding processes. Alternatively, by means of a comparison of the observed binding constants with those obtained from the partition function, information is obtained about the conformational changes which occur on binding different substances.

The possibility of multi-point binding of ligands, combined with flexibility, may also result in alterations of the kinetics of association–dissociation reactions. This may be important in the evaluation of results obtained by relaxation techniques (O. Jardetzky, personal communication).

As indicated in Section 4, the partition function can also be used for a study of the stability of protein conformations and of the extent of fluctuations from the most stable structure.

These applications must make use of the general formulation of the partition function Z, presented elsewhere. In order to be able to apply the theory to proteins whose tertiary structure is not known in complete detail, it will also be necessary to derive generalizations for the formulation of the sets of interactions $\{m_{ps}\}$ and $\{m_{pp}\}$ on the basis of limited information about the structure of the protein.

REFERENCES

Brandts, J. F. (1964). *J. Am. chem. Soc.* **86,** 4291.
Brandts, J. F. (1966). Abstr., First Middle Atlantic Regional Meeting of the American Chemical Society, p. 84.
Hein, G. E. & Niemann, C. (1962). *J. Am. chem. Soc.* **84,** 4495.
Koshland, D. E., Jr. (1958). *Proc. natn. Acad. Sci. U.S.A.* **44,** 98.
Koshland, D. E., Jr. (1964). *Fedn. Proc. Fedn. Am. Socs. exp. Biol.* **23,** 719.
Koshland, D. E., Jr., Némethy, G. & Filmer, D. (1966). *Biochemistry, N.Y.* **5,** 365.
Lifson, S. (1964). *J. chem. Phys.* **40,** 3705.

Lifson, S. & Roig, A. (1961). *J. chem. Phys.* **34,** 1963.

Monod, J., Wyman, J. & Changeux, J.-P. (1965). *J. molec. Biol.* **12,** 88.

Némethy, G., Leach, S. J. & Scheraga, H. A. (1966). *J. phys. Chem., Ithaca,* **70,** 998.

Némethy, G. & Scheraga, H. A. (1962). *J. phys. Chem., Ithaca,* **66,** 1773.

Némethy, G., Steinberg, I. Z. & Scheraga, H. A. (1963). *Biopolymers,* **1,** 43.

Ogston, A. G. (1948). *Nature, Lond.* **162,** 963.

Poland, D. C. & Scheraga, H. A. (1965). *Biopolymers,* **3,** 275, 283, 305, 315, 335, 357, 369, 379, 401.

Schellman, J. A. (1955). *C. r. Trav. Lab. Carlsberg, Sér. chim.* **29,** 230.

Scheraga, H. A., Scott, R. A., Vanderkooi, G., Leach, S. J., Gibson, K. D., Ooi, T. & Némethy, G. (1967). Proceedings of this meeting.

Steinberg, I. Z. & Scheraga, H. A. (1963). *J. biol. Chem.* **238,** 172.

Zimm, B. H. & Bragg, J. K. (1959). *J. chem. Phys.* **31,** 526.

The Co-operativity of Helix–Coil Transitions in Polypeptide Chains

O. B. Ptitsyn

*Institute of High Molecular Weight Compounds of the
U.S.S.R. Academy of Sciences, Leningrad, U.S.S.R.*

In this work a method is proposed for the qualitative comparison of the degrees of co-operativity of helix–coil transitions for various polypeptide–solvent systems. The method is based on the fact that the relative dimensions of a polypeptide molecule in the region of the helix–coil transition is greater (for a given helix content) the greater the degree of co-operativity of the transition. This is because the contribution of helical sections to the mean square of the end-to-end distance of a macromolecule is proportional to the mean length of a helical section, which increases with increase of the degree of co-operativity of the transition The method has been applied to the comparison of the degrees of co-operativity of helix–coil transitions in poly-γ-benzyl-L-glutamate (PBG) induced by changing the solvent composition in mixtures of dichloroacetic acid with dichloroethylene, and of helix–coil transitions in poly-L-glutamic acid (PGA) in various solvents induced by the ionization of the macromolecules.

The intrinsic viscosity and the dispersion of the optical activity of these polypeptides were investigated for the various stages of the transition, and the curves of intrinsic viscosity *versus* helix content were compared. The results of these experiments confirm the fact (also obtained earlier by other methods) that the transition of PBG in the mixture of organic solvents is more co-operative in comparison with the transitions of PGA in aqueous solutions with low ionic strengths. However, the increase of the ionic strength and especially the addition of organic solvents (2-chloroethanol and dioxan) to aqueous solutions of PGA increases the degree of co-operativity of the transition in PGA, making it closer to that of the transition in PBG. This leads to the conclusion that the difference between the degrees of co-operativity of helix–coil transitions for PBG in the mixture of organic solvents and for PGA in aqueous solutions is due not only to the difference between the side groups of these polypeptides, but also to the difference between solvents. The dependence of the degree of co-operativity of the transition on the solvent is compared with the existing theoretical attempts at calculating this quantity. This dependence cannot be described in the "hard sphere" approximation for intramolecular interactions, and leads to the suggestion about the marked influence of dipole–dipole interactions on the conformations of polypeptide chains and particularly on the co-operativity of helix–coil transitions.

1. Introduction

It is well known that the generating of the helical conformation of a polypeptide chain can be described by two parameters (Zimm & Bragg, 1959; Birshtein & Ptitsyn, 1964): $S = \exp\left(-\Delta F/kT\right)$ and $\sigma = \exp\left(-F_{\text{init}}/kT\right)$.

Here ΔF is the free energy change of a monomer unit accompanying its transition from the free state to the helical state (tied by a hydrogen bond) and F_{init} is the additional change of the free energy during the initiation of a new helical section of the chain. The existence of F_{init} is due primarily to the fact that prolongation of the helical section involves a fixation of the conformation of one monomer unit and an initiation of the section involves that of three monomer units (Zimm & Bragg, 1959). This circumstance leads to the co-operativity of the helix–coil transition in synthetic polypeptides; the average number of monomer units in a helical (or statistically coiled) section in the middle of the transition region is much greater than unity, and is equal to (Birshtein & Ptitsyn, 1964):

$$v = \exp\left(\frac{F_{\text{init}}}{2kT}\right) = \frac{1}{\sqrt{\sigma}}. \tag{1}$$

The nature of the co-operativity of the helix–coil transition of a polypeptide chain has not been studied till now, mainly because of the lack of a sufficiently universal method for evaluating the parameter σ.

The only reliable method for evaluating σ that has been proposed till now is applicable only to polypeptides that undergo helix–coil transitions produced by a change of temperature; it is also necessary for the transition to occur in a sufficiently narrow interval of temperature in order that the heat of transition, ΔH, can be measured calorimetrically. From the expression for the fraction of monomer units in helical conformation in the middle part of the transition, $\vartheta = S^v/(1-S^v)$, we obtain that in the middle point ($S = 1$)

$$d\vartheta/dT = v\Delta H/4kT^2.$$

It means that the heat capacity of the polypeptide chain in the middle point of the transition is equal to:

$$C_{\text{max}} = \left(\frac{d\vartheta}{dT}\right)_{\text{max}} \Delta H = \frac{v(\Delta H)^2}{4kT^2} = \frac{(\Delta H)^2}{4\sqrt{\sigma}kT^2}. \tag{2}$$

From the value of C_{max} determined from the height of the maximum of the heat capacity–temperature curve and the value of ΔH determined from the area under this curve, it is possible to calculate v or σ.

By this method values of $\Delta H = 950 \pm 30$ cal/mole and $v = 100$ (i.e. $\sigma = 1 \times 10^{-4}$) for poly-$\gamma$-benzyl-L-glutamate (PBG) have been determined in a mixture of dichloroacetic acid with dichloroethylene (DCA + DCE; 81 + 19) (Ackerman & Rüterjans, 1964). These values have been obtained by an extrapolation of calorimetric data to zero concentration of the polypeptide. An alternative method involves comparing the calorimetric value of ΔH with the value of $d\vartheta/d(1/kT) \simeq -v\Delta H/4$, which can be obtained from the temperature dependence of ϑ (by means of the optical-activity dispersion data).

The comparison of the calorimetric value ΔH with the value of $v\Delta H = 70$ kcal/ mole, which was evaluated by this method for PBG by Applequist (1963), gives $v = 70$ ($\sigma = 2 \times 10^{-4}$). The same value of σ for PBG was obtained still earlier by Zimm et al. (1959) from the comparison of helix–coil transitions in short and long chains of PBG.

The calorimetric method for evaluating σ was applied, other than to PBG, only to poly-ε-carbobenzoxy-L-lysine (PCBL) (also in a DCA + DCE mixture) (Karasz et al., 1965), but the value $\sigma \approx 0.1 \times 10^{-4}$ that was obtained corresponds to a finite concentration of the PCBL and therefore must be refined.

Nagasawa & Holtzer (1964) (see also Snipp et al., 1965) have proposed a method for evaluating σ for polypeptides that undergo pH-induced helix–coil transitions. The method is based on the analysis of the potentiometric titration curves of these polypeptides in the transition region. Elementary calculations lead to the equation:

$$\int_{\mathrm{pH_0}}^{\mathrm{pH}} (\alpha_h - \alpha_c)\mathrm{d(pH)} = 0.43\,\frac{\Delta F_0}{kT} + \frac{1}{v}\log\frac{\vartheta}{1-\vartheta}. \tag{3}$$

Here α_h and α_c are the degrees of ionization of the pure helical and pure coiled polypeptide corresponding to the given pH value (these values can be obtained by extrapolation of titration curves of the helical and statistically coiled polypeptides to the given pH), $\mathrm{pH_0}$ is the value of pH corresponding to $\alpha_h = \alpha_c$ (it is the case for small degrees of ionization) and ΔF_0 is the free-energy difference between the helical and the statistically coiled state of the uncharged chain. Equation (3) means that the integral

$$\int_{\mathrm{pH_0}}^{\mathrm{pH}} (\alpha_h - \alpha_c)\mathrm{d(pH)}$$

must linearly depend on $\log(\vartheta/1-\vartheta)$ (ϑ is the helix content for the given pH, which can be determined, for instance, from the optical-activity dispersion data; it is also possible to evaluate ϑ directly from potentiometric titration curves by making an approximation that $\alpha = \alpha_c\vartheta - \alpha_h(1-\vartheta)$) and that the slope of this graph must be equal to $1/v$. This method has been applied to the evaluation of v for poly-L-glutamic acid (PGA) in aqueous solutions of NaCl. Various authors (Nagasawa & Holtzer, 1964; Nekrasova et al., 1965; Snipp et al., 1965) have obtained results that are relatively close one to another and are grouped near the value $v = 20$ (i.e. $\sigma = 2.5 \times 10^{-3}$). The shortcoming of this method is the need for extrapolating titration curves, which always leads to some uncertainty. For the completeness of the picture it is also necessary to mention the method of evaluating σ that was proposed recently by Rifkind & Applequist (1964); this method is based on the influence of external pressure of the degree of helicity of a polypeptide. This method has also been applied to PGA in an aqueous solution of NaCl, and the result is close to that of the previous method ($v = 15$, i.e. $\sigma = 5 \times 10^{-3}$) (Rifkind & Applequist, 1964).

Consequently the existing fragmentary experimental data show that the parameter σ can be smaller in PBG than in PGA at least by an order of magnitude, which is in contradiction with the assumption of Zimm & Bragg (1959) about the constancy of this parameter for all polypeptides. A more detailed investigation of this problem is hindered by the lack of a method for evaluating σ that would be applicable in principle to all polypeptides that undergo helix–coil transitions and to all solvents (it is necessary to remember that the data for PBG and PGA correspond to different solvents; PBG has been investigated in a mixture of organic solvents and PGA in aqueous solution).

In this paper a method is proposed that allows one to make at least a qualitative investigation of the co-operativity of helix–coil transitions of various polypeptides in various solvents. The results of the comparison of PBG and PGA made by this method are also presented. The method is based on the theory of dimensions of polypeptide molecules in the region of the helix–coil transition that was first proposed by Nagai (1960,1961) (see also Ptitsyn & Skvortsev, 1965). This theory shows that, in the region of the helix–coil transition, the dimensions of macromolecules have a minimum (if σ is not very small). It also shows that *for a given helix content of a polypeptide chain, the molecular dimensions are greater the smaller is σ* (see Fig. 3(a) of the paper by Nagai, 1961, and Fig. 1 of the paper by Ptitsyn & Skvortsev, 1965). This permits in principle the evaluation of σ from the dependence of macro-molecular dimensions (or related quantities) on the helix content in the region of the helix–coil transition, as was first proposed by the author together with Skvortsev (Ptitsyn & Skvortsev, 1965).

2. Theory

The dependence of the dimensions of a polypeptide chain on the degree of co-operativity in the region of the helix–coil transition can be qualitatively illustrated by means of the following simple model (Nagai, 1961; Ptitsyn & Skvortsev, 1965). Let us suppose that the polypeptide chain consists of the helical and statistically coiled sections that are freely linked one to another. In this case the mean square of the end-to-end distance of a chain, $\overline{h^2}$, is equal to the sum of the mean squares of the end-to-end distances of two hypothetical chains consisting only of statistically coiled sections or only of helical sections (these chains have correspondingly $n(1-\vartheta)$ and $n\vartheta$ monomer units, where n is the degree of polymerization and ϑ is the fraction of monomer units in helical conformation). For $n \to \infty$, $\overline{h^2}$ of the first chain is equal simply to

$$\overline{h^2}_{\text{coiled part}} = (1-\vartheta)\overline{h^2}_{\text{coil}},$$

where $\overline{h^2}_{\text{coil}}$ is the mean square of the end-to-end distance of a statistically coiled chain consisting of n monomer units, and $\overline{h^2}$ of the second chain can be expressed by means of Eyring's equation (Eyring, 1932) as:

$$\overline{h^2}_{\text{helical part}} = n\vartheta l_h^2 \frac{1+\cos\theta}{1-\cos\theta} \tag{4}$$

where l_h is the length of a monomer unit in the direction of the helix axis and $\overline{\cos\theta}$ is the mean value of the cosine of the angle between the end-to-end vectors of neighbour monomer units included in the helical sections of the chain. As $\overline{\cos\theta}$ is 1 if two neighbouring units belong to one helical section and 0 if they belong to different sections, $\overline{\cos\theta} = 1 \times (1-p) + 0 \times p = 1-p$, where p is the probability of the "breaking" of the helix (see also Birshtein & Ptitsyn, 1966). Substituting this value of $\overline{\cos\theta}$ in equation (4), we obtain:

$$\overline{h^2} = \overline{h^2}_{\text{coiled part}} + \overline{h^2}_{\text{helical part}} = (1-\vartheta)\overline{h^2}_{\text{coil}} + 2n\vartheta l_h^2 \bar{v}_h \tag{5}$$

where $\bar{v}_h = 1/p$ is the mean number of monomer units included in a helical section (the model is correct only for $\bar{v}_h \gg 1$).

In order to express $\bar{v}_h$ through ϑ and σ, we can use the simplest version of the Zimm and Bragg theory of helix–coil transition (Zimm & Bragg, 1959), in which the end effects are neglected and the state of each monomer is supposed to be dependent only on the state of the preceding monomer unit. In this approximation (see equation (9.45) in the book of Birshtein & Ptitsyn, 1964):

$$\bar{v}_h = \frac{\lambda_0}{\lambda_0 - S}. \tag{6}$$

Here λ_0 is the maximal root of the characteristic equation:

$$(\lambda-1)(\lambda-S) = \sigma S \tag{7}$$

of the matrix that describes the set of the states of a monomer unit (Zimm & Bragg, 1959; Birshtein & Ptitsyn, 1964). Eliminating S from equations (6) and (7) we obtain:

$$\bar{v}_h = \frac{\lambda-1}{\sigma} + 1. \tag{8}$$

However, we obtain by differentiating equation (7) with respect to λ (see equation (9.43) in Birshtein & Ptitsyn, 1964):

$$\vartheta = \frac{\lambda-1}{2\lambda-1-S}. \tag{9}$$

By including equation (9) in equation (7) and solving it for λ, we obtain (for $\sqrt{\sigma} \ll 1$):

$$\lambda_0 \simeq 1 + \sqrt{\sigma \cdot \frac{\vartheta}{1-\vartheta}} \tag{10}$$

from which:

$$\bar{v}_h \simeq \frac{1}{\sqrt{\sigma}} \sqrt{\frac{\vartheta}{1-\vartheta}}. \tag{11}$$

As a result we obtain in our approximation ($n \to \infty$, $v = 1/\sqrt{\sigma} \gg 1$)†:

$$\overline{h^2} = (1-\vartheta)\overline{h^2_{\text{coil}}} + \frac{2nl_h^2}{\sqrt{\sigma}} \frac{\vartheta^{\frac{3}{2}}}{\sqrt{(1-\vartheta)}} \tag{12}$$

or

$$\frac{\overline{h^2}}{\overline{h^2_{\text{coil}}}} = 1-\vartheta + \frac{2l_h^2}{\sqrt{\sigma}l_c^2} \frac{\vartheta^{\frac{3}{2}}}{\sqrt{(1-\vartheta)}} \tag{13}$$

where $l_c = (\overline{h^2_{\text{coil}}}/n)^{\frac{1}{2}}$ is the effective length of one monomer unit in a statistically coiled chain. The curves $\overline{h^2}/\overline{h^2_{\text{coil}}}$ versus ϑ obtained from equation (13) for various values of the parameter $l_h^2/\sqrt{\sigma}l_c^2$ are shown in Fig. 1. From the Figure one can see that the dependence of $\overline{h^2}/\overline{h^2_{\text{coil}}}$ on ϑ is very sensitive, to the value of this parameter, i.e. for the given l_h and l_c to the value of σ.

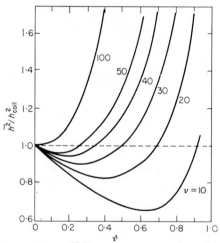

FIG. 1. The theoretical curves of $\overline{h^2}/\overline{h^2_{\text{coil}}}$ versus ϑ for infinitely long polypeptide chains, obtained from equation (13). $l_h = 1 \cdot 5\,\text{Å}$; $l_c = 11 \cdot 3\,\text{Å}$; the values of $v = 1/\sqrt{\sigma}$ are marked near the curves.

† In Ptitsyn & Skvortsev (1965) the lengths of all the helical sections were supposed to be equal; as a result, the second term in the right side of equation (12) was two times smaller, in accordance with the difference between h^2 of "regular" and "statistical" zigzag chains (Birshtein & Ptitsyn, 1966).

Equation (13) cannot always serve as a basis for the quantitative determination of σ in real polypeptide chains since it neglects the end effects, which were shown by Nagai (1961) to be important even for a rather long polypeptide chain. The approximation $v = 1/\sqrt{\sigma} \gg 1$, which is involved in this equation, can sometimes also introduce smaller, but still not negligible, errors. Further, equation (13) does not take into account the influence on $\overline{h^2}$ of long-range interactions in a macromolecule (a crude estimate of these interactions was proposed in the work of Ptitsyn & Skvortsev, 1965). And, last but not least, the quantity $\overline{h^2}$, which can be calculated by means of equation (13), cannot be directly determined from experiment, and the connection between $\overline{h^2}$ and the experimentally determinable quantities (e.g. the mean square of the radius of gyration of a macromolecule or the intrinsic viscosity) also depends on the helix content (Nagai, 1961). Nevertheless equation (13) well illustrates the great sensitivity of the curves $\overline{h^2}(\vartheta)/\overline{h^2_{coil}}$ to σ and can serve as a basis for a qualitative comparison of σ for various polypeptides with the same n (or for a comparison of σ for the same polypeptide in various solvents).

3. Comparison of the Degrees of Co-operativity of Helix–Coil Transitions in Poly-γ-benzyl-L-glutamate and in Poly-L-glutamic Acid in various solvents

It follows from the preceding section that, for the comparison of the degrees of co-operativity of helix–coil transitions in various polypeptide–solvent systems, it is necessary to measure the dependence of some property of the polypeptide molecules related to its dimensions (e.g. intrinsic viscosity $[\eta]$) on its helix content. These experimental investigations were made by the author together with T. V. Barskaya, I. A. Bolotina and N. G. Illarionova for poly-γ-benzyl-L-glutamate (PBG) and poly-L-glutamic acid (PGA). We have investigated the helix–coil transitions in PBG due to change of solvent composition in mixtures of dichloroethylene (DCE) with dichloroacetic acid (DCA) and the transitions in PGA due to the ionization of its macromolecules both in aqueous solutions of PGA with various ionic strengths (0·02, 0·2, 1·0 and 2·0 M NaCl) and in mixtures of an aqueous solution of 0·2 M NaCl with 2-chloroethanol and dioxan (2 to 1 v/v). The intrinsic viscosities of the samples investigated were measured for various stages of the transition; the helix content of macromolecules was determined from the specific rotation $[\alpha]_{546}$ and from the dispersion of optical activity (the constant b_0 in the Moffitt and Yang equation (Moffitt & Yang, 1956)).

The sample of PBG which had been synthetized in the laboratory of Yu. V. Mitin in our Institute was investigated. It had $n = 550$, determined from its intrinsic viscosity in DCA by means of an empirical equation proposed by Doty et al. (1956). The sample of PGA (in the form of Na salt) with $n = 560$, kindly placed at our disposal by Prof. G. Fasman, was also investigated. The viscosity was measured in an Ostwald viscometer at $22 \pm 0.02°C$ at concentration intervals from 0·05–0·3 g per 100 ml. (depending on the time of flowing of the solution) to 0·6–0·9 g per 100 ml. The viscosities of PGA solutions in 0·02 M NaCl were measured by using isoionic dilution. The optical activity was measured at room temperature by means of a spectropolarimeter "Pepol-60" in the range $\lambda = 350$–590 mμ. All measurements were made in distilled water and in organic solvents distilled immediately before the experiment

In Figs. 2 to 6, the results of experiments are presented in a form of the curves $[\alpha]_{546}$ and $[\eta]$ of PBG *versus* the solvent composition and the curves $[\alpha]_{546}$ and $[\eta]$ of PGA in various solvents *versus* pH. In all the systems investi-

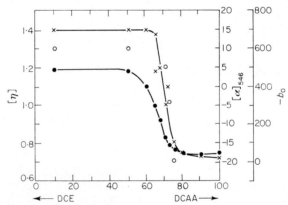

FIG. 2. The dependence of $\times$, $[\alpha]_{546}$ and $\bullet$, $[\eta]$ for PBG in DCE + DCA mixtures on the solvent composition. The open circles are the corresponding values of the Moffitt and Yang constant b_0.

gated, the curves of $[\alpha]_{546}$ and $[\eta]$ clearly demonstrate the existence of helix–coil transitions. The values of $[\eta]$ and $[\alpha]_{546}$ for the statistically coiled molecules of PBG and PGA as well as the values $[\eta]$, $[\alpha]_{546}$ and b_0 for maximal helix contents reached in our experiments are presented in Table 1. $[\eta]$ always reflects the "melting" of the helices earlier than $[\alpha]_{546}$, which is in accordance with the usual point of view that the "melting" begins with the appearance of a few breaking points of the system of hydrogen bonds. These breaking points practically do not influence the mean degree of short-range order in the chain (which determines the value of $[\alpha]$), but markedly decrease the rigidity of the chain, and as a result decrease $[\eta]$. The curves of $[\eta](pH)$ for PGA in all solvents except 0·02 M aqueous NaCl have

TABLE 1. Viscosity and optical-activity parameters for PBG and PGA in various solvents

Solvent	$[\eta]_{coil}$	$[\eta]_m$†	$[\alpha]_c$	$[\alpha]_m$†	$(-b_0)_{max}$	$(-b_0)_h$	$[\alpha]_h$	ϑ_{max}
				Poly-γ-benzyl-L-glutamate				
Dichloroethylene + dichloroacetic acid	0·74	1·19	−19°	+15°	600°	640°	+17°	0·95
				Poly-L-glutamic acid				
0·02 M NaCl	2·60	1·0	−112°	−5°	620°	730°	+10°	0·88
0·2 M NaCl	1·28	0·84	−100°	−3°	590°	730°	+20°	0·81
1 M NaCl	0·82	0·64	−100°	−20°	590°	730°	0°	0·80
2 M NaCl	0·70	0·55	−87°	−26°	570°	730°	−7°	0·76
0·2 M NaCl : dioxan (2 to 1)	0·58	1·37	−82°	+7°	610°	610°	+7°	1·0
0·2 M NaCl : 2-chloroethanol (2 to 1)	0·93	1·5	−89°	−3°	730°	730°	−3°	1·0

† $[\eta]_m$ and $[\alpha]_m$ are the values of $[\eta]$ and $[\alpha]_{546}$ corresponding to maximal values of $-b_0$ reached in the experiments, i.e. to the maximal helix content.

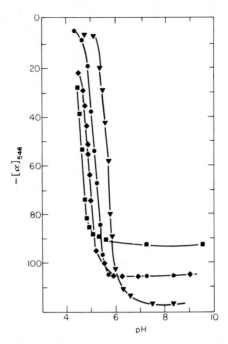

FIG. 3. The pH dependence of $[\alpha]_{546}$ for the Na salt of PGA in ▼, 0·02; ●, 0·2; ◆, 1·0 and ■, 2·0 M aqueous NaCl.

strongly pronounced minima,† the existence of which is predicted by the theory (see above) for macromolecules with a small degree of co-operativity of the transition. The curve of $[\eta]$ of PBG *versus* solvent composition has no minimum in accordance with the theoretical prediction for macromolecules with a high degree of co-operativity of the transition.

It is interesting to note that the curves $[\alpha]_{546}$ (pH) and especially $[\eta]$ (pH) for PGA differs markedly in water and in water–organic solvents. In water–organic solvents, $[\eta]$ increases sharply with decrease of pH below the point of the minimum, reaching a saturation at acidic pH. In water solutions, such a sharp increase was not observed (see Figs. 4 and 6 as well as the third column of Table 1), since in the last case, the minimum is close to the values of pH corresponding to the loss of solubility of PGA. It suggests that PGA does not reach 100% of helix content in aqueous solutions at room temperature (see also the ninth column of Table 1), which is in accordance with the results of the work of Cassim & Taylor (1965b).

† In the mixtures of water with organic solvents, such minima for PGA have been observed also by other authors (Doty *et al.*, 1957; Goldstein & Katchalsky, 1960).

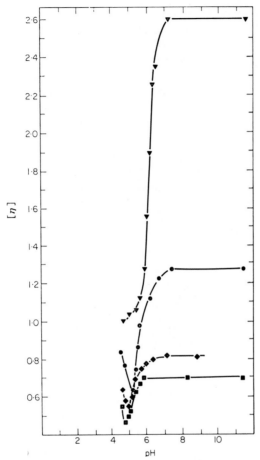

FIG. 4. The pH dependence of $[\eta]$ for the Na salt of PGA in ▼, 0·02; ●, 0·2; ◆, 1·0 and ■, 2·0 M aqueous NaCl.

The evaluation of the helix content of PGA molecules from the optical activity data was made by means of the equation:

$$\vartheta = \frac{[\alpha]_{546} - [\alpha]_c}{[\alpha]_h - [\alpha]_c} \qquad (14)$$

where $[\alpha]_h$ and $[\alpha]_c$ are the values of $[\alpha]_{546}$ for the completely helical and completely coiled conformations. The use of equation (14) was justified by the special experiments that have shown that for all the systems investigated, $[\alpha]_{546}$ changes during the helix–coil transition proportionately to the change of the Moffitt and Yang constant b_0 (it is also in accordance with the data for PGA published in the literature). The quantity $[\alpha]_c$ in equation (14) can easily be determined, since the curves of $[\alpha]_{546}$ became parallel to the abscissa in the region of statistically coiled conformations (see Figs. 2, 3 and 5). The resulting values of $[\alpha]_c$ are presented in the fourth column of Table 1. The values of $[\alpha]_h$ are connected with some uncertainty, especially for PGA molecules, which did not reach 100% of the helix content in some of the systems investigated. We have put $[\alpha]_h$ equal to the values of $[\alpha]_{546}$ obtained as a result of the extrapolation of the empirical curves $[\alpha]_{546}$ versus b_0 to the values of b_0 corresponding to 100% of the helix content. (The values of b_0 corresponding to 100% of the helix content were evaluated by means of the empirical equation $b_0 = -1701 + 730 \cdot 3\, n_s$, where n_s is the refractive index of the solution, proposed recently by Cassim & Taylor (1965a)). The resulting values of $(b_0)_h$ and $[\alpha]_h$ are presented in the seventh and eighth columns of Table 1; in the ninth column of the Table, the maximum values of helix contents, ϑ_{max}, are presented, which values have been calculated for the given

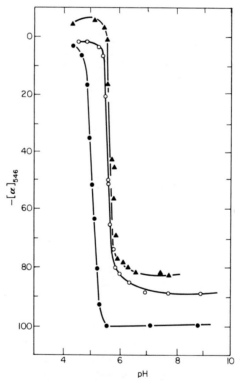

Fig. 5. The pH dependence of $[\alpha]_{546}$ for Na salt of PGA in a mixture of 0·2 M aqueous NaCl with ○, dioxan and ▲, 2-chloroethanol (2 : 1 v/v). For comparison purposes, the curve of $[\alpha]_{546}$ (pH) for PGA in 0·2 M aqueous NaCl (●) (taken from Fig. 3) is also presented.

system by means of equation (14). However, the shape of the curves $[\eta](\vartheta)$ (see Fig. 8) does not change markedly if we put $[\alpha]_h$ simply equal to the values of $[\alpha]_{546}$ corresponding to the maximal values of $-b_0$ reached in the experiment (see fifth and sixth columns of Table 1).

The $[\eta]$-values of PGA for a given pH depend markedly on the solvent, decreasing with increase of ionic strength and with the addition of organic solvents (see Figs. 4 and 6). It can be explained, of course, by the influence of the electrostatic interactions of charged groups in the completely or partly ionized molecules of PGA.† As a measure of these interactions, we can consider the values $[\eta]_{coil}$ of statistically coiled, completely ionized macromolecules at neutral and basic pH values (see Figs. 4 and 6 as well as the second column of Table 1). As our special experiments have shown, $[\eta]_{coil}$

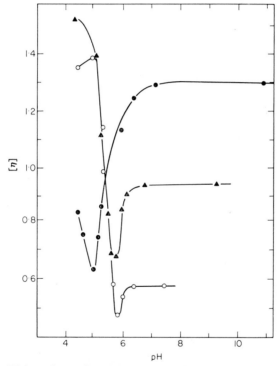

FIG. 6. The pH dependence of $[\eta]$ for Na salt of PGA in the mixture of 0.2 M aqueous NaCl with $\bigcirc$, dioxan and $\blacktriangle$, 2-chloroethanol ($2:1$ v/v). For comparison purposes the curve of $[\eta]$ (pH) for PGA in 0.2 M aqueous NaCl, shown by filled circles (taken from Fig. 4), is also presented.

† It is possible that it is the influence of electrostatic interactions (increasing with the increase of pH) that is responsible for the absence of the minimum in the curve of $[\eta]$ (pH) in 0.02 M NaCl, where these interactions are especially large.

of PGA in aqueous solutions is linearly dependent on $1/\sqrt{\mu}$, where μ is the ionic strength of the solvent (see Fig. 7, where $[\eta]$ of PGA at pH 7 is presented for eight ionic strengths from 0·02 to 3 M NaCl). The same dependence has been observed earlier (Pals & Hermans, 1952; Cox, 1960; Takahashi & Nagasawa, 1964) for other flexible polyelectrolyte molecules. It has been explained theoretically (Yelyashevich & Ptitsyn, 1964) on the basis of the assumption that the ionic-strength dependence of the dimensions of flexible polyelectrolyte molecules is due mainly to the long-range interactions of charged groups.

The value of $[\eta]_{coil}$, extrapolated from the graph of Fig. 7 to infinitely large ionic strength (which corresponds to the absence of electrostatic interactions) is equal to $[\eta]_{\infty} = 0·50$. For samples of relatively low molecular

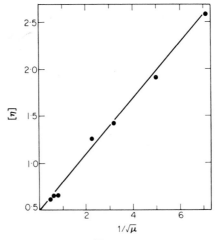

FIG. 7. The dependence of $[\eta]$ on $1/\sqrt{\mu}$ (μ is the ionic strength of the solution) for the Na salt of PGA in aqueous solutions of NaCl (pH 7·0).

weight (which is the case for our sample of PGA), the non-electrostatic long-range interactions must be rather small and, therefore, this value of $[\eta]_{\infty}$ must be near to the value of $[\eta]_{coil}$ in θ solvent, i.e. in the absence of both electrostatic and van der Waals long-range interactions. It means that it is possible to calculate from $[\eta]_{\infty}$ the effective length l_c of a monomer unit in a state unperturbed by the long-range interactions in a statistical coil. By means of Flory's equation (Flory, 1953):

$$[\eta]_{\infty} = \Phi \frac{(\overline{h^2})^{\frac{3}{2}}}{M} = \Phi \frac{\sqrt{n} l_c^3}{M_0} \tag{15}$$

where M is the molecular weight of the polypeptide, M_0 is the molecular weight of the monomer unit, which for the Na salt of PGA is 151 and $\Phi = 2\cdot1 \times 10^{21}$ dl/g. We thus obtain a value of $11\cdot5$ Å for l_c. This value is in excellent agreement with the value of $11\cdot3$ Å that was obtained recently by Brant & Flory (1965a) for several polypeptides (including PGA) from measurements of $[\eta]$, M_w and the second virial coefficient in good solvents.

The addition of organic solvents to the aqueous PGA solution, as was pointed out above, leads to the decrease of $[\eta]_{coil}$. It suggests that the addition of organic solvents decreases the electrostatic interactions in PGA molecules. It can probably be explained by the increase of counter-ion binding of the charged polyelectrolyte molecules with the decrease of the dielectric constant of the solvent.

In Fig. 8 the curves of relative values of intrinsic viscosities $[\eta]/[\eta]_{coil}$ versus ϑ (calculated from equation (13)) are presented. The shape of the curves $[\eta](\vartheta)/[\eta]_{coil}$ is absolutely different for the aqueous PGA solutions and for the solution of PBG in a mixture of organic solvents. This difference decreases, however, when we increase the ionic strength of the aqueous solutions of PGA and especially when we go from aqueous solutions of PGA to its solutions in mixtures of water with organic solvents. As it was pointed out above, the dependence of $[\eta]/[\eta]_{coil}$ on ϑ may be determined in principle first by the degree of co-operativity of the transition (i.e. the parameter σ), secondly by the degree of polymerization, n, and thirdly by the long-range interactions in macromolecules. The degrees of polymerization of our samples of PGA and PBG are practically equal, and therefore the difference in the shape of the curves cannot be due to the difference in n. In order to evaluate the role of long-range interactions, we may compare two lower curves on Fig. 8, which correspond to PGA in $0\cdot2$ M and $0\cdot02$ M NaCl, i.e. in the solvents in which the long-range interactions are especially great. We can see that these two curves coincide practically in the region of ϑ from 0 to $0\cdot6$ for these two solvents, notwithstanding that $[\eta]_{coil}$ values in them are more than two times different one from another (see Fig. 4 and the second column of Table 1). However, the shape of the curves $[\eta]/[\eta]_{coil}$ for PGA in 2 M NaCl and in the mixture of $0\cdot2$ M NaCl with dioxan are essentially different, notwithstanding that the long-range electrostatic interactions in both these cases are relatively small. Comparison of Fig. 8 with Table 1 shows clearly the absolute absence of correlation between the shape of $[\eta]/[\eta]_{coil}$ curves for PGA in various solvents and the $[\eta]_{coil}$ values in these solvents (these values are the measure of long-range interactions).

As a result, we can come to the conclusion that the reason for the different shape of the $[\eta]/[\eta]_{coil}$ curves for PGA and PBG as well as for PGA in various solvents can only be due to the difference in the degrees of co-operativity of the helix–coil transition. Figure 1 shows the fact that the increase of the degree of co-operativity of the transition must lead to an increase of

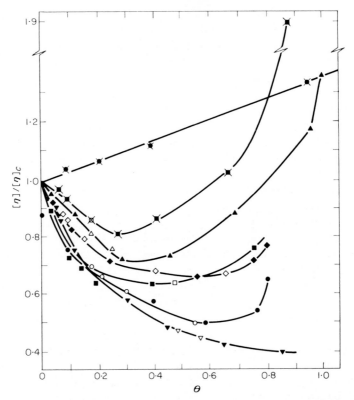

FIG. 8. The dependence of $[\eta]/[\eta]_{coil}$ on the helix content ϑ for the systems investigated: for PGA ($n = 560$) in ▼, ▽, 0·02, ●, ○, 0·2, ◆, ◇, 1·0 and ■, □, 2·0 M aqueous NaCl and in the mixtures of 0·2 M aqueous NaCl with ▲, △, 2-chloroethanol and ■, ⊠, dioxan (2 : 1 v/v) and ● for PBG ($n = 550$) in DCE + DCA mixtures. Black circles correspond to the values of pH (for PGA) or of solvent composition (for PBG) for which both $[\eta]$ and $[\alpha]_{546}$ have measured; white circles correspond to the values of pH for which only $[\alpha]_{546}$ have been measured and $[\eta]$ values have been interpolated from the $[\eta]$ (pH) curve. The curves are drawn through the experimental points.

$\overline{h^2}/\overline{h^2}_{coil}$ and hence of $[\eta]/[\eta]_{coil}$ values for given ϑ in the transition region. This result of the theory is easy to understand qualitatively, since the helical sections of the polypeptide chains contribute more to $\overline{h^2}$ with increase in the mean length of a helical section (see equation (2)), and the mean length of a helical section increases with the increase of the degree of co-operativity of the transition (equation (11)).

The qualitative comparison of Fig. 8 with Fig. 1 shows that the great difference between the curves of $[\eta]/[\eta]_{coil}$ for PGA in aqueous solutions and for PBG is due to the much greater degree of co-operativity of the transition in PBG, which is in accordance with literature data (see section 1). The other point, however, is more important: the increase of values of $[\eta]/[\eta]_{coil}$ for a given ϑ with increase of ionic strength of the solvent, and especially with the addition of organic solvents to aqueous solutions means that the degree of co-operativity of helix–coil transitions in PGA depends markedly on the solvent. The evaluation of the degree of co-operativity of the transition in PGA, which was cited in the Introduction ($v \simeq 20$, i.e. $\sigma \simeq 2 \cdot 5 \times 10^{-3}$) corresponds to aqueous solutions of PGA with relatively small ionic strength ($\lesssim 0 \cdot 2$ M). The quantitative evaluation of the parameter for PGA from the data of Fig. 8 cannot be made without further development of the theory. Our results show, however, that the degree of co-operativity of the helix–coil transition in PGA increases with increase of ionic strength, and especially with the addition of organic solvents to aqueous solutions. It shows that the difference between the degrees of co-operativity of the transition for PGA in aqueous solutions and PBG in organic solvents is due not only to the difference of side groups between PGA and PBG, but also to the difference of the solvents.

4. The Nature of the Co-operativity of Helix–Coil Transitions in Polypeptide Chains

As was pointed out in section 1, the co-operativity of helix–coil transition in polypeptide chains is due mainly to the fact that the initiation of a helical section involves the fixation of the conformations of three monomer units, whereas the prolongation of a helical section involves the fixation of the conformation of only one monomer unit (in both cases, the process is accompanied by the formation of one hydrogen bond). Brant & Flory (1965b) have shown that in a statistically coiled chain, the short-range interactions between all non-neighbour monomer units can be neglected. As a result, the free energy of such a chain is equal to the sum of individual terms, each of which depends only on two angles of internal rotation, which determine the orientation of the given monomer unit with respect to the precedent one. Supposing that this approximation is valid also for the α-helical conformation of the chain for all interactions except hydrogen bonds, we can state that the additional free energy of the initiation of a helical section is $F_{init} = 2\Delta F_{conf}$ and that:

$$\sigma = \exp\left(-F_{init}/kT\right) = \exp\left(-2\Delta F_{conf}/kT\right). \tag{16}$$

The short-range interactions of near, but not neighbouring, monomer units can also be effectively included in ΔF_{conf}.

In the first stage of development of the theory describing the helical state of polypeptide chain, it was commonly accepted (see for instance Kauzmann, 1954; Schellman, 1955; Birshtein & Ptitsyn, 1964) that a monomer unit in a free state has q rotational isomers and in a helical state only one rotational isomer, and therefore:

$$\Delta F_{conf} = -T\Delta S_{conf} = kT \log q. \tag{17}$$

Various values for q have been proposed: 6 (Schellman, 1955); 8 (Kauzmann, 1954); or 9 (Birshtein & Ptitsyn, 1964). These values lead to $\Delta F_{conf} \simeq 1\cdot2$ kcal/mole (it was supposed that q and therefore also ΔF_{conf} and σ are equal for all polypeptides). It follows from this value of ΔF_{conf} that $F_{init} \simeq 2\cdot4$ kcal/mole and $\sigma \simeq 10^{-2}$, which contradicts the experimental data at least for PBG and PCBL.

The investigations of the conformations of polypeptide monomer units not forbidden by steric interactions (Sasisekharan, 1962; Ramachandran et al., 1963a,b; Ramakrishnan, 1964; Schellman & Schellman, 1964; Ramakrishnan & Ramachandran, 1965; Ramachandran et al., 1965; Némethy & Scheraga, 1965; Leach et al., 1966) as well as the first attempts at calculating the potential surfaces of the monomer units as a function of the angles of internal rotation (Brant & Flory, 1965; de Santis et al., 1965; Liquori, 1966; Gibson & Scheraga, 1966) show, however, that the real angle dependence of the potential energy of the monomer units cannot be described by the rotational-isomer approximation. Therefore, in order to calculate ΔF_{conf} we must make the averaging on the whole potential surface of a monomer unit in a free state. More quantitatively:

$$\Delta F_{conf} = -kT \log \frac{z_h}{z_c} \tag{18}$$

where z_h and z_c are the partition functions of a monomer unit in helical and statistically coiled states. The appropriate calculations were made recently by Némethy et al. (1966) in a "hard sphere" approximation, in which all the sterically non-forbidden conformations of a monomer unit have equal energy. In this approximation:

$$\Delta F_{conf} = -T\Delta S_{conf} = -kT \log \frac{\gamma_h}{\gamma_c} \tag{19}$$

where γ_h is the conformational phase volume allowed for a monomer unit in the α-helical conformation and γ_c is the conformational phase volume allowed for a free monomer unit by steric interactions. Némethy, Leach and Scheraga have actually calculated only differences between ΔF_{conf} for the given monomer unit and for glycine, since the previous calculations of these authors (Leach et al., 1966) and others have shown that γ_c depends on the nature of side group. In these calculations, it has been taken into account that the steric interactions in various polypeptides first exclude the different fractions of the conformations of the main chain and secondly limit the number of possible side-group conformations in a different way. The results of the work of Némethy *et al.* (1966) show that in an approximation involved in equation (19), the values of ΔF_{conf} must be nearly equal for most of the amino acid residues (with the exception of valine, isoleucine, threonine and, to a small extent, leucine).

The results of our work show clearly that the degree of co-operativity of helix–coil transitions in PGA depends markedly on the solvent, and suggest that the difference between the degrees of co-operativity in PGA and PBG is also due at least partly to the difference between the solvents for these polypeptides. It means that the parameter σ depends markedly on the intra-molecular energy of the chain in various sterically possible conformations, since the fraction of sterically possible conformations itself cannot appreciably depend on the solvent. In other words, the "hard sphere" approximation that was the basis of equation (19) is insufficient for the proper calculation of the parameter σ.

Discussing the intramolecular interactions in polypeptide chains that depend on the solvent, we may firstly consider dipole–dipole interactions of peptide groups as well as electrostatic interactions in PGA molecules. The role of dipole–dipole interactions of neighbouring peptide groups was recently discussed in detail by Brant & Flory (1965*b*) (see also Gibson & Scheraga, 1966). These authors have shown that the account of dipole–dipole inter-action of neighbouring peptide groups increases very markedly the energy difference between the deepest minimum of the potential surface of monomer unit (which is near to the conformation corresponding to the β-structure of the chain) and the second minimum that corresponds to the conformation near to the right-handed α-helix (see also Arridge & Cannon, 1964).† It means that the dipole–dipole interactions must appreciably increase the value of ΔF_{conf}, and therefore decrease σ, i.e. increase the degree of co-operativity of helix–coil transitions in polypeptide chains. It is quite possible that the short-range dipole–dipole interactions of near, but not neighbouring, peptide groups can also contribute to the value of σ, but it does not change the general picture.

Changing from the aqueous solutions of PGA to the water–organic solutions of PGA and further to the solutions of PBG in organic solvents, we decrease the dielectric constant of the medium. This must lead to an increase of the contribution of dipole–dipole interactions and, therefore, to an increase

† It is interesting to note in this connection (Birshtein & Ptitsyn, 1967) that the inter-action of the dipoles of the peptide groups of the main chain with the dipole moments of side groups in polyserine, polycysteine and their derivatives leads to an additional increase of the energy of the right-handed α-helix and to the decrease of the energy of the β-structure. This circumstance probably explains the well-known fact (see for instance Blout *et al.*, 1960; Fasman & Blout, 1960; Bradbury *et al.*, 1962; Imahori & Yahara, 1964; Anufrieva *et al.*, 1965; Anufrieva *et al.*, 1966; Illarionova *et al.*, 1966) that the derivatives of poly-L-serine and poly-L-cysteine form β-structures rather than α-helices in a bulk state and in solutions.

of the degree of co-operativity of helix–coil transition, which is in accordance with the results presented in Fig. 8. Thus one can treat the results of our work as the corroboration of Brant and Flory's idea about the appreciable influence of dipole–dipole interactions on the conformations of polypeptide chains.

At a first view, this conclusion contradicts the experimental results of Brant & Flory (1965a) which show that the value of $\overline{h^2_{\text{coil}}}$ for a polypeptide chain does not depend practically on the solvent. This contradiction seems, however, to be only apparent, since the value of σ depends mainly on the statistical weight of the hardly probable conformation of a free monomer unit, and the contribution of this conformation to $\overline{h^2_{\text{coil}}}$ is very small. Therefore the dipole–dipole interactions that contribute to the statistical weight of this conformation can influence σ much more than $\overline{h^2_{\text{coil}}}$.

The discussion of the role of electrostatic interactions must certainly involve an account of the interactions of all charged groups with mutual distances smaller than the Debye–Hückel radius $1/\varkappa$. The influence of the interactions of neighbouring ionizable groups on σ cannot be great, because the distance between these groups is nearly equal in a helical and in a statistically coiled chain (Zimm & Rice, 1960). However, the ionizable groups belonging to the neighbouring turns of the α-helix are closer to each other in a helix than in a statistical coil (Zimm & Rice, 1960), which as a matter of fact explains the pH-induced helix–coil transitions in polypeptides of the type of PGA. The electrostatic interactions may decrease the mean length of a helical section of the chain (for a given helix content), because the electrostatic energy of monomer units at the beginning of a helical section must be smaller than this in the middle part (because of the absence of the preceding turn of the helix at the beginning of a helical section). This circumstance may explain our results about the decrease of the degree of co-operativity of helix–coil transition in PGA with the diminution of the ionic strength of the solvent. The electrostatic interactions can also contribute to the difference between the degrees of co-operativity of helix–coil transitions in PBG and PGA.

The subsequent development of the theory of the dimensions and the other characteristics of macromolecules in the region of helix–coil transitions will probably permit one to determine quantitatively σ or ΔF_{conf} for various polypeptides. This approach may lead to useful information about the free energy of the helix state of polypeptide chains.

ACKNOWLEDGMENTS

The experimental part of this work was made together with T. V. Barskaya, I. A. Bolotina and N. G. Illarionova, and the theoretical part together with A. M. Skvortsev. I am very grateful to these collaborators. I also thank T. M. Birshtein for valuable discussions of the results, and Prof. G. Fasman and Yu. V. Mitin for the samples of PGA and PBG.

REFERENCES

Ackerman, Th. & Rüterjans, H. (1964). *Ber. Bunsen. phys. Chem.* **68**, 850.

Anufrieva, E. V., Birshtein, T. M., Bolotina, I. A., Burstein L. L., Eskin, V. E., Frolov, V. I., Illarionova, N. G., Kalikhevich, V. I., Korotkina, O. Z., Mitin, Yu. V., Ptitsyn, O. B.. Purkina, A. V. & Volchek, B. Z. (1966). *J. Polymer Sci.* (in press).

Anufrieva, E. V., Bolotina, I. A., Volchek B. Z., Illarionova, N. G., Kalikhevich, V. I., Korotkina, O. Z., Mitin, Yu. V., Ptitsyn, O. B., Purkina, A. V. & Eskin, V. E. (1965). *Biofizika*, **10**, 918.

Applequist, J. (1963). *J. chem. Phys.* **38**, 934.

Arridge, R. G. C. & Cannon C. G. (1964). *Proc. R. Soc.* **A278**, 91.

Birshtein, T. M. & Ptitsyn, O. B. (1964). "Konformatsii makromolekul". Moscow: Nauka. (English translation "Conformations of Macromolecules". New York: Interscience (1966).)

Birshtein, T. M. & Ptitsyn, O. B. (1966). *J. Polym. Sci.* (in press).

Birshtein, T. M. & Ptitsyn, O. B. (1967). *Biopolymers* (in press).

Blout, E. R., de Lozé, C., Bloom, S. M. & Fasman, G. D. (1960). *J. Am. chem. Soc.* **82**, 3787.

Bradbury, J. H., Elliott, A. & Hanby, W. (1962). *J. molec. Biol.* **5**, 487.

Brant, D. A. & Flory, P. J. (1965a). *J. Am. chem. Soc.* **87**, 2788.

Brant, D. A. & Flory, P. J. (1965b). *J. Am. chem. Soc.* **87**, 2791.

Cassim, J. Y. & Taylor, E. W. (1965a). *Biophys. J.* **5**, 553.

Cassim, J. Y. & Taylor, E. W. (1965b). *Biophys. J.* **5**, 573.

Cox, R. A. (1960). *J. Polym. Sci.* **47**, 441.

Doty, P., Bradbury, J. H. & Holtzer, A. M. (1956). *J. Am. chem. Soc.* **78**, 947.

Doty, P., Wada, A., Yang, J. T. & Blout, E. R. (1957). *J. Polym. Sci.* **23**, 851.

Eyring, H. (1932). *Phys. Rev.* **39**, 746.

Fasman, G. D. & Blout, E. R. (1960). *J. Am. chem. Soc.* **82**, 2262.

Flory, P. J. (1953). "Principles of Polymer Chemistry". Ithaca: Cornell University Press.

Gibson, K. D. & Scheraga, H. A. (1966). *Biopolymers*, **4**, 709.

Goldstein, L. & Katchalsky, E. (1960). *Bull. Res. Coun. Israel, Sect. A*, **9**, 138.

Illarionova, N. G., Bolotina, I. A., Volchek, B. Z., Kalikhevich, V. I., Mitin, Yu. V., Ptitsyn, O. B. & Purkina, A. V. (1966). *Biofizika* (in press).

Imahori, K. & Yahara, Y. (1964). *Biopolymers Symposia No.* 1, 421.

Karasz, F. E., O'Reilly, I. M. & Bair, H. E. (1965). *Biopolymers*, **3**, 241.

Kauzmann, W. (1954). *In* "The Mechanism of Enzyme Action", ed. by W. D. McElroy and B. Glass, p. 70. Baltimore: Johns Hopkins University.

Leach, S. J., Némethy, G. & Scheraga, H. A. (1966). *Biopolymers*, **4**, 369.

Liquori, A. M. (1966). *J. Polym. Sci.* Part C (18), 209.

Moffitt, W. & Yang, J. T. (1956). *Proc. natn. Acad. Sci., U.S.A.* **42**, 596.

Nagai, K. (1960). *J. phys. Soc. Japan*, **15**, 407.

Nagai, K. (1961). *J. chem. Phys.* **34**, 887.

Nagasawa, M. & Holtzer, A. M. (1964). *J. Am. chem. Soc.* **86**, 538.

Nekrasova, T. N., Anufrieva, E. V., Yelyashevich, A. M. & Ptitsyn, O. B. (1965). *Vȳsokomolek. Soedin.* **7**, 913.

Némethy, G., Leach, S. J. & Scheraga, H. A. (1966). *J. phys. Chem.* **70**, 998.

Némethy, G. & Scheraga, H. A. (1965). *Biopolymers*, **3**, 155.

Pals, D. T. F. & Hermans, J. J. (1952). *Recl. Trav. chim. Pays Bas Belg.* **71**, 456.

Ptitsyn, O. B. & Skvortsev, A. M. (1965). *Biofizika*, **10**, 909.

Ramachandran, G. N., Ramakrishnan, C. & Sasisekharan, V. (1963a). *In* "Aspects of Protein Structure", ed. by G. N. Ramachandran, p. 121. London: Academic Press.

Ramachandran, G. N., Ramakrishnan, C. & Sasisekharan, V. (1963b). *J. molec. Biol.* **7**, 95.

Ramachandran, G. N., Ramakrishnan, C. & Venkatachalam, C. M. (1965). *Biopolymers*, **3**, 592.

Ramakrishnan, C. (1964). *Proc. Indian Acad. Sci.* **A59**, 327.

Ramakrishnan, C. & Ramachandran, G. N. (1965). *Biophys. J.* **5**, 909.

Rifkind, J. & Applequist, J. (1964). *J. Am. chem. Soc.* **86**, 4207.

de Santis, P., Giglio, E., Liquori, A. M. & Ripamonti, A. (1965). *Nature, Lond.* **206**, 456.

Sasisekharan, V. (1962). *In* "Collagen", ed. by N. Ramanathan, p. 39. New York: Interscience Publishers.

Schellman, J. A. (1955). *C.r. Trav. Lab. Carlsberg, Sér. chim.* **29**, 230.

Schellman, J. A. & Schellman, C. (1964). *In* "The Proteins", ed. by H. Neurath, Vol. II, p. 1. New York: Academic Press.

Snipp, R. L., Miller, W. G. & Nylund, R. E. (1965). *J. Am. chem. Soc.* **87**, 3547.

Takahashi, A. & Nagasawa, M. (1964). *J. Am. chem. Soc.* **86**, 543.

Yelyashevich, A. M. & Ptitsyn, O. B. (1964). *Dokl. Akad. Nauk SSSR*, **156**, 1145.

Zimm, B. H. & Bragg, J. (1959). *J. chem. Phys.* **31**, 526.

Zimm, B. H., Doty, P. & Iso, K. (1959). *Proc. natn. Acad. Sci., U.S.A.* **45**, 1601.

Zimm, B. H. & Rice, S. A. (1960). *Molec. Phys.* **3**, 391.

Macromolecular Cooperative Phenomena

JON APPLEQUIST

*Department of Biochemistry and Biophysics
Iowa State University, Ames, Iowa, U.S.A.*

The theory of cooperative transitions in linear chain molecules is reviewed and extended. Derivations are given for the fraction of residues in a specified state B, the mean length of B-sequences, and the mean square fluctuation in the number of B-states for infinitely long one- and two-stranded molecules. The latter two quantities are employed as measures of cooperativity. The behavior of finite chains is discussed for the limit of high cooperativity in the one-stranded case and the limit of infinite dilution for the two-stranded case. In these limits simple formulas result, expressing the chain length dependence of the transitions. The nature of apparent thermodynamic quantities obtained from comparison of theory and experiment is explored. The theory is applied to studies of the temperature and pressure transitions in poly-γ-benzyl-L-glutamate, poly-L-glutamic acid, and poly-L-proline, and to the one- and two-stranded helix–coil transitions in poly-adenylic acid and its oligomers. The occurrence of a second-order phase transition in two-stranded polyadenylic acid is noted and interpreted in terms of the theory.

1. Introduction

Cooperative phenomena have become very familiar in the study of macro-molecules in dilute solution. Any large change in the equilibrium molecular properties occurring as a result of a small change in environmental conditions (temperature, pressure, or solvent composition) is usually considered to be a cooperative phenomenon. (This definition is not strictly adequate, as will be seen below.) The most common examples are the equilibria between helical and randomly coiled states of various biological polymers. The shift in equilibrium occurring upon variation of the environmental conditions is commonly called a "helix–coil transition". Another type of cooperative phenomenon occurs in the equilibrium between the two helical forms of poly-L-proline. Certain features of all of these phenomena can be understood in similar theoretical terms. It is the object of this paper to review the theory and to show some recent applications to experimental observations.

The systems to be discussed here can be classified as one-dimensional, in the sense that the molecular structures are periodic in one topological dimension. While cooperative phenomena in three-dimensional systems are usually in the form of phase transitions, this is not generally the case for one-dimension. (However, some such cases do occur, and will be discussed presently.) Thus it is necessary to characterize a one-dimensional cooperative phenomenon in some manner that will distinguish it from ordinary chemical equilibria. This can be done in terms of a "cooperative effect", which is defined here as a tendency for residues in the same state to group together, or to "aggregate" in linear sequences. The sharpness of the transition involved is directly related to this tendency. This point of view will be stated more quantitatively in the following.

The above definition leads naturally to the concept of an "anti-cooperative" effect, in which a residue tends to prefer neighbors in the opposite state. Examples of such systems are polyacids undergoing dissociation and the one-dimensional anti-ferromagnet (Ising, 1925). A "non-cooperative" system is one in which there is no preference on the part of a given residue regarding the state of its neighbors.

2. Some Definitions

The models with which we are concerned consist either of a single chain of N residues or of two chains, each with N residues, associated in a side-by-side complex. Each residue is regarded as having two accessible states, A and B. The nature of these states for particular systems to be described below are specified in Table 1. The object of the equilibrium theory is to obtain

TABLE 1. Specification of residue states for various systems

System	State A	State B
α-Helical polypeptide	Carbonyl not hydrogen bonded	Hydrogen bonded carbonyl
One-stranded polynucleotide	No stacking interaction with (arbitrary) specified neighbor	Stacking interaction with specified neighbor
Poly-L-proline	Amide bond in *trans* conformation	Amide bond in *cis* conformation
Two-stranded polynucleotide	Base not hydrogen bonded	Base hydrogen bonded to another base in opposite strand

information about the manner in which residues are distributed between the two states, expressed in terms of certain basic parameters. This information is obtained from the configurational partition function Z_N for a molecule of chain length N.

A basic parameter that is appropriate in all models is the stability constant s, which is the equilibrium constant for the conversion of a residue from state A to state B at the end of an existing sequence of one or more residues in state B. The magnitude of the stability constant is assumed to be independent of any cooperative effects, so that it is independent of chain length or the length of the B-sequence to which a new B-state is added. The cooperative effects are conveyed by the interruption constant ω_j, which is the equilibrium constant for the conversion of a molecular state containing a single sequence of n B-states (in each strand for two-stranded cases) to a state containing two B-sequences totalling n B-states, separated by j repeating units (residaes or residue pairs, depending on the model) in A-states. The relative populutions of all possible sequences of A's and B's may be readily deduced in terms of s and the ω_j's. The sum of these relative populations is Z_N.

The main object of the following discussion is to derive, in summary form, equations which are of value in the interpretation of experimental data. The groundwork for these derivations has been laid largely by S. Lifson and by B. H. Zimm.

3. Infinite Chains

The limiting behavior of infinitely long chains is of interest for comparison with experimental data on high molecular weight materials, and is expressible in simpler form than the behavior of finite chains. A convenient mathematical approach (adapted from Lifson, 1964) is based on the convergence properties of the power series

$$F(x) = \sum_{N=1}^{\infty} Z_N x^N \tag{1}$$

where x is an arbitrary variable. An important theorem on power series (Whittaker & Watson, 1915) states that the limit (assuming it exists) approached by $Z_N^{1/N}$ as $N \to \infty$ is $1/\rho$, where ρ is the radius of convergence of $F(x)$. From the treatment by Lifson & Zimm (1963), it is found that $F(x)$ converges in the same range of x as the sum

$$\sum_{i=1}^{\infty} [sG(x)]^i \tag{2}$$

where

$$G(x) = x + \sum_{j=1}^{\infty} \omega_j x^{\delta j + 1} \tag{3}$$

and where δ has the value 1 or 1/2, depending on the particular model. Assuming $G(\rho)$ converges, ρ can thus be found from the condition

$$sG(\rho) = 1. \tag{4}$$

A quantity that can often be determined at least approximately from experiment is the fraction of residues in state B, designated f. The theory (see, for example, Zimm & Bragg, 1959) yields this quantity as

$$f = \frac{1}{N} \left(\frac{\partial \ln Z_N}{\partial \ln s} \right)_{\tau} = -\left(\frac{\partial \ln \rho}{\partial \ln s} \right)_{\tau} \tag{5}$$

where τ represents variables other than s appearing in the partition function, and is replaced for particular models by one of the symbols σ, b or β (see below). From equations (4) and (5) one obtains the Lifson–Zimm result

$$f = \frac{1}{s\rho G'(\rho)}. \tag{6}$$

For the two-stranded models, equation (5) gives the fraction f_0 of residues in state B among those chains which are associated as two-stranded complexes. If the fraction of chains so associated is α, then the overall fraction f of residues in state B is

$$f = \alpha f_0. \tag{7}$$

For very long chains, however, α is very nearly unity over a wide range of s (Zimm, 1960; Litan & Lifson, 1965). In the limit of $N = \infty$, it is therefore correct to set $f = f_0$.

We may characterize cooperative effects by means of the average length $\langle l \rangle$ of a sequence of B-states, given by

$$\langle l \rangle = -\left(\frac{\partial \ln \tau}{\partial \ln s}\right)_\rho. \tag{8}$$

If ω_j is proportional to τ, as is true for all cases discussed here, then it follows that

$$\langle l \rangle = 1/(1 - s\rho). \tag{9}$$

(See also Crothers & Zimm, 1964.)

TABLE 2. Summary of formulas f•

Model	ω_j	δ	$G(x)$
Ising model	σ	1	$x + \dfrac{\sigma x^2}{1 - x}$
Two-strand polymer: matching case $a = 2$	$\dfrac{b_1}{(j + 1)^2}$	1	$x + b_1[\text{Li}_2(x) - x]$
Two-strand polymer: mismatching case $a = 2$	$\dfrac{b_2(j + 1)}{(j + 2)^2}$	1/2	$x - b_2\left[\dfrac{x}{4} + \ln(1 - x^{1/2}) + \text{Li}_2(x^{1/2})\right]$
Two-strand polymer: mismatching case $a = 3$	$\dfrac{b_3(j + 1)}{(j + 2)^3}$	1/2	$x - b_3\left[\dfrac{x}{8} + \text{Li}_3(x^{1/2}) - \text{Li}_2(x^{1/2})\right]$

• Where a phase transition occurs, the inflection point is the transition point.

A second measure of cooperativity is the equilibrium fluctuation ϕ in the number of B-states in a chain, defined by $\phi = n - \langle n \rangle$, where the brackets indicate the average value. $\langle \phi^2 \rangle$ is related to the sharpness of the transition by

$$\langle \phi^2 \rangle / N = (\partial f / \partial \ln s)_\tau \qquad (10)$$

which is exact for all N. The quantities $\langle l \rangle$, $\langle \phi^2 \rangle / N$ and $(\partial f / \partial \ln s)$ are closely related characteristics of a cooperative system, since all may be increased by the same basic causes. (For further discussion of this matter, see Applequist, 1963.)

Table 2 summarizes the important formulas for particular models. In each case $G(x)$ converges for $|x| < 1$, and the expressions for $G(x)$ hold in this interval. For the two-stranded models it is simplest to express f as a function of s, b and ρ, although it is understood that one variable may be eliminated by equation (4). The models are described below.

(a) *Ising model*

The one-dimensional Ising model (Ising, 1925) is characterized by the fact that interactions between nearest neighbors only are included, with the result that a single interruption constant σ applies to interruptions of all lengths. A one-stranded polynucleotide which is able to form a helix by attractive interactions between nearest neighbor bases is an excellent example of the Ising problem, since it is reasonable in this case to neglect all but nearest

g-chain cooperative phenomena

f	$\langle l \rangle$ at inflection[a]	$(\partial f / \partial \ln s)_\tau$ at inflection[a]
$1/2 + \dfrac{s-1}{2[(1-s)^2 + 4\sigma s]^{1/2}}$	$1 + \sigma^{-1/2}$	$\dfrac{1}{4\sigma^{1/2}}$
$\dfrac{1}{s\rho - b_1 s[\rho + \ln(1-\rho)]}$	$1 + \dfrac{1}{0.6449 b_1}$	∞
$\dfrac{1}{s\rho + \dfrac{b_2 s}{2}\left[\dfrac{\rho^{1/2}}{1-\rho^{1/2}} - \dfrac{\rho}{2} + \ln(1-\rho^{1/2})\right]}$	No simple expression found	$0.38 + \dfrac{0.1447}{b_2}$ $(b_2 \leqslant 0.3)$
$\dfrac{1}{s\rho - \dfrac{b_3 s}{2}\left[\dfrac{\rho}{4} + \ln(1-\rho^{1/2}) + \mathrm{Li}_2(\rho^{1/2})\right]}$	$1 + \dfrac{1}{0.3179 b_3}$	∞

$\mathrm{Li}_a(x)$ is the polylogarithm function defined by $\mathrm{Li}_a(x) = \sum\limits_{i=1}^{\infty} x^i / i^a$ for $|x| \leq 1$ (Lewin, 1958).

neighbor interactions. The α-helical polypeptides are stabilized mainly by further-neighbor interactions, and it is less obvious that the Ising model should apply. Refinements of the Ising model to take into account the effects peculiar to the α-helix (Zimm & Bragg, 1959; Lifson & Roig, 1961; Applequist, 1963) have led to the conclusion that the simple Ising model is a good approximation as long as σ is much less than unity. The reason is that those molecular states that are strongly affected by the further-neighbor nature of the interactions are relatively unpopulated when σ is small. The Ising model approximation is convenient because the important expressions are relatively simple. The model will be adopted here for all of the one-stranded polymers. The transition curves are characterized by the fact that $f = 1/2$ at $s = 1$ for all σ.

The non-cooperative system is a special case of the Ising model with $\sigma = 1$. From the formulas in Table 2 it is seen that $\langle l \rangle = 2$ and $\langle \phi^2 \rangle / N = 0.25$ at the midpoint of the transition for this case. These values serve as a point of reference in considering cooperative systems. The "anti-cooperative" systems mentioned above are examples of the Ising model with $\sigma > 1$.

(b) Two-stranded model, matching case

In the two-stranded models, state B in one strand is bonded to a state B in the opposite strand. Thus an interruption between B-sequences consists of a closed loop of residues in state A. The matching case (Hill, 1959; Zimm, 1960) is characterized by the fact that a loop of size j consists of j A-states in each strand. The interruption constant ω_j must contain as a factor the probability of ring closure, which we take to be $\mu/(j+1)^a$ where μ and a are constants. The value $a = 2$ was found by Wall et al. (1955), and will be used in some of the following examples. (This choice departs from the usual random-flight approximation, in which $a = 3/2$.) The parameter b, which is given various subscripts in Table 2 to distinguish it for the various models, is related to ΔF_{st}, the molar free energy of stacking of a pair of B-states on an adjacent pair of B-states, by

$$b = \mu \exp \frac{\Delta F_{st}}{RT} \tag{11}$$

where R is the gas constant and T is the absolute temperature. The significance of ΔF_{st} can be understood somewhat better by considering that the free energy of formation of a new pair of B-states at the end of a B-sequence is $\Delta F_{st} + \Delta F_{pr}$, where ΔF_{pr} is the free energy of formation of the bond between the paired residues in opposite strands. Thus s is given by

$$s = \exp \left(-\frac{\Delta F_{st} + \Delta F_{pr}}{RT} \right). \tag{12}$$

The formation of this new residue pair is accompanied by a change of configurational entropy of the residues in the amount $R \ln \mu_0$, where μ_0 is the probability of closure of the ring consisting of two adjacent residue pairs. (Since there is most likely only one stable conformation of this ring in the polynucleotides, it is reasonable to assume that μ_0 is considerably less than μ.) Thus ΔF_{st} can be written

$$\Delta F_{st} = \varepsilon - RT \ln \mu_0 \qquad (13)$$

where ε is that part of the stacking free energy discussed by Crothers & Zimm (1964), and includes only contributions other than that from the configurational entropy. Thus we have

$$b = \frac{\mu}{\mu_0} e^{\varepsilon/RT}. \qquad (14)$$

The above analysis differs somewhat from that of Crothers and Zimm, who have for convenience assumed $\mu = \mu_0$.

An interesting characteristic of the matching case with $a = 2$ is the occurrence of a true second order phase transition. The expression for f in Table 2 drops steeply to zero (in continuous fashion) at a critical value s_t of the stability constant, given by

$$s_t = \frac{1}{1 + 0 \cdot 6449 b_1} \qquad (15)$$

(see also Zimm, 1960). For $s < s_t$, the formula given for f does not hold, due to the fact that equation (4) has no solution. Under these conditions ρ is the radius of convergence of $G(x)$: i.e. $\rho = 1$. Thus f vanishes for all $s < s_t$, by equation (5). If one takes $a > 2$, then it can be shown that a first order transition would occur, i.e. f would show a discontinuous jump from some finite value to zero. The necessary proofs have been outlined elsewhere (Applequist, 1966; Poland & Scheraga, 1966).

Only in recent years has it become evident that a phase transition in a one-dimensional system is theoretically possible (Baker, 1961; Baur & Nosanow, 1962; Kac et al., 1963). The present case is of particular interest because it suggests that the observation of such a transition is experimentally feasible as well.

(c) Two-stranded model, mismatching case

The mismatching case is similar to the preceding case, except that a loop of size j is understood to consist of a total of j residues in A-states distributed in arbitrary manner between the two strands, all such distributions being regarded as equally probable. This case was first treated by Hill (1959), and has been further discussed by Steiner & Beers (1961) and by Crothers & Zimm (1964). The form of ω_j is similar to that for the matching case with the additional factor $j+1$, which is the number of ways of forming the specified interruption. The quantity δ takes the value 1/2 so that each *pair* of residues in a loop contributes a factor x to terms of the sum in equation (3).

No phase transition occurs for $a = 2$, because equation (4) has a solution for all s. The qualitative behavior is then similar to that of the Ising model, with transition midpoints occurring in the vicinity of $s = 1$.

A phase transition occurs for $a > 2$, and is of second order for $a = 3$, being very similar to the transition described for the matching case. The critical value of s is then

$$s_t = \frac{1}{1+0 \cdot 3179b_3}. \tag{16}$$

Formulas for the cases $a = 2$ and 3 are given in Table 2 to illustrate the significant differences.

4. Finite Chains

Several more or less exact treatments of finite chains are available for various models (Zimm & Bragg, 1959; Lifson & Roig, 1961; Applequist & Damle, 1965,1966). Since the formulas are generally too complicated for routine use, the discussion here will be restricted to certain limiting forms which provide insight into the behavior of short chains, and which should be useful in some quantitative applications.

For sufficiently large cooperative effects, one may simplify the problem by assuming that there is at most one B-sequence per chain. In addition to the stability constant, one then needs only an equilibrium constant for the formation of the first B state in a chain to describe the system.

(a) One-stranded model

The equilibrium constant for the formation of the first B state is just σs, where σ has the same significance as before. Expressions for f under the above simplifying assumption have been given by Schellman (1958) and by Zimm & Bragg (1959). To simplify further, we note that for $\sigma \ll 1$, we must have $s \gg 1$ in order to achieve appreciable formation of B states. Under these conditions the relative population σs^N of chains entirely in state B is much greater than that of all of the partially-B chains, and one may neglect the latter. Thus the equilibrium approaches the all-or-none case. This approximation breaks down as the chains become long, due to the increasing multiplicity of ways of forming partially-B molecules. The calculations by Schellman (1958) illustrate the nature of this approximation. Some useful formulas are given in Table 3. These are increasingly valid as σ and N decrease. The stability constant s_m at the midpoint of the transition serves as a fixed point in analysing experimental data. The manner in which the temperature T_m at

TABLE 3. Formulas for short-chain cooperative phenomena

	One-strand model $(\sigma \ll 1)$	Two-strand models (infinite dilution)
f	$\dfrac{\sigma s^N}{1 + \sigma s^N}$	$\dfrac{1 + 4\gamma s^N - (1 + 8\gamma s^N)^{1/2}}{4\gamma s^N}$
$\left(\dfrac{\partial f}{\partial \ln s}\right)_\tau$ (max)	$\dfrac{N}{4}$	$\dfrac{N}{6}$
s_m	$\sigma^{-1/N}$	$\gamma^{-1/N}$
$\dfrac{1}{T_m}$	$\dfrac{1}{T_c} + \dfrac{R \ln \sigma}{N\Delta H_s}$	$\dfrac{1}{T_c} + \dfrac{R \ln \gamma}{N\Delta H_s}$

the midpoint varies with chain length is also shown, and provides a simple means of evaluating σ. In the formula given, T_c is the temperature at which $s = 1$, and ΔH_s is the enthalpy change per mole of residues when an A-residue is converted to a B-residue at the end of a sequence of B-residues.

(b) Two-stranded model

The equilibrium constant (in terms of molar concentrations) for the formation of the first pair of B states between two strands is βs, where β has units of l/mole. Since dilution of the system favors dissociation of the strands, a large value of s will be required at very low concentrations to achieve appreciable association of strands. Thus, for the reason given in the one-stranded case, the residues in associated strands will be almost entirely in state B. Returning to the discussion of equation (7), we see that this means $f_0 \cong 1$ and thus $f \cong \alpha$. The important formulas are then easily derived (Applequist & Damle, 1965), and appear in Table 3. We define $\gamma = \beta c$, where c is the total molar concentration of strands if the strands are identical, or c is the concentration of each type of strand if the two differ and are present in equal amounts. By this convention, βs is the equilibrium constant for formation of a species with a symmetry number of two. If the two strands differ, and if each has a symmetry number of unity, then all species have symmetry number unity, and the true equilibrium constant for formation of the first pair of B states is $2\beta s$.

ΔH_s for this model is the enthalpy change per mole of residue pairs when a pair of A-residues is converted to a pair of B-residues at the end of a B-sequence.

The formulas of Table 3 are increasingly valid as γ and N decrease. Since it is possible to vary the concentration, it is feasible to approach this limit experimentally for any two-stranded system, provided the strands are not too long.

It is seen in both the one- and two-stranded models that a strong dependence of the equilibrium on chain length is expected. In the one-stranded case, this is the direct result of cooperative effects, since no chain length dependence occurs in the non-cooperative case. For the highly dilute two-stranded case, however, the effect is the direct result of the chain length dependence of the association equilibrium constant, since this quantity reduces to βs^N in the transition region, regardless of the magnitude of the cooperative effects. Thus an observed dependence of the transition curve on chain length is an indicator of cooperative effects only if the equilibrium is not strongly influenced by a strand-dissociation process.

5. Relating Experiment to Theory

The observable properties of interest in the present discussion are those which measure the relative number of residues in each state. Typically such a property can be classified as an intensive quantity q which takes the value q_n for B-residues in sequences of n B-residues and the value q_A for all A-residues. Defining $\Delta\bar{q} = \bar{q} - q_A$, where $\bar{q}$ is the observed value for the system, and $\Delta q_n = q_n - q_A$, we have

$$\Delta\bar{q} = \sum_{n=1}^{N} \Delta q_n w_n \qquad (17)$$

where w_n is the fraction of residues in sequences of n B-residues.

If q_n takes the value q_∞ for all n, then equation (17) reduces to $f = \Delta\bar{q}/\Delta q_\infty$. Another approximation of interest is that where $\Delta q_n/\Delta q_\infty = 1 - 1/n$, as is approximately the case for certain optical properties of polynucleotides. Experiment then yields the quantity $f^* = \Delta\bar{q}/\Delta q_\infty$, which is, by virtue of equation (17), given by

$$f^* = f\left(1 - \frac{1}{\langle l \rangle}\right). \qquad (18)$$

Incorporating equations (6) and (9), we obtain for infinite chains

$$f^* = fs\rho = \frac{1}{G'(\rho)}. \qquad (19)$$

One can understand f^* as the fraction of residues which are in state B and have a nearest neighbor in a specified direction along the chain also in state B.

It is interesting to note that an equation analogous to equation (5) holds for f^*, namely

$$f^* = \frac{1}{N}\left(\frac{\partial \ln Z_N}{\partial \ln s}\right)_{\tau^*} \qquad (20)$$

where $\tau^* = \tau s$. Equation (20) can be derived by a simple identity from equations (5), (8) and (18). Thus it may sometimes be convenient to regard f^* and Z_N as functions of the explicit variables s and τ^*, rather than s and τ.

The observation of f (or f^*) as a function of temperature T and pressure P can yield useful thermodynamic information. All of the models discussed here have in common a dependence of f on two parameters, s and τ, which have the properties of equilibrium constants. (One may substitute τ^* for τ throughout the remainder of this section if the former is chosen as an explicit variable.) We may write

$$RT \ln s = T\Delta S_s - \Delta H_s = T\Delta S_s - \Delta E_s - P\Delta V_s \qquad (21)$$

$$RT \ln \tau = T\Delta S_\tau - \Delta H_\tau = T\Delta S_\tau - \Delta E_\tau - P\Delta V_\tau \qquad (22)$$

where S, H, E and V are the entropy, enthalpy, energy and volume, respectively, per mole of the repeating unit whose state is changed in the process for which s or τ serves as equilibrium constant. (More explicitly, S, H, E and V as used here are standard partial molal quantities. While their recognition as such is of minor importance at present, it is worth noting that a calorimetric ΔH (or a dilatometric ΔV) contains a contribution from the change in partial molal enthalpy (or volume) of the solvent, and is therefore not strictly equivalent to the corresponding quantity in equations (21) or (22). One case where this consideration seems significant will be cited below.)

The analysis of data can be simplified by assuming that τ is constant over the range of T and P of interest. However, ΔH_τ and ΔV_τ are not necessarily zero, and the assumption is not strictly correct. The effects on the analysis will be explored by means of an example.

Suppose f is known as a function of T from experiment at constant pressure. One may then determine an "apparent" enthalpy change $\Delta H_s'$ from theory by means of the relation

$$\left(\frac{\partial f}{\partial T}\right)_P = \frac{\Delta H_s'}{RT^2}\left(\frac{\partial f}{\partial \ln s}\right)_\tau. \qquad (23)$$

However, $(\partial f/\partial T)_P$ is related to the true enthalpy changes by

$$\left(\frac{\partial f}{\partial T}\right)_P = \frac{\Delta H_s}{RT^2}\left(\frac{\partial f}{\partial \ln s}\right)_\tau + \frac{\Delta H_\tau}{RT^2}\left(\frac{\partial f}{\partial \ln \tau}\right)_s. \qquad (24)$$

Thus we readily find

$$\Delta H_s' = \Delta H_s - \xi\Delta H_\tau \qquad (25)$$

where

$$\xi = \left(\frac{\partial \ln s}{\partial \ln \tau}\right)_f. \qquad (26)$$

Since $\Delta S_s'$ is found as $\Delta H_s'/T_c$, where T_c is the temperature at which $s = 1$, we find also

$$\Delta S_s' = \Delta S_s - \frac{\xi\Delta H_\tau}{T_c}. \qquad (27)$$

A similar relationship holds for volume changes found from $(\partial f/\partial P)_T$:

$$\Delta V_s' = \Delta V_s - \xi \Delta V_\tau. \tag{28}$$

For the various long-chain models the curves of f against s at various fixed τ cross somewhere near their midpoints. A common point of intersection corresponds to $\xi = 0$, and it is seen from the above that the apparent quantities are equal to the true quantities at such a point. For the finite chains in the approximation discussed above, we find $\xi = -1/N$ for both one- and two-stranded models. This relationship would enable one to determine both ΔH_s and ΔH_τ from sufficiently accurate data on oligomers.

The above considerations play a role in the choice of the τ parameter which is regarded as constant. Using the two-stranded case as an example, we recall that either b or b^* $(= bs)$ may conveniently be regarded as a constant. (Other choices are equally possible.) From equations (11) and (12) it is evident that the appropriate enthalpies are

$$\Delta H_s = \Delta H_{pr} + \Delta H_{st} \tag{29}$$

$$\Delta H_b = -\Delta H_{st} \tag{30}$$

$$\Delta H_{b*} = \Delta H_{pr}. \tag{31}$$

Thus, if one determines $\Delta H_s'$ from equation (23) with $\tau = b$, one has

$$\Delta H_s' = \Delta H_{pr} + \Delta H_{st}(1 + \xi), \tag{32}$$

whereas if one takes $\tau = b^*$, then

$$\Delta H_s' = \Delta H_{st} + \Delta H_{pr}(1 - \xi). \tag{33}$$

If either ΔH_{st} or ΔH_{pr} is negligible, then an obvious choice for τ will yield a $\Delta H_s'$ which is equal to the larger of the two.

The distinction between the "apparent" and "true" thermodynamic quantities may become significant as the precision of experimental data is improved. In the examples described below the distinction is not made, either because ξ vanishes or because the quality of the data does not warrant it.

We conclude this section by stressing the utility of combined pressure and temperature studies, as illustrated by the following consideration. We have, by definition of $\Delta V_s'$,

$$\left(\frac{\partial f}{\partial P}\right)_T = -\frac{\Delta V_s'}{RT}\left(\frac{\partial f}{\partial \ln s}\right)_\tau. \tag{34}$$

By combination with equation (23) we obtain

$$\left(\frac{\partial P}{\partial T}\right)_f = \frac{\Delta H_s'}{T \Delta V_s'}. \tag{35}$$

Equation (35) is the analog of the Clapeyron equation for the types of systems discussed here. It is a valuable relationship between thermodynamic quantities since it makes no reference to a particular theoretical model, except through the ambiguity in $\Delta H_s'$ and $\Delta V_s'$ which can in many cases be made insignificant.

6. Experimental Data

(a) *Applications of Ising model*

(i) *α-Helical polypeptides*

The helix–coil transition in α-helical polypeptides is one of the best-known macromolecular cooperative phenomena (Urnes & Doty, 1961). Data will be given here on two of the most widely-studied compounds, poly-γ-benzyl-L-glutamate (PBLG) and poly-L-glutamic acid (PGA), in order to demonstrate the utility of the study of pressure effects on the equilibrium. Figure 1 shows the results obtained by Rifkind (1966; see also Rifkind & Applequist, 1964). The same study also provided measures of $(\partial f/\partial T)_P$, though these merely confirmed values from earlier data, namely $+0.098$ deg^{-1} for PBLG (Doty & Yang, 1956) and -0.0116 deg^{-1} for PGA in 0.2 M NaCl (Fasman *et al.*, 1962), both values being taken at $f = 1/2$.

Table 4 shows the parameters calculated from these data on the basis of the Ising model, and the solid curves in Fig. 1 are calculated using these

TABLE 4. Data from helix–coil transitions in α-helical polypeptides

Polymer	ΔV_s (cm^3 mole^{-1})	ΔH_s (cal mole^{-1})	ΔS_s (cal deg^{-1} mole^{-1})	σ
PBLG	$+1.0$	$+950$[a]	$+3.2$	2×10^{-4}
PGA	$+1.0$[b]	-630	-2.0	5×10^{-3}

[a] Calorimetric value from Ackermann & Rüterjans (1964). The value was extrapolated to infinite dilution, and is therefore free of any contribution from a change in partial molal enthalpy of the solvent.
[b] Dilatometric value from Noguchi & Yang (1963).

values. The height of the peak is proportional to $\Delta V_s/\sigma^{\frac{1}{2}}$, and this quantity is assumed to be constant throughout. The experimental errors are large enough that we cannot draw any strong conclusions from the discrepancies between the curves and the experimental points. However, these data suffice to establish a quantitative difference between PBLG and PGA, such that the cooperative effect is higher in the former. Zimm & Bragg (1959) showed that values of σ in the observed range are largely accounted for by the loss of internal rotation in the backbone bonds of two residues when an interruption is formed. While it is possible that additional effects due to the nature of the side chains are present, it is interesting to speculate that the difference between PBLG and PGA arises from a lesser freedom of internal rotation of the random coil in the latter. This would be the case, for example, if a poly-electrolyte effect in PGA forces the random chains into extended conformations.

Gill & Glogovsky (1965) have reported a similar pressure study on PBLG. Snipp *et al.* (1965) have obtained a similar estimate of σ for PGA from the

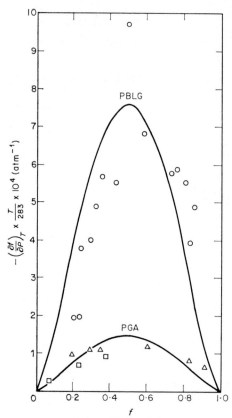

FIG. 1. Pressure coefficient of helix content f from optical rotation measurements at 436 and/or 546 mμ in the pressure range 1–136 atm. $\bigcirc$, PBLG in dichloroacetic acid–ethylene dichloride (3 : 1 by volume) at various temperatures between 17·8 and 26·0°C. $\square$, PGA in 0·01 M NaCl. $\triangle$, PGA in 0·2 M NaCl. Points for PGA correspond to pH's between 4·50 and 5·60 and temperatures between 9 and 25°C.

charge-induced transition. Bradbury *et al.* (1965) determined the volume change for the helix–coil transition in PBLG by a dilatometric method, and found the value $-0·077$ cm^3/mole. The discrepancy in sign and magnitude with our result may very well be due to the occurrence of a change in the partial molal volume of the solvent, as mentioned above.

(ii) *Poly-L-proline*

Poly-L-proline exists in two helical forms, designated I and II. All peptide bonds are in the *cis* conformation in form I and the *trans* conformation in form II. It was discovered by Gornick *et al.* (1964) that a cooperative transition from *trans* to *cis* occurs as n-propanol is added to a solution of the polymer in acetic acid. The equilibrium between the two forms was insensitive to temperature, indicating that $\Delta H_s \cong 0$. It is therefore of particular interest to explore the cooperative effects by means of pressure studies. Figure 2 shows the data of Rifkind (1966) on the pressure transition. In this study high pressures were achieved in the apparatus of Walling & Pellon (1957). Generally, a week or more was required for attainment of equilibrium. Optical rotations at the time of removal from the pressure vessel were obtained by extrapolation from a series of measurements shortly after that time.

The curve in Fig. 2 is calculated for the Ising model, taking

$$\Delta V_s/\sigma^{\frac{1}{2}} = -43\cdot5 \text{ cm}^3/\text{mole},$$

where ΔV_s applies to the reaction *trans → cis*. (The shape of the curve is insensitive to σ as long as $\sigma \ll 1$.) It is clear that σ cannot be as large as unity, since this would require a volume change comparable to the molar volume of a residue. A more reasonable estimate of ΔV_s would be in the range -1 to -2 cm^3/mole, as found for *trans → cis* reactions involving ethylenic

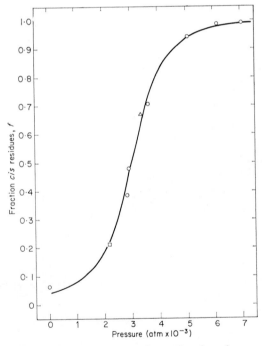

Fig. 2. Fraction of *cis* residues in poly-L-proline as function of pressure in acetic acid + n-propanol (60 : 40 by volume), determined by optical rotation measurements at 365, 436 and 546 mμ. ○, Equilibrium approached from low f at 28°C. □, Equilibrium approached from low f at 40°C. △, Equilibrium approached from high f at 28°C.

double bonds (Hamann, 1963). Thus we may tentatively place σ in the range 5×10^{-4}–3×10^{-3}. It may then be concluded that the cooperative effect is comparable in magnitude to that found in α-helical polypeptides, although the two effects must be quite different in origin.

(iii) One-stranded polyadenylic acid

Polyadenylic acid in aqueous solution at neutral pH is believed to form a one-stranded helix by stacking of bases with their planes more or less perpendicular to the helix axis (see evidence cited by Holcomb & Tinoco, 1965). Figure 3 shows the transition curves for this polymer and its oligomers as given by the relative hypochromicity $\bar{G}/G_\infty$. These data have recently been discussed in some detail elsewhere (Applequist & Damle, 1966), and only certain relevant features will be brought out here. A number of similar

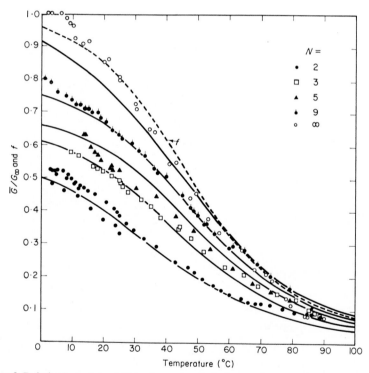

FIG. 3. Relative hypochromicities of one-stranded oligo- and polyadenylic acids at 257 mμ in 0·15 M NaCl + 0·015 M sodium citrate, pH 7·3. Curves are calculated for the chain lengths shown on the basis of the Ising model. The experimental data are those of J. R. Fresco, R. Blake and P. Doty (unpublished), discussed by Applequist & Damle (1966).

studies of this system have also been described (Poland et al., 1966; Leng & Felsenfeld, 1966; Brahms et al., 1966).

In treating these data it was assumed that the formalism of equation (17) applies by letting $q = -\varepsilon/\varepsilon_A$, where ε is the molar extinction coefficient. Then $\Delta\bar{q}/\Delta q_\infty$ is identical to $\bar{G}/G_\infty$. (Equation (17) is identical to equation (2) of our 1966 paper if one recognizes that $G_n = \Delta q_n n/(n+1)$ and $x_n = w_n(n+1)/n$, and that $w_N = 0$ because at most $N-1$ residues are in B-states.)

The dashed curve in Fig. 3 shows f calculated for the infinite Ising model, taking $\Delta H_s = -9.4$ kcal per residue-mole, $\Delta S_s = -29.3$ cal/deg per residue-mole, and $\sigma = 0.6$. The solid curves were calculated for the various chain lengths using the same parameters by direct application of equation (17). These calculations required the w_n derived for the Ising model and the Δq_n (or G_n) based on the data for the oligomers. It follows from the foregoing that $\bar{G}/G_\infty$ would be identical to f if Δq_n were independent of n. While this is only roughly correct, it can be seen that this approximation would lead to f curves with approximately the observed dependence on N by virtue of the fact that one end residue cannot be in state B, according to our definition. The trend in the observed curves does not follow the relations given in Table 3, since σ is close to unity.

There is clearly some uncertainty in the numerical parameters for this system, but it appears that a small cooperative effect is present. This can be attributed to the loss of rotational freedom about one glycosidic bond when an interruption is formed (Poland et al., 1966; Applequist & Damle, 1966).

(b) Two-stranded systems

(i) Oligoadenylic acids

Polyadenylic acid and its oligomers at acid pH associate to form a two-stranded helix with bases stacked in a helical array and hydrogen bonded in pairs (Fresco & Doty, 1957; Rich et al., 1961). Figure 4 shows the transition curves for the oligomers as given by the hypochromicity data taken at strand concentrations in the micromolar range. These data were discussed recently (Applequist & Damle, 1965) in connection with a model in which a single sequence of B-states was allowed in the molecule, while the strands were allowed to be staggered with respect to each other (the "staggering zipper model"). The solid curves were calculated on the basis of equation (17), making the identifications $\bar{G} = \Delta\bar{q} + (1-f)\Delta q_A$, $\Delta q_n = 1 - \varepsilon_n/\varepsilon$ and $\Delta q_A = 1 - \varepsilon_A/\varepsilon'$, where ε' is the molar extinction coefficient of isolated residues. Values of G_n (identical to Δq_n) were taken in accordance with the theoretical calculations of Rich & Tinoco (1960), and w_n was calculated for the staggering zipper model. The parameters used were $\Delta H_s = -7.98$ kcal per mole of base pairs, $\Delta S_s = -20.9$ cal/deg per mole of base pairs and $\beta = 2.2$ cm^3/mole. For details of the calculation, the original paper should be consulted. For

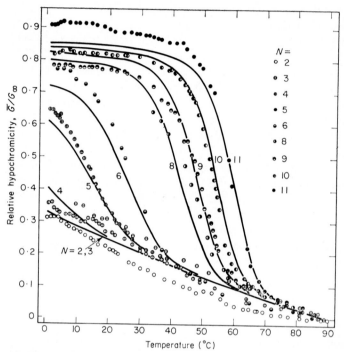

Fig. 4. Relative hypochromicities of two-stranded oligoadenylic acids at 257 mμ in 0·15 M NaCl + 0·015 M sodium citrate, pH 4·00. The experimental data are those of J. R. Fresco, R. Blake and P. Doty (unpublished) discussed by Applequist & Damle (1965).

present purposes, it is relevant to note that the trend in the transition curves is approximately that predicted for a two-stranded system at infinite dilution, as given by the relations in Table 3. The reason for this is that the populations of two-stranded species are heavily weighted in favor of the fully-bonded helix at the concentrations employed. Because even a non-cooperative system would show this behavior at infinite dilution, it can be said that the role of cooperative effects in this case is merely to produce this distribution of populations at finite dilutions. Thus cooperativity affects the observations only indirectly, and it is not possible to obtain parameters which measure the cooperativity in this case.

In the calculations for Fig. 4 an empirical temperature dependence was assigned to ε_A to account for the slopes at the high temperature limit. It is now evident that these slopes result from the superposition of the one- and two-stranded helix–coil transitions. An analysis in terms of this hypothesis would be straightforward, though probably not warranted by the available data.

(ii) *Long-chain polyadenylic acid*

The transition curves for a sample of high molecular weight two-stranded polyadenylic acid at various pH are shown in Fig. 5, as adapted from unpublished data generously supplied by J. R. Fresco. It was assumed that f^* could be calculated from the absorbance measurements (at 257 mμ) by identifying q with the molar extinction coefficient and employing the approximation $\Delta q_n/\Delta q_\infty = 1 - 1/n$, as suggested by the data on the oligomers. The actual shapes of the absorbance curves can be seen in the similar data of Massoulié (1965).

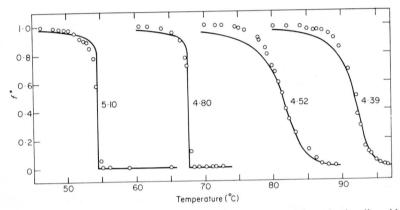

FIG. 5. Transition curves for two-stranded high molecular weight polyadenylic acid in 0·15 M NaCl + 0·015 M sodium citrate at pH indicated on curves. Solid curves are theoretical, based on parameters in Table 5.

The most striking feature of the experimental data is the qualitative change in the shape of the transition curve between pH 4·80 and 4·52. In the higher pH region there appears to be a true discontinuity in the slopes of the curves. This implies a discontinuity in the second derivative of free energy with respect to temperature, and therefore corresponds to a second order phase transition.

Both the matching and mismatching models have been shown to exhibit phase transitions of this type under certain conditions. The two leftmost curves in Fig. 5 are calculated for either of these models, being indistinguishable for the two, taking $a = 2$ for the matching case and $a = 3$ for the mismatching case. The two rightmost curves in Fig. 5 were calculated for the mismatching model with $a = 2$. The other parameters used to fit the curves are given in Table 5. For this purpose it was assumed throughout that $\Delta S_s = -23\cdot0$ cal/deg per mole of base pairs, since this appeared to be one of the more reliable of the values obtained at pH 4·00 (Applequist & Damle,

TABLE 5. Parameters for long two-stranded polyadenylic acid transitions

pH	Model	a	ΔH (cal)	b^*	
4·39	Mismatching	2	− 8364	0·0227	(b_2^*)
4·52	Mismatching	2	− 8122	0·0329	(b_2^*)
4·80	Mismatching	3	− 7822	0·080	(b_3^*)
	Matching	2	− 7822	0·040	(b_1^*)
5·10	Mismatching	3	− 7519	0·080	(b_3^*)
	Matching	2	− 7519	0·040	(b_1^*)

1965). Thus it was necessary to adjust only ΔH_s in order to position the curves correctly on the temperature axis. The values of ΔH_s fall in a reasonable range, although they cannot be regarded as accurate. The curves were calculated on the assumption that b^* is independent of temperature. The significance of this assumption will be seen from the earlier discussion, but it should be added that it makes little difference for present purposes whether b or b^* is chosen as the constant parameter. The two are approximately equal in the transition region.

It appears that the models are reasonable representations of the system. However, the fact that two different models account semiquantitatively for the behavior of the system above pH 4·8 leaves doubt as to the nature of the changes that occur between pH 4·5 and 4·8. While the matching model is not a very appealing one in the case of a homopolymer, where there are no obvious constraints on the shifting of strands with respect to each other, the present observations open the possibility that such constraints do exist. On the other hand, it is possible that random mismatching of loops is in fact maintained if a can be increased as a result of titration of the adenine groups. It would then be necessary to abandon the notion that a is known *a priori*, and regard it as an additional adjustable parameter. The values of a assumed here are, therefore, not necessarily accurate. A third possibility is that the system is actually intermediate between the matching and mismatching models, such that mismatching of loops is relatively unfavorable, but not ruled out.

The order of magnitude of b^* seen in Table 5 appears to be significant, although the precise values remain in doubt. It would be possible to say something about the stacking free energy on the basis of equations (11) and (14) if μ and μ_0 were known, but it is doubtful that meaningful results could be obtained at present. Suffice it to say that ε must be substantially negative, since μ/μ_0 is most likely much greater than unity. This conclusion is in qualitative agreement with that of Crothers & Zimm (1964), although our quantitative interpretations differ considerably.

7. Some Comparisons

A comparison of the (theoretical) magnitudes of the cooperative effects in the systems discussed here is given in Table 6. Most of the data are subject to large uncertainties, but should be of semiquantitative value. It is possible,

TABLE 6. Measures of cooperativity for various substances

Polymer	$\langle l \rangle$	$\langle \phi^2 \rangle / N$
Poly-γ-benzyl-L-glutamate	72	18
Poly-L-glutamic acid	15	3·5
Poly-L-proline	~ 34	~ 8
Polyadenylic acid		
One-stranded, pH 7·3	2·3	0·32
Two-stranded, pH 4·8	39	∞
Two-stranded, pH 4·5	13	4·75

for example, to see among the various systems similarities and differences that were not evident from the thermal transition data alone, since ΔH_s strongly influences the latter.

The cooperativity of two-stranded polyadenylic acid at pH 4·8, where a phase transition occurs, is considerably greater than that at pH 4·5, where there is no phase transition. This conclusion appears to be independent of the model chosen for the phase transition, since the same values of $\langle l \rangle$ and $\langle \phi^2 \rangle / N$ are obtained for either of the models treated here. More generally, calculations for the matching and mismatching models (with $a = 2$ in both cases) show that $\langle l \rangle$ at the inflection is an order of magnitude greater in the former for the same stacking free energy. For those cases where a second order phase transition appears, it can thus be concluded that a significant cooperative effect arises from the entropy loss which occurs on formation of a looped state. In such cases $\langle \phi^2 \rangle / N$ becomes infinite at the transition point regardless of the magnitude of b^*. However, a significant cooperative effect results from a negative stacking free energy. This is the *major* cooperative effect in the mismatching case if a is not too large, as Crothers & Zimm (1964) have also found, taking $a = 3/2$. As a corollary to this statement, it is interesting to note that a positive free energy of base pairing can be an equally important source of the cooperative effect, since $\Delta F_{st} = -\Delta F_{pr}$ when $s = 1$. This fact is perhaps conveyed more clearly by the relation $b^* = \mu \exp(-\Delta F_{pr}/RT)$, found from equations (11) and (12).

It is seen from the above comparisons that either $\langle l \rangle$ or $\langle \phi^2 \rangle / N$ would place a given system at the same relative position on a "cooperativity scale", with the exception of those cases where a phase transition occurs. For future studies, it will thus be of interest to consider both quantities in characterizing cooperative (or anti-cooperative) systems.

I am indebted to Prof. Jacques R. Fresco for supplying the many unpublished polyadenylic acid data, which have proven to exhibit essentially all of the effects predicted by the theory. This investigation was supported by a U.S. Public Health Service research grant (GM–13684) from the National Institute of General Medical Sciences, Public Health Service. A travel grant from the National Science Foundation is gratefully acknowledged.

REFERENCES

Ackermann, Th. & Rüterjans, H. (1964). *Ber. Bunsen. phys. Chem.* **68**, 850.
Applequist, J. (1963). *J. chem. Phys.* **38**, 934.
Applequist, J. (1966). *J. chem. Phys.* **45**, 3459.
Applequist, J. & Damle, V. (1965). *J. Am. chem. Soc.* **87**, 1450.
Applequist, J. & Damle, V. (1966). *J. Am. chem. Soc.* **88**, 3895.
Baker, G. A., Jr. (1961). *Phys. Rev.* **122**, 1477.
Baur, M. E. & Nosanow, L. H. (1962). *J. chem. Phys.* **37**, 153.
Bradbury, J. H., Fenn, M. D. & Gosney, I. (1965). *J. molec. Biol.* **11**, 137.
Brahms, J., Michelson, A. M. & Van Holde, K. E. (1966). *J. molec. Biol.* **15**, 467.
Crothers, D. M. & Zimm, B. H. (1964). *J. molec. Biol.* **9**, 1.
Doty, P. & Yang, J. T. (1956). *J. Am. chem. Soc.* **78**, 498.
Fasman, G. D., Lindblow, C. & Bodenheimer, E. (1962). *J. Am. chem. Soc.* **84**, 4977.
Fresco, J. R. & Doty, P. (1957). *J. Am. chem. Soc.* **79**, 3928.
Gill, S. J. & Glogovsky, R. L. (1965). *J. phys. Chem.* **69**, 1515.
Gornick, F., Mandelkern, L., Dorio, A. F. & Roberts, D. E. (1964). *J. Am. chem. Soc.* **86**, 2549.
Hamann, S. D. (1963). *In* "High Pressure Physics and Chemistry", ed. by R. S. Bradley, p. 133. London: Academic Press.
Hill, T. L. (1959). *J. chem. Phys.* **30**, 383.
Holcomb, D. & Tinoco, I., Jr. (1965). *Biopolymers*, **3**, 121.
Ising, E. (1925). *Z. Physik*, **31**, 253.
Kac, M., Uhlenbeck, G. E. & Hemmer, P. C. (1963). *J. math. Phys.* **4**, 216.
Leng, M. & Felsenfeld, G. (1966). *J. molec. Biol.* **15**, 455.
Lewin, L. (1958). "Dilogarithms and Associated Functions". London: Macdonald.
Lifson, S. (1964). *J. chem. Phys.* **40**, 3705.
Lifson, S. & Roig, A. (1961). *J. chem. Phys.* **34**, 1963.
Lifson, S. & Zimm, B. H. (1963). *Biopolymers*, **1**, 15.
Litan, A. & Lifson, S. (1965). *J. chem. Phys.* **42**, 2528.
Massoulie, J. (1965). *C. r. hebd. Séanc., Acad. Sci., Paris*, **260**, 5554.
Noguchi, H. & Yang, J. T. (1963). *Biopolymers*, **1**, 359.
Poland, D. & Scheraga, H. A. (1966). *J. chem. Phys.* **45**, 1464.
Poland, D., Vournakis, J. N. & Scheraga, H. A. (1966). *Biopolymers*, **4**, 223.
Rich, A. & Tinoco, I., Jr. (1960). *J. Am. chem. Soc.* **82**, 6409.
Rich, A., Davies, D. R., Crick, F. H. C. & Watson, J. D. (1961). *J. molec. Biol.* **3**, 71.
Rifkind, J. M. (1966). Ph.D. Thesis, Columbia University.

Rifkind, J. & Applequist, J. (1964). *J. Am. chem. Soc.* **86,** 4207.
Schellman, J. A. (1958). *J. phys. Chem.* **62,** 1485.
Snipp, R. L., Miller, W. G. & Nylund, R. E. (1965). *J. Am. chem. Soc.* **87,** 3547.
Steiner, R. F. & Beers, R. F. (1961). "Polynucleotides", Chap. 9. Amsterdam: Elsevier.
Urnes, P. & Doty, P. (1961). *Adv. Protein Chem.* **16,** 401.
Wall, F. T., Hiller, L. A. & Atchison, W. F. (1955). *J. chem. Phys.* **23,** 2314.
Walling, C. & Pellon, J. (1957). *J. Am. chem. Soc.* **79,** 4776, 4786.
Whittaker, E. T. & Watson, G. N. (1915). "A Course of Modern Analysis", 2nd Ed., p. 30. Cambridge University Press.
Zimm, B. H. (1960). *J. chem. Phys.* **33,** 1349.
Zimm, B. H. & Bragg, J. K. (1959). *J. chem. Phys.* **31,** 526.